D1545529

PEARSON

Prentice
Hall

Needham, Massachusetts
Upper Saddle River, New Jersey

Copyright © by Pearson Education, Inc., publishing as Pearson Prentice Hall, Upper Saddle River, New Jersey 07458. All rights reserved. Printed in the United States of America. This publication is protected by copyright, and permission should be obtained from the publisher prior to any prohibited reproduction, storage in a retrieval system, or transmission in any form or by any means, electronic, mechanical, photocopying, recording, or likewise. The publisher hereby grants permission to reproduce student worksheets and tests, for classroom use only, the number not to exceed the number of students in each class. Notice of copyright must appear on all copies. For information regarding permission(s), write to: Rights and Permissions Department.

Pearson Prentice Hall™ is a trademark of Pearson Education, Inc.
Pearson® is a registered trademark of Pearson plc.
Prentice Hall® is a registered trademark of Pearson Education, Inc.

Lab zone™ is a trademark of Pearson Education, Inc.

Planet Diary® is a registered trademark of Addison Wesley Longman, Inc.

Discovery Channel School® is a registered trademark of Discovery Communications, Inc., used under license. The Discovery Channel School logo is a trademark of Discovery Communications, Inc.

SciLinks® is a trademark of the National Science Teachers Association. The SciLinks® service includes copyrighted materials and is owned and provided by the National Science Teachers Association. All rights reserved.

Science News® is a registered trademark of Science Services, Inc.

ISBN 0-13-190285-7   1 2 3 4 5 6 7 8 9 10   08 07 06 05 04

All in One Teaching Resources

Everything you need for daily planning is in one place! *Science Explorer* blackline masters, teaching support, and all answer keys are organized by chapter, making it easy for you to find what you need—when you need it.

Teaching Support

Lesson Plans—Streamline your path through every section with a core set of activities and teaching suggestions.

Color Transparency Planner—Provides you with easy access to the transparencies to help you plan your lessons.

Teacher Notes—Includes support for hands-on teaching for projects, labs, and assessment.

Complete Answer Keys—Find all the answers at the end of each chapter.

Reading & Review

Target Reading Skills Handbook—Guides student understanding of target reading skills and shows how to apply them.

Guided Reading and Study Worksheets—Promote active reading and help enhance students' study skills with worksheets that apply Target Reading Skills and guide students through the text with questioning strategies and exercises.

Section Summaries—Support all readers and English language learners with easily accessible content summaries.

Review & Reinforce Worksheets—Motivate students to build vocabulary, review main ideas, and interpret diagrams, charts, and graphs.

Enrichment

Enrich Worksheets—Encourage all students to read, write, and visualize as they apply core concepts in a new context.

Interdisciplinary Exploration Worksheets—Explore a topic from the perspective of four disciplines: science, mathematics, social studies, and language arts.

Labs & Activities

Laboratory Safety—Offers teacher support and safety symbols for ready reference.

Laboratory Investigations—In-depth labs apply and extend key concepts for each chapter and include teaching support, pre-lab discussions, and critical-thinking questions.

Student Edition Lab Worksheets—Help students get organized with blackline masters of Student Edition labs—each in an easy-to-grade format.

Chapter Project Support—Guide students through the Chapter Projects in the student text with extensive teacher notes, scoring rubrics, and student worksheets with project rules and checklists.

Assessment

Performance Assessment—Assess student problem-solving and process skills using scoring rubrics and suggested outcomes.

Chapter and Book Tests—Monitor student mastery of standards-driven content and skills with a variety of questions. Thousands more questions can be found on the *ExamView*® Computer Test Bank CD-ROM.

© Pearson Education, Inc., publishing as Pearson Prentice Hall. All rights reserved.

Chemical Interactions

Contents

PRENTICE HALL

TeacherEXPRESS™
Plan • Teach • Assess

The TeacherExpress CD-ROM is a new suite of instructional tools to help teachers plan, teach, and assess.

- Powerful lesson planning
- Resource management
- Testing
- Interactive teacher's edition
- **All in One** *Teaching Resources*

Having everything in one place makes class preparation quick and easy!

© Pearson Education, Inc., publishing as Pearson Prentice Hall. All rights reserved.

Name _____ Date_____ Class _____

Interdisciplinary Exploration ▪ *Science*

Bubble Formulas

Have you ever blown bubbles? Did you ever try to blow bubbles with soapy water and find that the bubbles burst too quickly? In this activity, you will compare different bubble formulas and experiment to see if you can find a better formula. *Record your findings on a separate sheet of paper.*

1. Below are three different formulas for bubble solution. Make up a batch of each bubble solution.

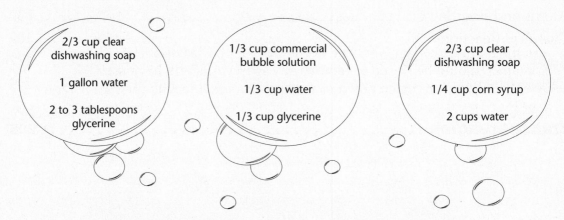

2. Test each solution. You can make different sized bubble wands by bending paper clips or other thin wire into rings. Make notes about each formula. Evaluate questions such as the following:

 ■ How difficult is it to form bubbles?

 ■ How long do the bubbles last?

 ■ How large can you make your bubbles?

 ■ What colors do you see in your bubbles?

 ■ Can you catch your bubble on a ring such as the open top of a glass jar?

 ■ Does the formula behave differently after it has sat overnight?

3. If you can, catch a bubble and put it somewhere where it won't be touched or vibrated. See how long the bubble lasts. Some bubbles are alleged to have stayed whole for over 300 days! They do not pop but they gradually shrink as air escapes through the film of soap.

4. What do you think makes a good bubble formula? Modify one of the formulas above. Measure your ingredients carefully and record what formula you tried. Record how your new solution performed. Continue experimenting with different formulas and see if you can find a formula that makes exceptional bubbles. An exceptional bubble is very large or lasts a long time.

© Pearson Education, Inc., publishing as Pearson Prentice Hall. All rights reserved.

How Soap Removes Dirt

One reason why soap is good at removing dirt is that it changes the surface tension of water. In this activity, you will explore surface tension and see how it changes when soap is added. *Record your findings on the lines.*

1. Attractions between molecules of water give them a property called surface tension. The surface of water has a very thin skin of water molecules bonded together. You can see the skin by performing the following experiment.

2. Fill a clean shallow container with cold water. The container should be 5 to 10 centimeters in diameter and 1 to 2 centimeters deep. You might use the lid of a glass jar, a saucer, or the lid of a plastic bowl. The container should be rinsed to remove any soap you might have used while washing it. Crouch down so your eyes are in line with the top surface of the container. Using a small jug or a plastic dropper, fill the container slowly to the top.

3. Take a clean, unused paper clip about 3 centimeters long. Make sure the ends of the paper clip are level with the rest of the paper clip. You are going to try to make it float. First lay the paper clip on the edge of the container, as level as you can. Gently ease the end of the paper clip onto the surface of the water. If you work slowly and gently, you will be able to make the paper clip float. Gently push the whole paper clip onto the water. Surface tension will hold the paper clip on the surface.

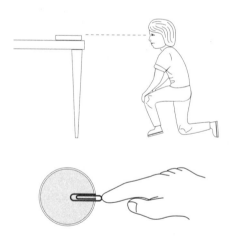

© Pearson Education, Inc., publishing as Pearson Prentice Hall. All rights reserved.

How Soap Removes Dirt *(continued)*

4. Get a bar of soap. Farthest away from the paper clip, gently dip one corner of the bar of soap into the water. If you make any waves, you will break the surface tension. Hold the soap steady for several seconds. As soap dissolves into the water, the soap will begin to change the surface tension. Eventually, the paper clip will drop to the bottom of the container.

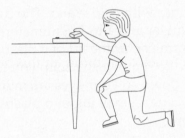

5. What affect did soap have on the surface tension? How do you know?

_____

_____

6. Water alone is not good at removing dirt because surface tension prevents water molecules from surrounding dirt particles. How do you think soap improves the ability of water to remove dirt?

_____

_____

_____

7. You know that temperature is a measure of the amount of energy of a substance. What effect would you expect a high temperature to have on the water molecules and therefore on the surface tension of the water?

_____

_____

_____

8. Rinse your container thoroughly to remove all traces of soap and repeat the experiment with warmer water. Use water that you can touch without burning yourself. What do you observe? Explain.

_____

_____

_____

© Pearson Education, Inc., publishing as Pearson Prentice Hall. All rights reserved.

Name _____ Date _____ Class _____

Interdisciplinary Exploration • *Social Studies*

What Is *Chlorogalum pomeridianum*?

In this activity, you will research this plant using encyclopedias, the Internet, and other research materials and discover how it relates to the subject of soap. Write your answers on the lines.

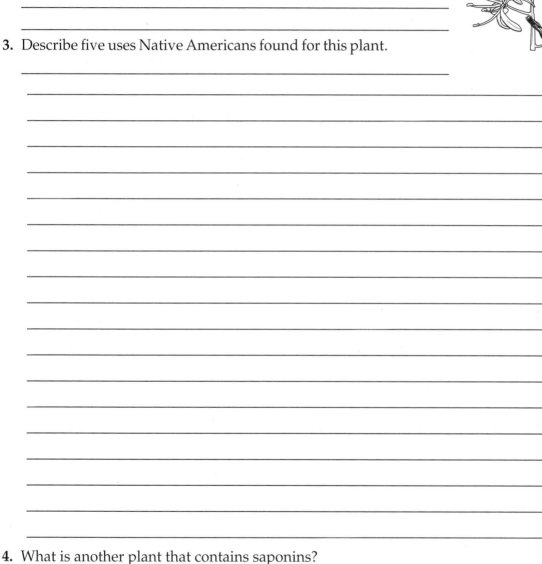

1. Find out the common name or names of this plant. *Chlorogalum pomeridianum* is the plant's botanical name.

   _____

2. What are saponins?

   _____

   _____

3. Describe five uses Native Americans found for this plant.

   _____

   _____

   _____

   _____

   _____

   _____

   _____

   _____

   _____

   _____

   _____

   _____

   _____

   _____

   _____

   _____

   _____

4. What is another plant that contains saponins?

   _____

© Pearson Education, Inc., publishing as Pearson Prentice Hall. All rights reserved.

Name _____ Date _____ Class _____

All American Soap Box Derby

Read the paragraphs about the soap box derby and then answer the questions on the lines below.

Years ago, a journalist in Dayton, Ohio, was assigned to photograph a home-town story about boys racing home-built cars. The journalist developed a national program of races to teach boys workmanship skills, competition, and perseverance. The first race was run in 1934. In 1935, the race moved to Akron because it was hillier than Dayton. In 1936, city leaders assigned the race a permanent track location. Girls began competing in 1971 and began winning in 1975.

All competitors design and build their cars. The total cost of their materials must not exceed a set amount. The cars use only gravity to propel them. Competitors must be 11 to 15 years old. They compete at local, state, and regional levels before the champions compete in Akron. Nowadays, competitors attend from several foreign countries.

At the championship race held in Akron, Ohio, each August, the regional champions compete on a 297-meter track. Before the race, their cars are weighed and inspected to ensure that the cars meet the competition's safety requirements. Speeds in the race average 42 kilometers per hour so safety is important.

The top racers each win scholarships and other prizes.

1. How does the terrain of Dayton compare to Akron?

    _____

2. How does the competition teach workmanship?

    _____

    _____

3. What force propels the cars to speeds of 42 kilometers per hour?

    _____

4. Have the competitors in Akron ever raced before? How do you know?

    _____

    _____

5. Do only Americans compete in the derby?

    _____

    _____

6. Would you want to build a car and compete in this race? Why or why not?

    _____

    _____

    _____

© Pearson Education, Inc., publishing as Pearson Prentice Hall. All rights reserved.

Name _____ Date _____ Class _____

Interdisciplinary Exploration • *Social Studies*

Soap and the Second World War

Read the paragraph below. Then, using encyclopedias, the Internet, and other research materials, find answers to the questions. Write your answers on the lines below.

During the Second World War, housewives were urged to save all cooking fat, bacon fat, meat drippings, and other fats and take them to their butcher. In return, they got extra ration points.

1. What was rationing?

   _____

   _____

   _____

2. In this unit, you learned about the soap-making process. After saponification, what is the byproduct that is pumped away?

   _____

3. How does this byproduct relate to fat?

   _____

   _____

4. What is nitroglycerin?

   _____

5. How does nitroglycerin relate to fat?

   _____

   _____

6. Why would the government want as much household fat as it could get during a war?

   _____

   _____

7. If the government was using all the fat to make explosives, how plentiful do you think soap was?

   _____

   _____

8. What effect do you think the war had on the development of detergents?

   _____

   _____

   _____

   _____

© Pearson Education, Inc., publishing as Pearson Prentice Hall. All rights reserved.

Name _____ Date _____ Class _____

The Case of the Curious Symbols

In this activity, you will solve a symbolic code and explain what it means. Write your answers on the lines provided.

1. While working for a secret government agency, you find in your shirt pocket the curious symbolic message shown below. Study the message.

a. _____
_____

b. _____
_____

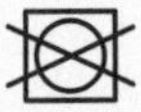

c. _____
_____

d. _____
_____

e. _____
_____

f. _____
_____

g. _____
_____

2. You contact an informant who tells you that the symbols are laundry care symbols, also called apparel care icons. These symbols, and others like them, appear on clothing labels.

3. Research what the symbols mean using reference books or electronic resources in the library.

4. On the lines beside the seven symbols, write a complete sentence explaining what each of the symbols means.

5. On the lines below, explain what the message is. Is there any significance to the message being in your shirt pocket?

_____
_____
_____
_____

© Pearson Education, Inc., publishing as Pearson Prentice Hall. All rights reserved.

Name _____ Date _____ Class _____

Write a Soap Story

The following vocabulary words all appeared in the text of the Interdisciplinary Exploration. Below each word, write a definition of the word. Use a dictionary if you need help.

1. antifreeze _____

   _____

2. ladle (verb) _____

   _____

3. detergent _____

   _____

4. colonists _____

   _____

5. spigot _____

   _____

6. consistency _____

   _____

7. continuously _____

   _____

8. germicide _____

   _____

9. Now write your soap story! On a separate sheet of paper, write a
   paragraph or two using as many of these words as you can.

© Pearson Education, Inc., publishing as Pearson Prentice Hall. All rights reserved.

Name _____ Date _____ Class _____

Lather Blather

In this activity, you will explore the claims of soap manufacturers and apply what you have learned about soap to evaluate whether the claims are reasonable. Write your answers on the lines provided.

1. For a few days, keep your eyes open for advertisements from bar soap manufacturers. What kinds of claims do the manufacturers make? Record some of the advertising slogans and claims on the lines.

    _____

    _____

    _____

    _____

    _____

    _____

    _____

2. Review what you learned in this unit about how soap works. Now think critically about the claims of manufacturers. For example, suppose an advertiser claims that their soap is so pure that it floats. Why would soap float? Does this property have any relation to purity? What do you think it means for a soap to be pure?

    _____

    _____

    _____

    _____

3. Look at some of the other claims that manufacturers made. Applying what you know about soap, which claim do you think is most reasonable? Explain.

    _____

    _____

    _____

    _____

4. Which claim do you think is most unreasonable? Explain.

    _____

    _____

    _____

    _____

© Pearson Education, Inc., publishing as Pearson Prentice Hall. All rights reserved.

Name _____ Date _____ Class _____

Can You Make Square Bubbles?

In this activity, you will explore why bubbles are round. You will need bubble mixture and paper clips or thin wire for this activity. You will also need modeling clay or dough. Write your answers on the lines.

1. Make a square bubble wand using a paper clip or a piece of thin wire. If you have extra wire, make a triangle shaped wand. Blow some bubbles using your wands. What shape are the bubbles?

   _____

2. Bubbles are always spherical because a sphere has the smallest possible surface area for its volume. You can explore this relationship using clay. Make a cube with modeling clay. Each side of your cube should be exactly 3 centimeters long.

3. What is the volume of your cube? Use the formula $V = 1^3$ (or $V = 1 \times 1 \times 1$).

   _____

4. What is the surface area of your cube? Use the formula: area = 6×1^2.

   _____

5. Now make your cube into a sphere. Use only the clay you used to make the cube. Estimate the radius of your sphere.

   _____

6. You know that the volume of the sphere has not changed because you used the same amount of clay as you used to make the cube. What is the approximate surface area of your sphere? Use the formula: surface area = $4\pi r^2$. Use 3.14 for π.

   _____

7. What do you conclude about the surface area of a sphere compared to a cube with the same volume?

   _____

   _____

© Pearson Education, Inc., publishing as Pearson Prentice Hall. All rights reserved.

Interdisciplinary Exploration • *Mathematics*

How Much Soap Do You Use?

The average American uses about 11 kilograms of soap per year to keep clean. In this activity, you will research and estimate how much soap you use each year. Write your answers on the lines.

1. Ask members of your household to estimate how long a bar of soap lasts in weeks or days. If your household uses liquid soap, include those amounts in your estimates. If you wish, you may keep the calculations separate and add together the masses in step 5.

   _____

   _____

2. Consider how many household members share the soap. About how long would one bar or one container last if only one person used it? Write your answer in weeks.

   _____

   _____

3. Using your answer to Question 2, calculate how many bars or containers of soap one person uses in one year. (*Hint:* How many weeks are in one year?)

   _____

   _____

4. What is the mass in grams of one bar or container of soap? If you cannot find a wrapper or container showing the mass, look at similar sized bars or containers of soap at the grocery store and estimate the mass of the soap you use.

   _____

   _____

5. Using your answers to Questions 3 and 4, calculate the mass of soap you use in one year.

   _____

   _____

6. Your answer may be different from the mass stated in the text and may differ from the answers of your classmates. Calculate the average mass of soap used in one year by you and your classmates.

   _____

   _____

© Pearson Education, Inc., publishing as Pearson Prentice Hall. All rights reserved.

Name _____ Date _____ Class _____

Comparing Soap Costs

Consumer research companies test and compare laundry soaps. In this activity, you will analyze cost data and conclude which brand of soap is the most cost-efficient. Write your answers on the lines.

1. The table shows several different laundry detergents, their price per box, and the number of washloads per box. The names of the laundry detergents have been replaced with letters so that researchers' personal biases do not influence the report. Each detergent in the table washes clothes equally well.

Laundry Detergent	Price per box ($)	Number of washloads per box	Cost per washload
A	2.82	9	
B	2.90	13	
C	3.00	12	
D	3.30	9	
E	3.80	12	
F	3.80	9	
G	3.85	12	
H	3.90	12	
I	3.99	30	
J	5.00	20	
K	5.60	16	
L	7.60	16	
M	23.95	60	

2. For each laundry detergent, calculate the cost per washload. Write your answers in the blank column in the table. Round each answer to the nearest penny.

3. Based on cost per washload, which detergent is the best purchase for consumers? If consumers cannot find this detergent, what three others would you recommend?

_____

4. Which detergent is the worst purchase?

_____

5. Could a consumer decide which detergent is the best purchase by just buying the cheapest box? Explain.

_____

© Pearson Education, Inc., publishing as Pearson Prentice Hall. All rights reserved.

Science: Bubble Formulas

2. Check that students make careful notes of each of the three bubble formulas.
3. Results will vary.
4. Check that students make careful notes about the formulas they tried and the results.

Science: How Soap Removes Dirt

5. The soap reduced the surface tension. The water no longer kept the paper clip afloat.
6. Soap reduces surface tension and allows the water molecules to surround the dirt particles.
7. Increasing the temperature of the water will give more energy to the water molecules. As the water molecules move with greater energy, the attractions between the water molecules should lessen, and the surface tension should weaken.
8. The paper clip won't float. The warmer water has a weaker surface tension.

Social Studies: What Is Chlorogalum pomeridianum?

1. amole or soap plant
2. Substances in plants that can be used to make soap
3. Answers will vary. Samples: They baked the bulbs for food. They made brushes from the fibers. Lather from the bulb made good soap. Lather from the bulb suffocated fish and made fish easier to catch. They made a glue from the bulb. The mashed bulb relieves sores, pains, and cramps. The leaves and shoots could be eaten. Juice from the leaves made a tattoo dye. Older leaves were wrapped around bread during baking.
4. Answers will vary. Samples: acacia, soapwort, soaproot, California pigweed

Social Studies: All-American Soap Box Derby

1. Dayton is flatter than Akron.
2. Competitors must build their own cars.
3. force of gravity
4. Yes, they are regional champions.
5. No, competitors from other countries compete too.
6. Accept all reasonable answers.

Social Studies: Soap and the Second World War

1. A government system of regulating how much each household can buy of certain items that are in short supply because of a national emergency such as a war

2. glycerin or glycerol
3. It is one of the compounds that makes up fat.
4. an explosive
5. It contains glycerol, which comes from fat.
6. To make explosives from the fat
7. Soap was probably hard to find.
8. The war probably encouraged detergents to be developed because people did not have very much soap.

Language Arts: The Case of the Curious Symbols

4. The symbols mean: **a.** Use gentle or delicate washer setting; **b.** The maximum water temperature should be 105°F or 40°C; **c.** Do not tumble dry the garment; **d.** Hang the garment wet and let it drip dry; **e.** Do not bleach the garment; **f.** Iron using a low temperature setting; **g.** The dry cleaner can dry-clean using any solvent.
5. The message provides instructions for proper care of a garment. They were probably put in the pocket by the manufacturer of the shirt.

Language Arts: Write a Soap Story

Students' definitions will vary. Samples follow:
1. Antifreeze is a liquid you put in a car radiator to keep the water in the radiator from freezing. (Some students may also find out antifreeze keeps a car from overheating, too.)
2. To serve liquid using a big deep spoon
3. A cleaner made from chemicals
4. The original settlers in a colony
5. faucet
6. thickness of a liquid
7. without stopping
8. Something that kills bacteria and other microorganisms
9. Accept all grammatically correct paragraphs that use at least half the words.

Language Arts: Lather Blather

1. Answers will vary. Query claims that seem unrelated to soap.
2. Soap floats because air is whipped into it. This has no relation to purity. Accept all reasonable answers about what "pure" means.
3. Accept all well thought-out answers.
4. Accept all well thought-out answers.

Mathematics: Can You Make Square Bubbles?

1. spherical
3. 27 cubic centimeters

© Pearson Education, Inc., publishing as Pearson Prentice Hall. All rights reserved.

4. Surface area is 54 square centimeters.
5. Radius is about 1.9 centimeters .
6. Surface area is about 45 square centimeters.
7. The surface area of a sphere is smaller than that of a cube with the same volume.

Mathematics: How Much Soap Do You Use?

1. Student answers will vary widely.
2. Student answers will vary widely.
3. Student answers will vary widely. Answers should be based on previous calculations, however.
4. A typical bar of soap has a mass of about 120 grams.
5. Student answers will vary widely. Answers should be based on previous calculations, however.
6. Accept all reasonable answers. Answers should be based on previous calculations.

Mathematics: Comparing Soap Cost

2.

Cost per washload
0.31
0.22
0.25
0.37
0.32
0.42
0.32
0.33
0.13
0.25
0.35
0.48
0.40

3. Detergent I is best. The next best are detergents B, C, and J.
4. Detergent L is the worst purchase.
5. No; the cheapest box, detergent A, is not the cheapest cost per washload.

© Pearson Education, Inc., publishing as Pearson Prentice Hall. All rights reserved.

Science Explorer ▪ *Target Reading Skills Handbook*

⟳ Target Reading Skills

Identifying Main Ideas

Identifying the main idea helps you understand what you are reading. Sometimes the main idea can be easy to find. For example, suppose that you are reading just one paragraph. Very often you will find the main idea in the first sentence, the topic sentence. The other sentences in the paragraph provide supporting details or support the ideas in the topic sentence.

Sometimes, however, the first sentence is not the topic sentence. Sometimes you may have to look further. In those cases, it might help to read the paragraph and summarize what you have read. Your summary can give you the main idea.

A textbook has many paragraphs, each one with its own main idea. However, just as a paragraph has a main idea and supporting details, so does the text under each heading in your textbook. Sometimes the main idea is the heading itself. Other times it is more difficult to find. You may have to infer a main idea by combining information from several paragraphs.

To practice this skill, you can use a graphic organizer that looks like this one.

Main Idea		
Detail	Detail	Detail
a.	b.	c.

Outlining

Outlining shows you how supporting details relate to main ideas. You can make an outline as you read. Using this skill can make you a more careful reader.

Your outline can be made up of sentences, simple phrases, or single words. What matters is that you follow a formal structure. To outline while you read, use a plan like this one.

I. Section Title
  A. Main Heading
    1. Subheading
      a. Detail
      b. Detail
      c. Detail

The main ideas or topics are labeled as Roman numerals. The supporting details or subtopics are labeled A, B, C, and so on. Other levels of supporting information can be added under heads. When you outline in this way, you are deciding just how important a piece of information is.

© Pearson Education, Inc., publishing as Pearson Prentice Hall. All rights reserved.

Science Explorer ▪ *Target Reading Skills Handbook*

Comparing and Contrasting

You can use comparing and contrasting to better understand similarities and differences between two or more concepts. Look for clue words as you read. When concepts or topics are similar, you will probably see words such as *also, just as, like, likewise,* or *in the same way.* When concepts or topics are different, you will see *but, however, although, whereas, on the other hand,* or *unlike.*

To use this skill, it sometimes helps to make a Venn diagram. In this type of graphic organizer, the similarities are in the middle, where the two circles overlap.

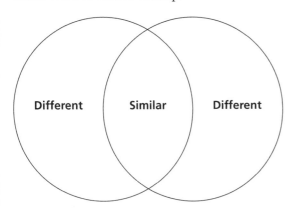

Relating Cause and Effect

Identifying causes and effects can help you understand the relationships among events. A cause is what makes something happen. An effect is what happens. In science, many actions cause other actions to occur.

Sometimes you have to look hard to see a cause-and-effect relationship in reading. You can watch for clue words to help you identify causes and effects. Look for *because, so, since, therefore, results, cause,* or *lead to.*

Sometimes a cause-and-effect relationship occurs in a chain. For example, an effect can have more than one cause, or a cause can have several effects. Seeing and understanding the relationships helps you understand science processes. You can use a graphic organizer like this one.

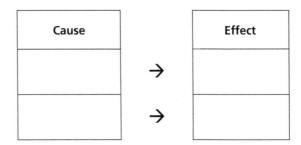

Asking Questions

Your textbook is organized using headings and subheadings. You can read the material under those headings by turning each heading into a question. For example, you might change the heading "Protecting Yourself During an Earthquake" to "How can you protect yourself during an earthquake?" Asking questions in this way will help you look for answers while reading. You can use a graphic organizer like this one to ask questions.

Question	Answer

© Pearson Education, Inc., publishing as Pearson Prentice Hall. All rights reserved.

Science Explorer ▪ *Target Reading Skills Handbook*

Sequencing

Sequencing is the order in which a series of events occurs. As you read, look for clue words that tell you the sequence or the order in which things happen. You see words such as *first, next, then,* or *finally.* When a process is being described, watch for numbered steps. Sometimes there are clues provided for you. Using the sequencing reading skill will help you understand and visualize the steps in a process. You can also use it to list events in the order of their occurrence.

You can use a graphic organizer to show the sequence of events or steps. The one most commonly used is a flowchart like this one.

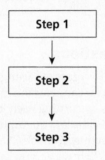

Sometimes, though, a cycle diagram works better.

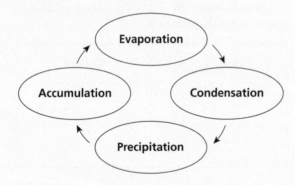

Using Prior Knowledge

Use prior knowledge to relate what you are reading to something that you already know. It is easier to learn when you can link new ideas to something that is already familiar to you. For example, if you know that fish are actually breathing oxygen that is dissolved in water, you wil be able to understand how or why gills work.

Using prior knowledge can help you make logical assumptions or draw conclusions about what you are reading. But be careful. Your prior knowledge might sometimes be wrong. As you read, you can confirm or correct your prior knowledge.

Use a graphic organizer like this one to link your prior knowledge to what you are learning as you read.

What You Know
1.
2.
3.

What You Learned
1.
2.
3.

© Pearson Education, Inc., publishing as Pearson Prentice Hall. All rights reserved.

Science Explorer ▪ *Target Reading Skills Handbook*

Previewing Visuals

Looking at visuals before you read can help you better understand a topic. Preview the visuals by reading labels and captions. For example, if you preview the visuals in a chapter about volcanoes, you will see more than just photographs of erupting volcanoes. You will see maps, diagrams, and photographs of rocks. These might tell you that you will learn where volcanoes are found, how they form, and what sort of rock is created when volcanoes erupt. Previewing visuals helps you understand and enjoy what you read.

One way to apply this strategy is to choose a few photographs, diagrams, or other visuals to preview. Then write questions about what you see. Answer the questions as you read.

Identifying Supporting Evidence

In science, you will read about hypotheses. A hypothesis is a possible explanation for scientific observations made by scientists or an answer to a scientific question. A hypothesis is tested over and over again. The tests may produce evidence that supports the hypothesis. When enough supporting evidence is collected, a hypothesis may become a theory.

Identifying supporting evidence in your reading can help you understand a hypothesis or theory. Evidence is made up of facts. Facts are information that can be confirmed by testing or observation.

When you are identifying supporting evidence, a graphic organizer like this one can be helpful.

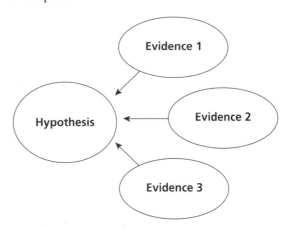

Building Vocabulary

To understand what someone is saying, you have to know the language that person is speaking. To understand science, you need to know what the words mean.

There are many ways to build your vocabulary. You can look up the meaning of a new word in a dictionary or glossary. Then you can write its definition in your own words. You can use the new word in a sentence. To figure out the meaning of a new word, you can use context clues or surrounding words. Look for prefixes and suffixes in the new word to help you break it down. Building vocabulary will get easier with practice.

Reading Skills Handbook

© Pearson Education, Inc., publishing as Pearson Prentice Hall. All rights reserved.

Guidelines for Laboratory Safety

This section on laboratory safety is included as a resource for the teacher. Rather than providing definitive rules and regulations, the information is intended to be the basis for the establishment of safe laboratory practice. Pearson Prentice Hall and its consultants make no claims as to the completeness of this material. Not all the precautions necessitated by the use, storage, and disposal of materials are covered here. Additional steps and safeguards may be required.

Responsibilities of the Teacher and the School

Laboratory safety is a shared responsibility. Both the school and the teacher need to be sure that all educational activities protect and promote the health and safety of students and the environment. To accomplish this goal, teachers need to understand the hazards, precautions, and emergency procedures associated with laboratory activities. When schools or teachers fail to live up to this responsibility, their behavior may be considered negligent. As a result, they may be liable for resulting injuries.

The best way to avoid being considered negligent is to ask yourself four simple questions:

1. What are the hazards?
2. What are the worst things that could happen?
3. What do I need to do if they do happen?
4. What are the prudent practices, protective facilities, and protective equipment needed to minimize the risk?

Be sure that you can answer all four of these questions before starting any science activity or demonstration. Then you can reduce the risks to an acceptable level—a level where the educational benefits of the activity outweigh the risks.

General Safety Strategies

Teachers should promote a "safety first" philosophy through personal example and by the careful planning and implementation of safety strategies.

The following strategies will help create an enjoyable, instructional, and safe environment.

1. Set up a safety committee made up of both teachers and administrators. Arrange to meet regularly to set safety policies for the school, discuss any safety problems that might arise, and organize periodic inspections of classrooms and laboratory equipment.

2. Establish a safety and health reference shelf in a resource center.

3. Develop detailed plans explaining what to do in case of emergency, including spills, cuts, burns, electric shock, poisoning, and fire. Review the procedures periodically throughout the school year.

4. Inform students of these emergency plans and carry out unannounced drills.

5. Explain to students how to use the intercom or other available means of communication to get help during an emergency.

6. Keep up to date in first aid and CPR (cardiopulmonary resuscitation) training.

7. Post emergency phone numbers for ambulance, fire, police, hospital, and the poison control center next to the telephone.

8. Perform laboratory investigations before assigning them to students. Take note of any potential hazards; devise plans for dealing with any possible mishaps or emergencies.

9. Emphasize safety considerations in pre-lab discussions. Display posters dealing with safety issues in the classroom as reminders.

10. Keep classroom aisles and exits free of obstructions.

© Pearson Education, Inc., publishing as Pearson Prentice Hall. All rights reserved.

11. During an investigation, move about the classroom to keep a constant watch for potentially dangerous situations.

12. Curtail inappropriate behavior immediately. Wild play and practical jokes are forbidden during labs. Once students realize that the practice of safety is a required part of the course, they will accept a serious approach to laboratory work.

13. Never leave students unattended while they are engaged in science activities.

14. Require proper clothing at all times. Insist that long hair, dangling jewelry, and loose clothing be restrained; do not allow students to wear open shoes.

15. Insist that students wear safety goggles when the lab requires it.

16. Encourage students to keep lab work space neat and clear of extraneous objects, such as books and jackets.

17. Make sure that investigations utilizing toxic, fuming, or flammable materials are performed under a fume hood.

18. Keep the fume hood clear of unnecessary chemicals and equipment. Have the fume hood checked periodically to ensure that it is operating safely and efficiently.

19. Demonstrate to students the proper handling of glass materials, such as beakers and graduated cylinders.

20. Only wastepaper should be discarded in wastepaper receptacles. Keep a separate container for broken glass.

21. Substitute plastic containers for glass ones whenever possible, including graduated cylinders and beakers.

22. Consider the use of dispensing containers for liquids. They help prevent spills, skin contact with chemicals, and waste.

23. Use hot plates in place of open flames whenever possible. Never use open flames or hot plates when flammables are present in the room.

24. Use only nonmercury thermometers in investigations that call for the measurement of temperature.

25. Do not permit students to insert glass tubing or thermometers into rubber stoppers. If necessary, do this task yourself. When inserting these items into rubber stoppers, use safety stoppers, which have holes with beveled edges and are easier to use. Use glycerin or water to lubricate the glass.

26. All electrical equipment used in the lab should have GFI (Ground Fault Interrupter) switches.

27. Do not leave equipment that is operating or plugged in unattended.

28. When working with live animals or plants, check ahead of time for students who may have allergies to the specimens.

29. Students should wear disposable nitrile, latex, or food-handling gloves when handling live animals or nonliving specimens.

30. Wearing safety equipment is required of all students.

31. Report in writing unsafe conditions to the department head, maintenance director, and principal.

32. Have clearly defined penalties for violations of safety rules. Have these penalties approved and supported by the principal.

33. Document safety training, rules violations, and penalties in your records.

34. Keep a record of injuries and incidents (close calls), no matter how minor they may seem. Discuss these events at a department meeting to avoid similar occurrences.

Laboratory Safety

© Pearson Education, Inc., publishing as Pearson Prentice Hall. All rights reserved.

Guidelines for Laboratory Safety *(continued)*

35. As a class, review the safety rules and symbols. Make sure students understand the safety rules.

36. Require students to sign the safety contract.

37. Conduct quarterly inspections of the classrooms and storage areas to maintain safe conditions.

Safety Equipment

Any classroom where laboratory investigations are performed should contain at least one each of the following pieces of safety equipment: (1) fire extinguisher, (2) fire blanket, (3) fire alarm, (4) phone or intercom to the office, (5) eyewash station, (6) safety shower, (7) safety hood, and (8) first-aid kit. If any of these basic pieces of safety equipment are not available, you may need to modify your laboratory program until the situation is remedied.

Make sure students know the location and proper use of all safety equipment. Where appropriate and practical, have students handle or operate the equipment so that they become familiar with it. Make sure all safety equipment is in good working order. All malfunctions should be promptly reported in writing to the proper school or district administrator.

Fire equipment At the beginning of the school year, you may wish to give each student the opportunity to actually operate a fire extinguisher, as the sound and action of a CO_2 fire extinguisher can be quite alarming to those who have never used one. You may also want to have students practice smothering imaginary flames on one another with the fire blanket.

Eyewash station The eyewash station should be used if chemicals are splashed onto the face or eyes. The exposed area should be left in the running water for five to ten minutes.

Safety shower The shower is used when chemicals have been spilled on a student's body or clothing. The student should stand under the shower until the chemical is completely diluted. Have a bathrobe or some type of replacement clothing handy in case the student's clothing is so badly contaminated that it must be removed.

You may want to set up one or two spill kits in your laboratory. The contents of a spill kit are used to neutralize chemicals, such as acids and bases, so that they can be cleaned up more easily. Baking soda (sodium bicarbonate) can be used to neutralize acids. Vinegar (acetic acid) can be used to neutralize bases. Commercial spill kits for acids, bases, and a number of other chemicals are available from supply houses.

Safety hood Use a safety hood whenever students are working with volatile or noxious chemicals. Make sure that the room is well ventilated when students are using any kind of chemicals or are working with preserved specimens. Warn students of the flammability and toxicity of various chemicals.

First-aid kit A typical first-aid kit contains an assortment of antiseptics, bandages, gauze pads, and scissors. Most also contain simple instructions for use. Be sure to read the instructions if you are not familiar with basic first-aid procedures. A first-aid kit should be taken on all field trips. For field trips, you may wish to add such items as a bee-sting kit, meat tenderizer, tweezers, and calamine lotion. Do not dispense medication (including aspirin).

© Pearson Education, Inc., publishing as Pearson Prentice Hall. All rights reserved.

Guidelines for the Use and Care of Animals

Animals are an essential part of a science curriculum. The judicious use of live or preserved animals can help students realize that the study of science is relevant, fascinating, and rewarding. It is important to be aware of and sensitive to ethical and practical concerns when studying animals. The purpose of this section is to discuss some realistic guidelines for using animals in the classroom.

1. Whenever possible, live animals should be observed in their natural habitats or in zoos, parks, and aquariums.

2. Check the state and federal codes regarding animal welfare that apply in your area. You may also wish to refer to guidelines published by the National Science Teachers Association, the National Association of Biology Teachers, and the International Science Fair. Make students aware of all safety rules and regulations regarding animals.

3. Before bringing a live animal into the classroom, determine whether a proper habitat can be maintained in the classroom. Such a habitat includes temperature, space, and type of food. Students should have a clear understanding of the appropriate care needed by the live animals brought into the classroom. Do not allow students to tap on animal enclosures or otherwise disturb the animals.

4. No wild vertebrate animals should be brought into the classroom. Purchase animals from a reputable dealer only.

5. Live animals should be nonpoisonous and healthy. Any mammals used in the classroom should be vaccinated against rabies unless the animals were purchased recently from a reliable scientific supply company. Quarantine any animal to make sure it is disease-free before bringing it into the classroom.

6. Make sure that the living quarters of classroom animals are clean, located away from stressful situations, appropriately spacious, and secure enough to confine the animal. You may wish to lock cages to prevent the accidental release of animals; the small padlocks used on luggage are good for this purpose.

7. Remove wastes from animal living quarters daily. Thoroughly clean animal living quarters periodically to ensure that they are odor and germ-free. Provide a daily supply of fresh water and any other needs specific to the particular animal.

8. Provide for the care of animals during weekends and school vacations. Inform the custodial staff of the presence of animals and warn them of any special requirements. For example, turning off the aquarium pump to save electricity or spraying the classroom for insects can be fatal to animals.

9. Students should be instructed how to handle each species brought into the classroom. Make students aware that they can receive painful wounds from the improper handling of some animals.

10. Animals should be handled only if necessary. If an animal is frightened or excited, pregnant, feeding, or with its young, special handling is required.

11. Students should thoroughly clean their hands after handling animals or the quarters containing animals.

12. Animals should be returned to their natural habitat after an observation period of not longer than 14 days. However, laboratory-bred animals or species that are not native to an area should not be released into the environment.

13. If an animal must be euthanized, do not allow students to watch. Contact the local humane society for advice.

Laboratory Safety

© Pearson Education, Inc., publishing as Pearson Prentice Hall. All rights reserved.

Guidelines for the Use and Care of Animals *(continued)*

14. Before performing any experiment involving live animals, check local and state regulations. In some states, certification is required before a teacher is permitted to experiment with animals.

15. No animal studies involving anesthetic drugs, pathogenic organisms, toxicological products, carcinogens, or radiation should be performed.

16. Any experiment requiring live animals should have a clearly defined objective relating to the teaching and learning of some scientific principle.

17. No experimental procedures that will cause pain, discomfort, or harm to animals should be done in the classroom or at home.

18. Surgical procedures should not be performed on live animals.

19. If fertilized bird eggs are opened, the embryo should be destroyed humanely two days before it would have hatched, at the latest.

20. When working with preserved animals, make sure that students maintain a serious and respectful attitude toward the specimens.

Handling Ethical Issues

There is much controversy regarding the use of animals in scientific research. This controversy extends to preserved animals in dissections as well as to live animals in experiments. Although the debate over what uses of animals are appropriate in a science classroom can be emotionally charged, it can also provide an opportunity for students to closely examine a current issue. You may wish to have students read current literature on the subject and contact groups and individuals with varying points of view.

Stress that it is important to make a rational, informed decision before taking a stand on any issue. Point out that it is vital to know and understand the arguments on all sides of an issue. Help students analyze the sources they find in terms of bias and the reliability and objectivity of the author(s). Help them to distinguish between fact and opinion. Encourage them to question what they read and hear. Challenge them to discover the hidden assumptions and implications of different points of view.

If dissections are a part of your curriculum and a student chooses to avoid dissections because of ethical concerns, respect that student's opinion. Point out, however, that no simulation or videotape can completely replace hands-on experience.

© Pearson Education, Inc., publishing as Pearson Prentice Hall. All rights reserved.

Guidelines for Safe Disposal of Laboratory Wastes

Every effort should be made to recover, recycle, and reuse materials used in the laboratory. When disposal is required, however, specific procedures should be followed to ensure that your school complies with local, state, and federal regulations.

1. Discard only dry paper into ordinary wastebaskets.

2. Discard broken glass into a separate container clearly marked "For Broken Glass Only."

3. Acidic or basic solutions need to be neutralized before disposal. Slowly add dilute sodium hydroxide to acids and dilute hydrochloric acid to bases until pH paper shows that they are no longer strongly acidic or basic. Then flush the solutions down the drain with a lot of water.

4. Before each investigation, instruct your students concerning where and how they are to dispose of chemicals that are used or produced during the investigation. Specific teacher notes addressing disposal are provided on each lab as appropriate.

5. Keep each excess or used chemical in a separate container; do not mix them. This allows for possible recycling or reuse. It also eliminates unexpected reactions or the need for expensive separation by a contractor if the wastes must be disposed of professionally.

6. Only nonflammable, neutral, nontoxic, nonreactive, and water-soluble chemicals should be flushed down the drain.

7. When growing bacterial cultures, use only disposable petri dishes. After streaking, the dishes should be sealed and not opened again by students. After the lab, students should return the unopened dishes to you and wash their hands with antibacterial soap.

8. For the safe disposal of bacterial cultures, autoclave the petri dishes and discard them without opening. If no autoclave is available, carefully open the dishes (never have a student do this), pour full-strength bleach into the dishes, and let them stand for a day. Then pour the bleach from the petri dishes down a drain and flush the drain with lots of water. Tape the petri dishes back together and place them in a sealed plastic bag. Wrap the plastic bag with a brown paper bag or newspaper and tape securely. Throw the sealed package in the trash. Thoroughly disinfect the work area with bleach.

9. To grow mold, use a new, sealable plastic bag that is two to three times larger than the material to be placed inside. Seal the bag and tape it shut. After the bag is sealed, students should not open it. To dispose of the bag and mold culture, make a small cut near an edge of the bag and cook the bag in a microwave oven on a high setting for at least one minute. Discard the bag according to local ordinance, usually in the trash.

Laboratory Safety

© Pearson Education, Inc., publishing as Pearson Prentice Hall. All rights reserved.

Science Explorer ▪ *Science Safety Rules*

Science Safety Rules

To prepare yourself to work safely in the laboratory, read the following safety rules. Then read them a second time. Make sure you understand and follow each rule. Ask your teacher to explain any rules you do not understand.

Dress Code

1. To protect yourself from injuring your eyes, wear safety goggles whenever you work with chemicals, flames, glassware, or any substance that might get into your eyes. If you wear contact lenses, notify your teacher.

2. Wear an apron or a lab coat whenever you work with corrosive chemicals or substances that can stain.

3. Tie back long hair to keep it away from any chemicals, flames, or equipment.

4. Remove or tie back any article of clothing or jewelry that can hang down and touch chemicals, flames, or equipment. Roll up or secure long sleeves.

5. Never wear open shoes or sandals.

General Precautions

6. Read all directions for an experiment several times before beginning the activity. Carefully follow all written and oral instructions. If you are in doubt about any part of the experiment, ask your teacher for assistance.

7. Never perform activities that are not assigned or authorized by your teacher. Obtain permission before "experimenting" on your own. Never handle any equipment unless you have specific permission.

8. Never perform lab activities without direct supervision.

9. Never eat or drink in the laboratory.

10. Keep work areas clean and tidy at all times. Bring only notebooks and lab manuals or written lab procedures to the work area. All other items, such as purses and backpacks, should be left in a designated area.

11. Do not engage in horseplay.

First Aid

12. Always report all accidents or injuries to your teacher, no matter how minor. Notify your teacher immediately about any fires.

13. Learn what to do in case of specific accidents, such as getting acid in your eyes or on your skin. (Rinse acids from your body with plenty of water.)

14. Be aware of the location of the first-aid kit, but do not use it unless instructed by your teacher. In case of injury, your teacher should administer first aid. Your teacher may also send you to the school nurse or call a physician.

15. Know the location of the emergency equipment such as the fire extinguisher and fire blanket.

16. Know the location of the nearest telephone and whom to contact in an emergency.

Heating and Fire Safety

17. Never use a heat source, such as a candle, burner, or hot plate, without wearing safety goggles.

18. Never heat anything unless instructed to do so. A chemical that is harmless when cool may be dangerous when heated.

19. Keep all combustible materials away from flames. Never use a flame or spark near a combustible chemical.

20. Never reach across a flame.

21. Before using a laboratory burner, make sure you know proper procedures for lighting and adjusting the burner, as demonstrated by your teacher. Do not touch the burner. It may be hot. Never leave a lighted burner unattended. Turn off the burner when it is not in use.

22. Chemicals can splash or boil out of a heated test tube. When heating a substance in a test tube, make sure that the mouth of the tube is not pointed at you or anyone else.

23. Never heat a liquid in a closed container. The expanding gases produced may shatter the container.

24. Before picking up a container that has been heated, first hold the back of your hand near it. If you can feel heat on the back of your hand, the container is too hot to handle. Use an oven mitt to pick up a container that has been heated.

© Pearson Education, Inc., publishing as Pearson Prentice Hall. All rights reserved.

Science Explorer • *Science Safety Rules*

Using Chemicals Safely

25. Never mix chemicals "for the fun of it." You might produce a dangerous, possibly explosive substance.

26. Never put your face near the mouth of a container that holds chemicals. Many chemicals are poisonous. Never touch, taste, or smell a chemical unless you are instructed by your teacher to do so.

27. Use only those chemicals needed in the activity. Read and double-check labels on supply bottles before removing any chemicals. Take only as much as you need. Keep all containers closed when chemicals are not being used.

28. Dispose of all chemicals as instructed by your teacher. To avoid contamination, never return chemicals to their original containers. Never pour untreated chemicals or other substances into the sink or trash containers.

29. Be extra careful when working with acids or bases. Pour all chemicals over the sink or a container, not over your work surface.

30. If you are instructed to test for odors, use a wafting motion to direct the odors to your nose. Do not inhale the fumes directly from the container.

31. When mixing an acid and water, always pour the water into the container first and then add the acid to the water. Never pour water into an acid.

32. Take extreme care not to spill any material in the laboratory. Wash chemical spills and splashes immediately with plenty of water. Immediately begin rinsing with water any acids that get on your skin or clothing, and notify your teacher of any acid spill at the same time.

Using Glassware Safely

33. Never force glass tubing or a thermometer into a rubber stopper or rubber tubing. Have your teacher insert the glass tubing or thermometer if required for an activity.

34. If you are using a laboratory burner, use a wire screen to protect glassware from any flame. Never heat glassware that is not thoroughly dry on the outside.

35. Keep in mind that hot glassware looks cool. Never pick up glassware without first checking to see if it is hot. Use an oven mitt. See rule 24.

36. Never use broken or chipped glassware. If glassware breaks, notify your teacher and dispose of the glassware in the proper broken-glassware container.

37. Never eat or drink from glassware.

38. Thoroughly clean glassware before putting it away.

Using Sharp Instruments

39. Handle scalpels or other sharp instruments with extreme care. Never cut material toward you; cut away from you.

40. Immediately notify your teacher if you cut your skin when working in the laboratory.

Animal and Plant Safety

41. Never perform experiments that cause pain, discomfort, or harm to animals. This rule applies at home as well as in the classroom.

42. Animals should be handled only if absolutely necessary. Your teacher will instruct you how to handle each animal species brought into the classroom.

43. If you know that you are allergic to certain plants, molds, or animals, tell your teacher before doing an activity in which these are used.

44. During field work, protect your skin by wearing long pants, long sleeves, socks, and closed shoes. Know how to recognize the poisonous plants and fungi in your area, as well as plants with thorns, and avoid contact with them. Never eat any part of a plant or fungus.

45. Wash your hands thoroughly after handling animals or a cage containing animals. Wash your hands when you are finished with any activity involving animal parts, plants, or soil.

End-of-Experiment Rules

46. After an experiment has been completed, turn off all burners or hot plates. If you used a gas burner, check that the gas-line valve to the burner is off. Unplug hot plates.

47. Turn off and unplug any other electrical equipment that you used.

48. Clean up your work area and return all equipment to its proper place.

49. Dispose of waste materials as instructed by your teacher.

50. Wash your hands after every experiment.

© Pearson Education, Inc., publishing as Pearson Prentice Hall. All rights reserved.

Science Explorer · *Science Safety Symbols*

Safety Symbols

These symbols appear in laboratory activities. They warn of possible dangers in the laboratory and remind you to work carefully.

Safety Goggles Wear safety goggles to protect your eyes in any activity involving chemicals, flames or heating, or glassware.

Lab Apron Wear a laboratory apron to protect your skin and clothing from damage.

Breakage Handle breakable materials, such as glassware, with care. Do not touch broken glassware.

Heat-Resistant Gloves Use an oven mitt or other hand protection when handling hot materials such as hot plates or hot glassware.

Plastic Gloves Wear disposable plastic gloves when working with harmful chemicals and organisms. Keep your hands away from your face, and dispose of the gloves according to your teacher's instructions.

Heating Use a clamp or tongs to pick up hot glassware. Do not touch hot objects with your bare hands.

Flames Before you work with flames, tie back loose hair and clothing. Follow instructions from your teacher about lighting and extinguishing flames.

No Flames When using flammable materials, make sure there are no flames, sparks, or other exposed heat sources present.

Corrosive Chemical Avoid getting acid or other corrosive chemicals on your skin or clothing or in your eyes. Do not inhale the vapors. Wash your hands after the activity.

Poison Do not let any poisonous chemical come into contact with your skin, and do not inhale its vapors. Wash your hands when you are finished with the activity.

Fumes Work in a ventilated area when harmful vapors may be involved. Avoid inhaling vapors directly. Only test an odor when directed to do so by your teacher, and use a wafting motion to direct the vapor toward your nose.

Sharp Object Scissors, scalpels, knives, needles, pins, and tacks can cut your skin. Always direct a sharp edge or point away from yourself and others.

Animal Safety Treat live or preserved animals or animal parts with care to avoid harming the animals or yourself. Wash your hands when you are finished with the activity.

Plant Safety Handle plants only as directed by your teacher. If you are allergic to certain plants, tell your teacher; do not do an activity involving those plants. Avoid touching harmful plants such as poison ivy. Wash your hands when you are finished with the activity.

Electric Shock To avoid electric shock, never use electrical equipment around water, or when the equipment is wet or your hands are wet. Be sure cords are untangled and cannot trip anyone. Unplug equipment not in use.

Physical Safety When an experiment involves physical activity, avoid injuring yourself or others. Alert your teacher if there is any reason you should not participate.

Disposal Dispose of chemicals and other laboratory materials safely. Follow the instructions from your teacher.

Hand Washing Wash your hands thoroughly when finished with the activity. Use antibacterial soap and warm water. Rinse well.

General Safety Awareness When this symbol appears, follow the instructions provided. When you are asked to develop your own procedure in a lab, have your teacher approve your plan before you go further.

© Pearson Education, Inc., publishing as Pearson Prentice Hall. All rights reserved.

Name _____ Date _____ Class _____

Laboratory Safety Contract

I, _____ ,
(please print full name)

have read the Science Safety Rules and Safety Symbols
sections, understand their contents completely, and agree to
demonstrate compliance with all safety rules and guidelines
that have been established in each of the following categories:

(please check)

❑ Dress Code

❑ General Precautions

❑ First Aid

❑ Heating and Fire Safety

❑ Using Chemicals Safely

❑ Using Glassware Safely

❑ Using Sharp Instruments

❑ Animal and Plant Safety

❑ End-of-Experiment Rules

_____
(signature)

Date _____

© Pearson Education, Inc., publishing as Pearson Prentice Hall. All rights reserved.

Laboratory Safety

Name _____ Date _____ Class _____

Chemical Interactions

Multiple Choice

Write the letter of the correct answer on the line at the left.

_____ 1. All of the following are properties of bases EXCEPT

    a. a bitter taste.   **b.** react with metals.

    c. a slippery feeling.   **d.** turn red litmus blue.

_____ 2. In the chemical equation $CH_4 + 2O_2 \rightarrow CO_2 + 2H_2O$, how does the total mass of the reactants compare to the total mass of the products?

    a. The reactants have greater mass.

    b. The products have greater mass.

    c. You need more information.

    d. The total masses are the same.

_____ 3. To start and maintain a fire, you need all of the following EXCEPT

    a. carbon dioxide.   **b.** oxygen.

    c. fuel.   **d.** heat.

_____ 4. The BEST evidence for a chemical reaction is

    a. the formation of a new substance.

    b. the production of a gas.

    c. a change in color.

    d. the formation of a solid.

_____ 5. An atom has a neutral charge because

    a. the atom has twice as many neutrons as protons.

    b. the atom has the same number of protons and neutrons.

    c. the atom has the same number of protons and electrons.

    d. the atom has the same number of electrons and neutrons.

_____ 6. Elements in the same group of the periodic table share characteristics because they have the same

    a. number of protons.   **b.** atomic mass.

    c. number of valence electrons.   **d.** atomic number.

_____ 7. Which of the following compounds contains covalent bonds?

    a. NaCl   **b.** CaF_2

    c. MgO   **d.** H_2O

_____ 8. A tablespoon of salt is thoroughly mixed into a cup of water. The water acts as a

    a. solvent.   **b.** solute.

    c. solution.   **d.** suspension.

_____ 9. An acid is a substance that

    a. forms hydrogen ions in water.   **b.** has a pH above 7.

    c. forms hydroxide ions in water.   **d.** turns red litmus paper blue.

© Pearson Education, Inc., publishing as Pearson Prentice Hall. All rights reserved.

____ **10.** The main function of enzymes in chemical digestion is

    a. to build up proteins.

    b. to convert starches to amino acids.

    c. to lower the pH of the digestive system.

    d. to speed up reactions by acting as catalysts.

Completion

Fill in the line to complete each statement.

11. A(n) _____ is a substance made of two or more elements chemically combined in a specific ratio.

12. A horizontal row in the periodic table is called a(n) _____.

13. When you have added so much solute to a solvent that no more solute dissolves, your solution is _____.

14. Polymers are made of smaller molecules called _____ linked together.

15. Like many _____ compounds, hydrocarbons mix poorly with water and are flammable.

True or False

If the statement is true, write true. *If it is false, change the underlined word or words to make the statement true.*

_____ **16.** A(n) <u>endothermic</u> reaction releases energy in the form of heat.

_____ **17.** A covalent bond in which electrons are shared equally is <u>nonpolar</u>.

_____ **18.** Increasing the surface area of a reactant <u>decreases</u> the rate of a chemical reaction.

_____ **19.** A <u>neutralization reaction</u> produces water and a salt.

_____ **20.** Different <u>nucleic acids</u> are made when different sequences of amino acids are linked into long chains.

Using Science Skills

Use the diagram below to answer the following questions.

$$K\cdot \quad \cdot \ddot{\underset{\cdot\cdot}{Cl}}:$$

21. Interpreting Illustrations What is this type of diagram called? What does each dot represent in the diagram?

_____

_____

© Pearson Education, Inc., publishing as Pearson Prentice Hall. All rights reserved.

Name _____ Date _____ Class _____

Chemical Interations · *Book Test*

22. Predicting Are these two atoms likely to form an ionic bond or a covalent bond? Explain your answer. What is the name of the compound formed?

_____

_____

_____

_____

23. Predicting Which of the three categories of chemical reaction will occur when the two atoms in the diagram react? Explain your answer.

_____

_____

Essay

Answer the following in the spaces provided.

24. Balance this chemical equation $Al + O_2 \rightarrow Al_2O_3$. Describe your reasoning.

_____

_____

_____

_____

25. What does pH tell you about a solution? Explain why pH can change when an acid is mixed with a base.

_____

_____

_____

_____

_____

Using Science Skills

Use the diagram below to answer the following questions.

a. 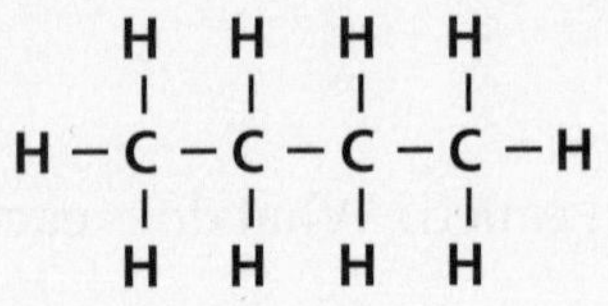
```
    H  H  H  H
    |  |  |  |
H − C −C −C −C −H
    |  |  |  |
    H  H  H  H
```

b.
```
    H  H  H
    |  |  |
H − C −C −C −H
    |  |  |
    H  |  H
     H − C − H
         |
         OH
```

c.
```
    H  H  H
    |  |  |
H − C −C −C −H
    |  |  |
    H  |  H
     H − C − H
         |
         H
```

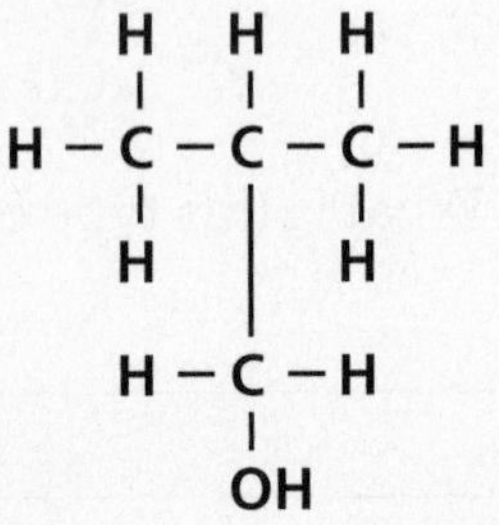

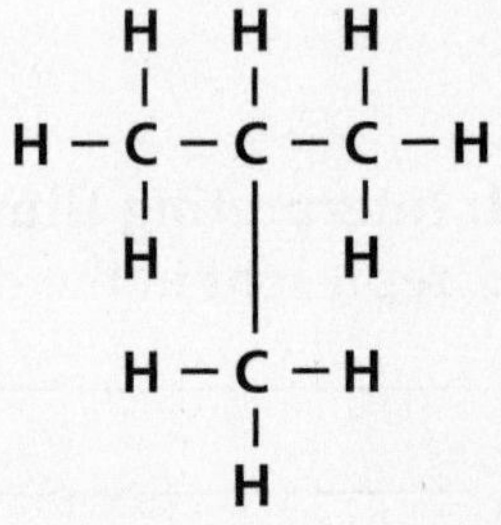

© Pearson Education, Inc., publishing as Pearson Prentice Hall. All rights reserved.

Name _____ Date _____ Class _____

Chemical Interations ▪ *Book Test*

26. Classifying Which of these organic compounds are isomers? Use the chemical formulas of these compounds to explain why they are isomers.

_____

_____

_____

_____

_____

27. Inferring Will any of these organic compounds dissolve in water? Explain.

_____

_____

_____

Essay

Write an answer for each of the following in the spaces provided.

28. Why are compounds with ionic bonds better conductors of electricity than compounds with covalent bonds?

_____

_____

_____

_____

_____

_____

29. If you chew a plain cracker for a few minutes, it begins to taste sweet. Explain why.

_____

_____

_____

_____

_____

_____

30. Describe four ways that a chemist might be able to speed up a chemical reaction.

_____

_____

_____

_____

_____

Book Test

© Pearson Education, Inc., publishing as Pearson Prentice Hall. All rights reserved.

Book Test

1. b
2. d
3. a
4. a
5. c
6. c
7. d
8. a
9. a
10. d
11. compound
12. period
13. saturated
14. monomers
15. organic
16. exothermic
17. true
18. increases
19. true
20. proteins
21. The diagram is called an electron dot diagram. Each dot represents a valence electron.
22. They are likely to form an ionic bond because Cl (chlorine) easily gains one electron, becoming a negative ion and K (potassium) easily loses an electron, becoming a positive ion. The oppositely charged ions attract each other. Potassium chloride is the name of the compound formed.
23. This is a synthesis reaction because two elements combine to make a more complex substance.
24. $4Al + 3O_2 \Rightarrow 2Al_2O_3$; Sample answer: To balance the oxygen atoms, there must be 6 on each side of the equation. Three molecules of O_2 and 2 molecules of Al_2O_3 works. Then there are 4 atoms of Al on the right, so 4 are needed on the left.
25. The pH measures the concentration of hydrogen ions (H^+) in a solution. It tells you how acidic or basic the solution is. When an acid is mixed with a base, the hydrogen ions react with hydroxide ions (OH^-) to form water. The new pH of the solution is higher than that of the original acid, but lower than that of the original base (closer to neutral).
26. Compounds a and c are isomers. Both have the chemical formula C_4H_{10}. Compounds that have the same chemical formula but different structures are isomers.
27. Yes. Compound b will dissolve in water because it is an alcohol and most alcohols dissolve well in water.
28. When an ionic compound is dissolved in water, the ions, which are charged particles, are free to move around; therefore, electricity can flow. In compounds with covalent bonds, there are no charged particles available to move around.
29. The saliva in your mouth contains an enzyme that helps break down the starch in the cracker into smaller sugar molecules. You taste these sugar molecules.
30. The rate of chemical reactions can be increased by increasing the surface area of reactants, increasing their temperature, increasing the concentration of reactants, or using a catalyst. The first three steps increase the number of particles that come together to react or increase the amount of energy the particles have. A catalyst usually works by lowering the activation energy required to start a reaction.

© Pearson Education, Inc., publishing as Pearson Prentice Hall. All rights reserved.

Atoms and Bonding

© Pearson Education, Inc., publishing as Pearson Prentice Hall. All rights reserved.

Lab zone | Chapter Project • Models of Compounds

The following steps will walk you through the Chapter Project. Use the hints and detailed directions as you guide your students through planning, model construction, and presentation.

Chapter Project Overview

To introduce the project, bring a ball-and-stick modeling kit into the classroom to show to students. Talk about how different colors of balls represent different elements. Also, discuss how bonds between atoms are represented in this kit.

Have students read the Chapter Project Overview. Review the project's rules, and hand out the Chapter Project Scoring Rubric that you will use for scoring students' work. Discuss with students what will be expected of them.

Set a deadline for the project presentation and interim dates for the Keep Students on Track at the ends of Section 1, Section 3, Section 4, and Section 5. Encourage students to copy the dates in the Project Timeline.

Group students. Have them brainstorm a list of possible materials they can use for modeling. Go over their suggestions and discuss the advantages and drawbacks of using these materials.

Distribute copies of Chapter Project Worksheet 1. Have students read over the questions that they will need to answer in the planning stage of this project. Students may then complete the worksheet.

Check over students' answers to Chapter Project Worksheet 1, and make sure that they have planned out how they will construct their models. Once students have your approval, they are ready to begin building their atoms.

Chapter Project Worksheet 2 will help students think about constructing their compounds. Distribute this worksheet after students have finished building their atoms.

Remind students to refer to the hints in the Chapter Project Overview as they plan and carry out the project.

Tell students they will be making a class presentation of their models in which they will explain how each aspect of the atoms and molecules is represented.

Consider organizing the class in groups to do the project. If space and time are limited, you may want to select the compounds that students will model.

Materials and Preparation

You will need a ball-and-stick model kit for the project launch.

When students are building their atoms, they will need a variety of materials such as raisins, gumdrops, jellied fruit candies, marshmallows, jellybeans, and clay. Allow students to be creative when selecting these materials. They will also need permanent markers to illustrate valence electrons on their atoms.

Additionally, students will require items such as tape, toothpicks, pipe cleaners, and paper clips when they begin joining their atoms into compounds.

Keep Students on Track— Section 1

Check each student's selection of materials for appropriateness before allowing students to begin making their atoms. If they select edible materials, make sure they know not to eat them. If the materials are perishable, have students plan ahead so they can make their models close to the date of the class presentations.

Make sure students have considered how they will attach atoms with chemical bonds. Using soft materials will make this easier.

Make sure students have thought about how they will illustrate the valence electrons. They should distribute these electrons evenly around their atoms. You may want to make some sample models of several different unbonded atoms to show that each model atom must include information on the number of valence electrons.

Check that students are making multiple models of each atom for later use in compound modeling.

© Pearson Education, Inc., publishing as Pearson Prentice Hall. All rights reserved.

Keep Students on Track— Section 3

Check that students are modeling several different ionic compounds. Check their models for accuracy. Make sure they are modeling compounds, not mixtures. They should understand the difference.

Point out that compounds containing ionic bonds do not occur as molecules. They are better modeled as crystals with indefinite boundaries.

Keep Students on Track— Section 4

Check students' models for accuracy. Make sure they have made several different molecules, including diatomic gases and compounds.

Students should understand the differences between single, double, and triple bonds. All three types should be demonstrated in their models.

Make sure students understand that each atom in molecules containing covalent bonds should have eight valence electrons (except for hydrogen, which should have two).

Keep Students on Track— Section 5

Tell students to be prepared to explain how they made their models and why they chose the materials they did.

Chapter Project Performance Assessment

In their class presentations, be sure that students fully explain how they represented different nuclei, valence electrons, ionic bonds, and covalent bonds in their models. Why did they make those particular choices? (*Samples: materials were soft and easily penetrated, came in several different colors, readily available*)

You may suggest that students make a chart giving an overview of all their atoms and compounds. This may help to make their presentations go more smoothly.

Have students turn in any written work you require. Students may then dispose of any perishable models. Make sure they do not eat any edible materials.

Extension/Options

Consider allowing students to work in pairs for this project. Make sure each partner contributes equally to the model planning and building.

Instead of allowing students to select the compounds that they will model, assign different compounds to different students. This will increase the diversity of compounds that will be modeled.

For some of the simpler molecular compounds modeled, have students speculate which may be polar or nonpolar. Ask students what further information they would need to know to be certain of their answers. (*An atom's pull on electrons; the arrangement in space of the atoms in the molecule*).

© Pearson Education, Inc., publishing as Pearson Prentice Hall. All rights reserved.

Atoms and Bonding · *Chapter Project*   **Overview**

Models of Compounds

In this chapter, you will be learning about atoms and the bonds that form between them. To illustrate bonding, chemists use ball-and-stick modeling kits. These kits usually contain balls that represent the atoms and sticks that represent the chemical bonds between the atoms. The balls are usually color-coded, with different colors representing different elements. Different stick types are usually included so that different types of chemical bonds (single, double, or triple) can be modeled.

In this project, you will create your own modeling kits. Your kits will contain several different atoms with their valence electrons clearly illustrated. They will also contain chemical bonds that you will use to join the atoms together. You will use these kits to create compounds that contain either ionic or covalent bonds. You can use your models to build simple molecules having single covalent bonds, as well as models of compounds containing double or triple bonds. At the end of the project, you will give a brief class presentation in which you explain your models and discuss why you used particular materials when constructing your models.

Project Rules

- Have your teacher approve your materials before you begin building your models.

- You must show valence electrons on your atom models.

- You should create at least six models of compounds—three with ionic bonds, and three with covalent bonds. You must model all three types of covalent bonds—single, double, and triple.

- You will be giving a brief class presentation in which you explain each of your models. You must be able to explain your choice of materials.

Suggested Materials

- Be creative when selecting the materials for building your models. Some suggestions include raisins, gumdrops, jellied fruit candies, marshmallows, jellybeans, and clay.

- Chemical bonds can be modeled by using items such as tape, toothpicks, pipe cleaners, and paper clips.

- Permanent markers can be used to illustrate valence electrons on your atoms.

© Pearson Education, Inc., publishing as Pearson Prentice Hall. All rights reserved.

Atoms and Bonding • *Chapter Project* Overview

Project Hints

- When selecting your materials for making atoms, think about how you will join your atoms together. Softer materials (marshmallows) may work better than harder items (hard candies) because you can join them with toothpicks or paper clips.

- If you plan on using materials that are perishable, make sure you construct your models close to the date of the class presentations so that the models do not spoil before you present them. You might also consider storing your models in a refrigerator to slow the decay process. **CAUTION:** *Do not eat any food materials you use in this project.*

- When making your atom models, make sure that you make multiples of each element because you will need several when creating your models of compounds.

- Compounds containing ionic bonds form crystals of indefinite size. Each ion is held in place by the attractive force between it and neighboring ions with opposite electric charges. Such compounds can be modeled as patterns of alternating ions with no two ions of the same element next to each other.

- Some of your models may include elements that exist as molecules made of one kind of atom.

- When preparing for your class presentation, it might be helpful to create a chart that gives an overview of all your models. This chart could act as a key, explaining how you have illustrated different elements and types of bonds.

Project Timeline

Task	Due Date
1. Materials selected.	_____
2. Materials approved.	_____
3. Atom models completed.	_____
4. Models of compounds with ionic bonds completed.	_____
5. Models of molecules with covalent bonds completed.	_____
6. Class presentation made.	_____

© Pearson Education, Inc., publishing as Pearson Prentice Hall. All rights reserved.

Atoms and Bonding • *Chapter Project*   **Worksheet 1**

Models of Compounds

Complete the following tasks using a separate sheet of paper. When the tasks have been completed, you are ready to get your teacher's approval and begin the Chapter Project.

Constructing Atoms

1. What materials will you use to model your atoms?
2. How will you differentiate between atoms of different elements?
3. How will you illustrate valence electrons on your atoms?
4. Here is a table of some elements that you will be modeling. Complete the table by recording the number of valence electrons for each element. Also, indicate what material you will use to model each element. For example, if you are using differently colored gumdrops, indicate the color that you will use for each element. Add to the table other elements you wish to model.

Element (Symbol)	Number of Valence Electrons	Model Key
Carbon (C)		
Chlorine (Cl)		
Fluorine (F)		
Hydrogen (H)		
Iodine (I)		
Magnesium (Mg)		
Nitrogen (N)		
Oxygen (O)		
Sodium (Na)		
Sulfur (S)		

© Pearson Education, Inc., publishing as Pearson Prentice Hall. All rights reserved.

Name _____ Date _____ Class _____

Models of Compounds

Compounds Containing Ionic Bonds

Complete this table with the compounds that you plan to model. List the ions that come together to form each compound and the charges of the ions. Also, describe how you plan to construct your model.

Compound	Ions	Ionic Charge	Plan for Model
Sodium Chloride (NaCl)	Na^+	1+	
	Cl^-		
Potassium Oxide (K_2O)			

Molecules Containing Covalent Bonds

Complete this table with the molecules that you plan to model. Name the type of covalent bond found in the molecule, and give a brief description of how you plan to construct your model.

Compound	Type of Bond (Single, Double, Triple)	Plan for Model
Water (H_2O)		
Carbon Dioxide (CO_2)		
Chlorine (Cl_2)		
Hydrogen (H_2)		

© Pearson Education, Inc., publishing as Pearson Prentice Hall. All rights reserved.

Atoms and Bonding ▪ *Chapter Project*

Scoring Rubric

Lab Zone Chapter Project — **Models of Compounds**

In evaluating how well you complete the Chapter Project, your teacher will judge your work in four categories. In each, a score of 4 is the best rating.

	4	3	2	1
Planning for Model Construction	Student's plans include all information about joining atoms, illustrating valence electrons, and differentiating between elements.	Student's plans include most information about joining atoms, illustrating valence electrons, and differentiating between elements. Makes minor omissions or errors.	Student fails to plan for one of the following: joining atoms, illustrating valence electrons, or differentiating between elements. Makes several omissions or errors.	Student makes significant omissions or errors in planning the joining of atoms, illustrating valence electrons, or differentiating between elements.
Constructing Atom Models	Student correctly builds multiple models of all required elements and includes the appropriate number of valence electrons on atoms.	Student correctly builds multiple models of most required elements and includes the appropriate number of valence electrons on atoms.	Student correctly builds models of most required elements, but fails to make multiples or include the appropriate number of valence electrons.	Student builds some models, but fails to make multiples or include the appropriate number of valence electrons.
Constructing Compound Models	Student correctly makes more than six model compounds and correctly distinguishes between ionic and covalent bonds. All three types of covalent bonds are represented.	Student correctly makes at least six models and correctly distinguishes between ionic and covalent bonds. Only two types of covalent bonds are represented.	Student makes four or five models, but fails to represent one or two types of covalent bonds. Distinction between ionic and covalent bonds is fairly clear.	Student makes fewer than four models and represents at most one type of covalent bond. Incorrectly distinguishes between ionic and covalent bonds.
Presenting the Models	Student makes a thorough, well-organized presentation with a clear explanation of reasons for material choices.	Student makes a good presentation with a mostly clear explanation of reasons for material choices.	Student makes a presentation, but it is hard to follow. Some reasons for material choices given.	Student gives a brief or confused presentation. Reasons for material choices are very sketchy.

© Pearson Education, Inc., publishing as Pearson Prentice Hall. All rights reserved.

SECTION LESSON PLAN

Elements and Atoms

⏱ *2–3 periods, 1–1 1/2 blocks*

Ability Levels Key
L1 Basic to Average
L2 For All Students
L3 Average to Advanced

Atoms and Bonding

Objectives

L.1.1.1 Explain why elements are sometimes called the building blocks of matter.

L.1.1.2 Describe how atomic theory developed and changed.

Key Terms

- matter • element • compound • mixture
- atom • scientific theory • model • electrons
- nucleus • protons • energy level • neutrons

Local Standards

PRETEACH

Build Background Knowledge

Students recall what they already know about elements and atoms from previous science courses.

 **Discover Activity** *How Far Away Is the Electron?* **L1**

Targeted Resources

☐ **All in One** **Teaching Resources**
   L2 Reading Strategy Transparency L1: Outlining
☐ 💿 **Presentation-Pro CD-ROM**

INSTRUCT

The Building Blocks of Matter Compare and contrast compounds and mixtures and relate them to elements.

Atomic Theory and Models Use questioning to guide students in understanding why atoms are represented by models.

Targeted Resources

☐ **All in One** **Teaching Resources**
   L2 Guided Reading, pp. 47–48
   L2 Transparencies L2, L3
☐ **PHSchool.com** Web Code: cgd-2011
☐ 💿 **Student Edition on Audio CD**

ASSESS

Section Assessment Questions

🕙 Have students use their completed outlines to answer the questions.

Reteach

Students name the particles making up atoms and identify their locations and electric charges.

Targeted Resources

☐ **All in One** **Teaching Resources**
   Section Summary, p. 46
   L1 Review and Reinforce, p. 49
   L3 Enrich, p. 50

© Pearson Education, Inc., publishing as Pearson Prentice Hall. All rights reserved.

Atoms and Bonding ▪ *Section Summary*

Elements and Atoms

Guide for Reading

■ Why are elements sometimes called the building blocks of matter?

■ How did atomic theory develop and change?

Elements are the simplest pure substances. They cannot be broken down into any other substances. Iron and oxygen are elements. **Elements are often called the building blocks of matter because all matter is composed of one element or a combination of two or more elements.**

Elements usually exist with other elements in the form of compounds. A **compound** is a pure substance made of two or more elements that are combined chemically in a specific ratio. Table salt is an example of a compound. Elements can also mix with other elements without combining chemically. A **mixture** is two or more substances that are in the same place but are not chemically combined. Air is an example of a mixture. The smallest particle of an element is an **atom**.

Scientific theories about the atom began to develop in the 1600s. A **scientific theory** is a well-tested idea that explains and connects a wide range of observations. Theories often include **models**—physical or other representations of an idea to help people understand what they cannot observe directly. **Atomic theory grew as a series of models that developed from experimental evidence. As more evidence was collected, the theory and models were revised.**

John Dalton proposed one of the first models of the atom. Dalton thought that atoms were like smooth, hard balls that could not be broken into smaller pieces. In 1897, J. J. Thomson discovered that atoms contained negatively charged particles. He proposed a model of the atom in which negatively charged particles were scattered throughout a ball of positive charge. The negatively charged particles later became known as **electrons**.

In 1911, Ernest Rutherford did experiments that showed that an atom is mostly empty space, with electrons moving around a small, positively charged center. Rutherford called this small positive region in the center of the atom the **nucleus**. He determined that the nucleus contained positively charged particles, which he named **protons**. In 1913, Niels Bohr revised the atomic model again. Bohr showed that electrons move around the nucleus in certain orbits according to their energy. According to Bohr, the electrons were like planets orbiting the sun. In the 1920s, the atomic model changed again. Scientists determined that electrons could be anywhere in a cloudlike region around the nucleus. A region where electrons of the same energy are likely to be found is called an **energy level**. In 1932, James Chadwick discovered another particle in the nucleus of the atom. It was called a **neutron** because it is electrically neutral. Since the 1930s, the model of the atom has not changed much. Scientists conclude the atom consists of a small, positively charged nucleus, containing protons and neutrons, which is surrounded by a cloudlike region of negatively charged electrons.

© Pearson Education, Inc., publishing as Pearson Prentice Hall. All rights reserved.

Atoms and Bonding · *Guided Reading and Study*

Elements and Atoms

This section describes elements and atoms. It also explains how atomic theory developed and changed.

Use Target Reading Skills

As you read the section, complete the outline about elements and atoms. Use the red headings for the main ideas and the blue headings for the supporting ideas.

Elements and Atoms
I. The building blocks of matter
A. Elements, compounds, and mixtures
B.
II. Atomic theory and models
A.
B.

The Building Blocks of Matter

1. The simplest pure substances are called _____ .

2. Why are elements often called the building blocks of matter?

   _____

   _____

3. Complete the table about combinations of elements.

Type of Combination	What Is Combined?	Combined Chemically (Yes/No)
Compound	a.	Yes
b.	Elements, compounds, or both	c.

4. Is the following sentence true or false? Sodium chloride is an example of a compound. _____

© Pearson Education, Inc., publishing as Pearson Prentice Hall. All rights reserved.

Atoms and Bonding • *Guided Reading and Study*

Elements and Atoms (continued)

5. Circle the letter of each choice that is an example of a mixture.

    a. air   **b.** soil

    c. gasoline   **d.** oxygen

6. The smallest particle of an element is a(n) _____.

Atomic Theory and Models

7. Why do scientists use models to help them understand atoms?

    _____

    _____

    _____

8. Circle the letter of each sentence that is part of John Dalton's atomic theory.

    a. All elements are composed of atoms.

    b. No two atoms of the same element are exactly alike.

    c. An atom of one element cannot be changed into an atom of a different element.

    d. Atoms cannot be created or destroyed in any chemical changes.

9. Is the following sentence true or false? With only a few changes, Dalton's atomic theory is still accepted today. _____

10. Who described the atom as negative charges scattered through a ball of positive charge? _____

11. What experiment convinced Ernest Rutherford that the atom has a small, positively charged nucleus? _____

12. The term Rutherford gave to the positively charged particles in the nucleus of an atom was _____.

13. The atomic model of _____ resembled planets orbiting the sun.

14. A region around the nucleus in which electrons of the same energy are likely to be found is called a(n) _____.

15. What particle did Chadwick discover in 1932 that was hard to detect because it had no electrical charge? _____

16. Is the following sentence true or false? Since the 1930s, the model of the atom has changed a great deal. _____

17. Circle the letter of each sentence that we now know to be true about atoms.

    a. Most of the mass of atoms is due to electrons.

    b. Atoms have no overall electrical charge.

    c. Atoms of different elements have the same number of protons.

    d. Most of the volume of atoms consists of protons and neutrons.

© Pearson Education, Inc., publishing as Pearson Prentice Hall. All rights reserved.

Name _____ Date _____ Class _____

Elements and Atoms

Label each model of the atom with the name of the scientist who developed it.

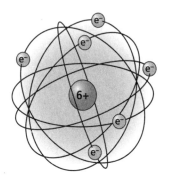  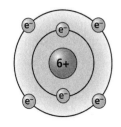 

1. _____   2. _____   3. _____   4. _____

Building Vocabulary

Match each term with its definition by writing the letter of the correct definition on the line beside the term in the left column.

_____ 5. matter

_____ 6. element

_____ 7. compound

_____ 8. mixture

_____ 9. atom

_____ 10. scientific theory

_____ 11. model

_____ 12. electron

_____ 13. nucleus

_____ 14. proton

a. two or more substances that are in the same place but not chemically combined

b. negatively charged particle in an atom

c. well-tested idea that explains and connects a wide range of observations

d. anything that has mass and takes up space

e. smallest particle of an element

f. positively charged region in the center of an atom

g. pure substance made of two or more elements that are combined chemically in a specific ratio

h. positively charged particle in the nucleus of an atom

i. physical or other representation of an idea to help people understand what they cannot observe directly

j. simplest pure substance that cannot be broken down into any other substance

© Pearson Education, Inc., publishing as Pearson Prentice Hall. All rights reserved.

Atoms and Bonding • *Enrich*

Discovery of the Electron

Scientists now know that an atom is made up of protons, neutrons, and electrons. However, as you read in the section, scientists once thought that atoms could not be divided into smaller parts. It wasn't until the late 1800s that electrons were discovered. At that time, scientists were studying the flow of electricity inside a glass tube. A simple diagram of one of these experiments is shown in the following figure.

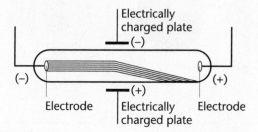

When the scientists sent an electric current through the tube, they found that the gas inside the tube began to glow. The glowing beam, or ray, started at the negatively charged end of the tube and traveled to the positively charged end. The ray was deflected by an electric field having a positive plate on one side and a negative plate on the other side. The deflection showed that the ray was composed of charged particles. These charged particles were later named eletrons.

Answer the following questions on a separate sheet of paper.

1. Electricity is the flow of electrons from one place to another. Explain how the above experiment confirms that statement.

2. Based on the results of the experiment described above, what charge does an electron have? Explain your answer.

3. What was the purpose of the electric field in the setup shown above? If the ray were composed of light, how would it be affected by the electric field?

4. Scientists did further experiments using the setup shown above. They used different metals for the disks at the ends of the tube, and also used different gases inside the tube. They found that the electrons behaved the same way every time. Based on their results, what can you infer about the electrons of various elements?

© Pearson Education, Inc., publishing as Pearson Prentice Hall. All rights reserved.

Atoms, Bonding, and the Periodic Table

Ability Levels Key
L1 Basic to Average
L2 For All Students
L3 Average to Advanced

Atoms and Bonding

⏱ *3–4 periods, 1 1/2–2 blocks*

Objectives

L.1.2.1 Explain how the reactivity of elements is related to valence electrons in atoms.

L.1.2.2 State what the periodic table tells you about atoms and the properties of elements.

Key Terms
- valence electrons • electron dot diagram
- chemical bond • symbol • atomic number
- period • group • family • noble gas
- halogen • alkali metal

Local Standards

PRETEACH

Build Background Knowledge
Students use a familiar analogy to understand why it is important for elements to be organized.

 *What Are the Trends in the Periodic Table?* **L1**

Targeted Resources

- ☐ **All in One Teaching Resources**
  L2 Reading Strategy: Building Vocabulary
- ☐ ⊙ **Presentation-Pro CD-ROM**

INSTRUCT

Valence Electrons and Bonding Introduce electron dot diagrams to help students visualize valence electrons and understand their role in bonding.

The Periodic Table Guide students in learning how to use the periodic table by asking them to locate information in the periodic table.

 Comparing Atom Sizes **L2**

Targeted Resources

- ☐ **All in One Teaching Resources**
  L2 Guided Reading, pp. 53–55
  L2 Transparencies L4, L5
  L2 Lab: *Comparing Atom Sizes,* pp. 58–60
- ☐ 📼 **Lab Activity Video/DVD**
  Lab: *Comparing Atom Sizes*
- ☐ **PHSchool.com** Web Code: cgp-1032
- ☐ ⊙ **Student Edition on Audio CD**

ASSESS

Section Assessment Questions
🔆 Have students use their completed definitions of key terms to answer the questions.

Reteach
Students identify properties of different types of elements, including noble gases, halogens and alkali metals.

Targeted Resources

- ☐ **All in One Teaching Resources**
  Section Summary, p. 52
  L1 Review and Reinforce, p. 56
  L3 Enrich, p. 57

© Pearson Education, Inc., publishing as Pearson Prentice Hall. All rights reserved.

Atoms and Bonding ▪ *Section Summary*

Atoms, Bonding, and the Periodic Table

Guide for Reading

■ How is the reactivity of elements related to valence electrons in atoms?

■ What does the periodic table tell you about atoms and the properties of elements?

The electrons of an atom are arranged in energy levels. **Valence electrons** are those electrons that are in the highest energy level and held most loosely. **The number of valence electrons in an atom of an element determines many properties of that element, including the ways in which the atom can bond with other atoms.** Each element has a specific number of valence electrons, ranging from 1 to 8. An **electron dot diagram** represents the valence electrons of an atom. It includes the symbol for the element surrounded by dots. Each dot stands for one valence electron.

Most atoms are more stable when they have eight valence electrons. When atoms react, they usually do so in a way that makes each atom more stable. Either the number of valence electrons increases to eight, or an atom gives up its most loosely held valence electrons. Atoms that react this way become chemically combined, or bonded together. A **chemical bond** is the force of attraction that holds two atoms together as a result of the rearrangement of electrons between them. When atoms bond, a chemical reaction occurs and new substances form.

The periodic table is a system for organizing the elements into categories. In the table, each element is represented by a **symbol** consisting of one or two letters. Above the symbol is the element's atomic number. The **atomic number** is the number of protons in the nucleus of an atom of that element. A row of elements across the periodic table is called a **period**. Within each period, atomic number increases from left to right. **As the number of protons (atomic number) increases, the number of electrons also increases. As a result, the properties of the elements change in a regular way across a period.**

Elements in the same column are called a **group** or **family**. Elements within a group always have the same number of valence electrons. As a result, all the members of a group have similar properties. Group 18 elements are the **noble gases**. Atoms of these elements except helium have eight valence electrons. This makes them very stable. Elements in Group 17 are the **halogens**. Their atoms have seven valence electrons. They react easily with elements whose atoms can give up or share electrons. Group 1 is the **alkali metal** family. Their atoms have only one valence electron. They can become stable by losing just one electron, so they also react easily. Elements in Groups 2 through 12 are also metals. Most of these elements have one, two, or three valence electrons, and they are reactive. Nonmetals are found in groups 13 through 18. They have four or more valence electrons. Nonmetals can combine with metals by gaining electrons and with other nonmetals by sharing electrons.

© Pearson Education, Inc., publishing as Pearson Prentice Hall. All rights reserved.

Atoms, Bonding, and the Periodic Table

This section explains how the reactivity of elements is related to the number of electrons in the highest energy level. It also describes what the periodic table can tell you about atoms and the properties of elements.

Use Target Reading Skills

After you read this section, reread the paragraphs that contain definitions of Key Terms. Use all the information you have learned to write a definition of each Key Term in your own words.

valence electrons

_____

_____

electron dot diagram

_____

_____

chemical bond

_____

_____

symbol

_____

_____

atomic number

_____

_____

period

_____

_____

group

_____

_____

family

_____

_____

noble gas

_____

_____

halogen

_____

_____

alkali metal

_____

_____

© Pearson Education, Inc., publishing as Pearson Prentice Hall. All rights reserved.

Atoms and Bonding • *Guided Reading and Study*

Atoms, Bonding, and the Periodic Table *(continued)*

Valence Electrons and Bonding

1. _____ are those electrons that are held most loosely in an atom.

2. Is the following sentence true or false? The number of valence electrons in an atom of an element determines the ways in which the atom can bond. _____

3. Identify each element and the number of valence electrons it has.

H ·   · C ·   · O :

a. _____   b. _____   c. _____

_____   _____   _____

4. Circle the letter of each sentence that is true about valence electrons and chemical bonding.

   a. Most atoms are less stable when they have eight valence electrons.
   b. Atoms with eight valence electrons easily form compounds.
   c. Having eight valence electrons makes atoms very reactive.
   d. Atoms with eight valence electrons are less likely to form chemical bonds than atoms with fewer valence electrons.

5. Is the following sentence true or false? When atoms bond, new substances are formed. _____

The Periodic Table

6. How are elements represented in the periodic table?

   _____

   _____

7. The _____ of an element is the number of protons in the nucleus of an atom.

8. What is a row of elements across the periodic table called?

   _____

9. Describe how atomic number changes across a period of elements.

   _____

   _____

10. What are elements in the same column of the periodic table called?

    _____

11. Elements within a group always have the same number of

    _____.

© Pearson Education, Inc., publishing as Pearson Prentice Hall. All rights reserved.

Atoms and Bonding · *Guided Reading and Study*

12. Complete the table about groups of elements in the periodic table.

Group Number	Group Name	Number of Valence Electrons	Reactivity (High/Low)
1	a.	1	b.
17	c.	7	d.
18	e.	8	f.

13. How many valence electrons do all nonmetals have?

_____

14. Describe two ways that nonmetals can combine with other elements.

_____

_____

_____

_____

15. How do metalloids differ from metals?

_____

_____

_____

16. Is the following sentence true or false? Hydrogen is considered to be a metal. _____

© Pearson Education, Inc., publishing as Pearson Prentice Hall. All rights reserved.

Name _____ Date _____ Class _____

Atoms, Bonding, and the Periodic Table

Understanding Main Ideas

Use the diagrams to answer questions 1–5 in the spaces provided.

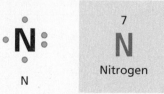

1. What is the atomic number of the element represented by the diagrams?
   _____

2. How many protons does the element have? _____

3. How many valence electrons does the element have?
   _____

4. Is the element reactive or stable? How do you know?
   _____

   _____

5. Is the element a metal or nonmetal? _____

Building Vocabulary

Fill in the blank to complete each statement.

6. An atom's _____ are those electrons that are in the highest energy level.

7. The force of attraction that holds two atoms together is called a(n)
   _____

8. Each element is represented in the periodic table by a(n)
   _____.

9. The number of protons in the nucleus of an atom is called the
   _____.

10. A row of elements across the periodic table is a(n)
    _____.

11. Elements in the same column of the periodic table are called a(n)
    _____.

© Pearson Education, Inc., publishing as Pearson Prentice Hall. All rights reserved.

Name _____ Date _____ Class _____

The Rockets' Red Glare

Many people enjoy fireworks displays on the Fourth of July. Did you know that chemistry plays a big part in the beauty and the noise? Depending on the chemical compound used in each firework rocket, a different color and effect is produced. A diagram of a typical rocket is shown at the right. When the gunpowder at the bottom of the rocket is lit, it lifts the rocket off the ground and into the air. When the rocket reaches its maximum height, a second fuse burns, setting the other chemicals in the rocket on fire. As these chemicals burn, they produce smoke, color bursts, loud noises, or a combination of these things.

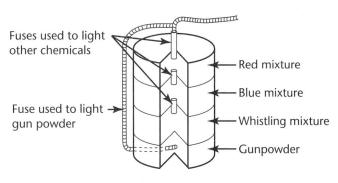

Fuses used to light other chemicals

Fuse used to light gun powder

Red mixture

Blue mixture

Whistling mixture

Gunpowder

The table below lists some chemicals and the effects they produce when combined in a rocket.

Element	Special effect
strontium	red color
barium	green color
copper	blue color
sodium	yellow color
magnesium or aluminum	white color
potassium or sodium	whistling sound
potassium and sulfur	white smoke

Answer the following questions on a separate sheet of paper.

1. What groups of the periodic table do the majority of the elements listed in the table above belong to? Why do you think elements in these groups are used in making fireworks?
2. What group of elements could you NOT use in making fireworks? Explain your answer.
3. Why would you want to have two or more separate fuses in a rocket?
4. Solutions of magnesium, barium, and strontium are clear and colorless. Predict what might happen if a drop of each solution was held in the flame of a lab burner.

© Pearson Education, Inc., publishing as Pearson Prentice Hall. All rights reserved.

Atoms and Bonding · *Skills Lab*

Comparing Atom Sizes

Problem

How is the radius of an atom related to its atomic number?

Skills Focus

making models, graphing, interpreting data

Materials

drawing compass

metric ruler

calculator

periodic table of the elements (Appendix D)

Procedure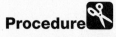

Review the safety guidelines in Appendix A.

1. Using the periodic table as a reference, predict whether the size (radius) of atoms will increase, remain the same, or decrease as you go from the top to the bottom of a group, or family, of elements.

2. The data table on the next page lists elements in Group 2 of the periodic table. The atomic radius of each element is given in picometers (pm). Record your data in the data table.

3. Calculate the relative radius of each atom compared to beryllium, the smallest atom listed. Do this by dividing each radius by the radius of beryllium. (*Hint:* The relative radius of magnesium would be 160 pm divided by 112 pm, or 1.4 pm.) Record these values, rounded to the nearest tenth, in the data table.

4. Using a compass, draw a circle for each element with a radius that corresponds to the relative radius you calculated in Step 3. Use centimeters as your unit for the radius of each of these circles. Use the space below or a separate sheet for your circles. **CAUTION:** *Do not push the sharp point of the compass against your skin.*

5. Label each model with the symbol of the element it represents.

© Pearson Education, Inc., publishing as Pearson Prentice Hall. All rights reserved.

Name _____ Date _____ Class _____

Atoms and Bonding · *Skills Lab*

Data Table

Atomic Number	Element	Radius (pm)*	Relative Radius
4	Be	112	1
12	Mg	160	
20	Ca	197	
38	Sr	215	
56	Ba	222	

* A picometer (pm) is one billionth of a millimeter.

Analyze and Conclude

Write your answers in the spaces provided.

1. **Making Models** Based on your models, was your prediction in Step 1 correct? Explain.

   _____

   _____

   _____

   _____

2. **Graphing** On a sheet of graph paper, make a graph of the data given in the first and third columns of the data table. Label the horizontal axis *Atomic Number*. Mark the divisions from 0 to 60. Then label the vertical axis *Radius* and mark its divisions from 0 to 300 picometers.

3. **Interpreting Data** Do your points fall on a straight line or on a curve? What trend does your graph show?

   _____

   _____

   _____

   _____

4. **Predicting** Predict where you would find the largest atom in any group, or family of elements. What evidence would you need to tell if your prediction is correct?

   _____

   _____

   _____

   _____

© Pearson Education, Inc., publishing as Pearson Prentice Hall. All rights reserved.

Atoms and Bonding ▪ *Skills Lab*

Comparing Atoms Sizes (*continued*)

5. **Communicating** Write a paragraph explaining why it is useful to draw a one- to two-centimeter model of an atom that has an actual radius of 100 to 200 pm.

_____

_____

_____

_____

_____

_____

_____

_____

_____

_____

_____

More to Explore
Look up the atomic masses for the Group 2 elements. Devise a plan to model their relative masses using real-world objects.

© Pearson Education, Inc., publishing as Pearson Prentice Hall. All rights reserved.

Ionic Bonds

3–4 periods, 1 1/2–2 blocks

Ability Levels Key
L1 Basic to Average
L2 For All Students
L3 Average to Advanced

Objectives

L.1.3.1 Describe ions and explain how they form bonds.

L.1.3.2 Explain how the formulas and names of ionic compounds are written.

L.1.3.3 Identify the properties of ionic compounds.

Key Terms

- ion • polyatomic ion • ionic bond
- ionic compound • chemical formula
- subscript • crystal

Local Standards

PRETEACH

Build Background Knowledge
Students recall what they have learned about electrons and electrical charge as a review of what they need to know to understand ions and ionic bonds.

 **Discover Activity** *How Do Ions Form?* **L1**

Targeted Resources

☐ **All in One Teaching Resources**
   L2 Reading Strategy Transparency L6: Previewing Visuals
☐ ⊙ **Presentation-Pro CD-ROM**

INSTRUCT

Ions and Ionic Bonds Introduce common ions that students will see throughout the book.

Chemical Formulas and Names Explain how chemical formulas reflect the composition of ionic compounds.

Properties of Ionic Compounds Have students compare and contrast different ionic compounds to infer their shared properties.

Skills Lab *Shedding Light on Ions* **L2**

Targeted Resources

☐ **All in One Teaching Resources**
   L2 Guided Reading, pp. 63–66
   L2 Transparencies L7, L8
   L2 Lab: *Shedding Light on Ions*, pp. 69–72
☐ ▭ **Lab Activity Video/DVD**
   Skills Lab: *Shedding Light on Ions*
☐ **PHSchool.com** Web Code: scn-1213
☐ ⊙ **Student Edition on Audio CD**

ASSESS

Section Assessment Questions
↻ Have students use their completed graphic organizers to answer the questions.

Reteach
Students describe properties of ionic compounds.

Targeted Resources

☐ **All in One Teaching Resources**
   Section Summary, p. 62
   L1 Review and Reinforce, p. 67
   L3 Enrich, p. 68

© Pearson Education, Inc., publishing as Pearson Prentice Hall. All rights reserved.

Atoms and Bonding • *Section Summary*

Ionic Bonds

Guide for Reading

■ What are ions, and how do they form bonds?

■ How are the formulas and names of ionic compounds written?

■ What are the properties of ionic compounds?

An **ion** is an atom or group of atoms that has an electric charge. **When an atom loses an electron, it loses a negative charge and becomes a positive ion. When an atom gains an electron, it gains a negative charge and becomes a negative ion.** Some ions are made of several atoms. Ions that are made of more than one atom are called **polyatomic ions**. You can think of polyatomic ions as a group of atoms that react as a unit. Like other ions, polyatomic ions have an overall positive or negative charge.

Positive ions and negative ions attract one another because they are oppositely charged. An **ionic bond** is the attraction between two oppositely charged ions. **Ionic bonds form as a result of the attraction between positive and negative ions.** A compound that consists of positive and negative ions is called an **ionic compound**. Sodium chloride is an example of an ionic compound. The sodium ion is positively charged, and the chloride ion is negatively charged.

Compounds can be represented by chemical formulas. A **chemical formula** is a combination of symbols that shows the ratio of elements in a compound. **When ionic compounds form, the ions come together in a way that balances out the charges on the ions. The chemical formula for the compound reflects this balance.** For example, the formula of magnesium chloride is $MgCl_2$. A magnesium ion has a charge of 2+, and a chloride ion has a charge of 1-. Therefore, two chloride ions are needed to balance one magnesium ion in the compound. The number "2" in the formula is a subscript. A **subscript** tells you the ratio of elements in the compound. An ionic compound is named according to certain rules. **For an ionic compound, the name of the positive ion comes first, followed by the name of the negative ion.**

All ionic compounds are similar in some ways. **Ionic compounds are hard, brittle crystals that have high melting points. When dissolved in water or melted, they conduct electricity.** The ions in ionic compounds form an orderly, three-dimensional arrangement called a **crystal**. Every ion is attracted to the oppositely charged ions above, below, and to all sides of it. The strength of these ionic bonds makes ionic crystals hard and brittle. Because ionic bonds are strong, a lot of energy is needed to break them. As a result, ionic compounds have high melting points and are solids at room temperature. When ionic compounds dissolve in water, the bonds are broken and the ions are free to move. This allows the solution to conduct electricity.

© Pearson Education, Inc., publishing as Pearson Prentice Hall. All rights reserved.

Atoms and Bonding · *Guided Reading and Study*

Ionic Bonds

This section explains how an atom becomes electrically charged. It also describes the characteristic properties of bonds formed by the attraction of electrically charged atoms.

Use Target Reading Skills

Before you read, preview Figure 17. Then write two questions that you have about the diagram in the graphic organizer below. As you read, answer your questions.

Formation of an Ionic Bond

Q.
A.
Q.
A.

Ions and Ionic Bonds

1. An atom or group of atoms that has an electric charge is called a(n) _____ .

2. What happens to an atom when it loses an electron?

   _____

   _____

   _____

3. What happens to an atom when it gains an electron?

   _____

   _____

   _____

© Pearson Education, Inc., publishing as Pearson Prentice Hall. All rights reserved.

Atoms and Bonding • *Guided Reading and Study*

Ionic Bonds *(continued)*

4. Ions that are made of more than one atom are called
   _____.

5. Use the table in the textbook to complete the table below.

Ions and Their Charges		
Name	**Charge**	**Symbol or Formula**
Sodium	a.	b.
Magnesium	c.	d.
Chloride	e.	f.
Sulfate	g.	h.

6. Compared to the number of protons, how many electrons does the
   carbonate ion (CO_3^{2-}) have? What is its charge?

   _____

   _____

7. What kinds of ions do a sodium atom and a chlorine atom become when
   a valence electron is transferred from one to the other?

   _____

   _____

   _____

8. What is an ionic bond?

   _____

   _____

   _____

9. What causes ionic bonds to form?

   _____

   _____

   _____

© Pearson Education, Inc., publishing as Pearson Prentice Hall. All rights reserved.

Name _____ Date _____ Class _____

Atoms and Bonding ▪ *Guided Reading and Study*

Chemical Formulas and Names

10. A(n) _____ is a combination of symbols that shows the ratio of elements in a compound.

11. Is the following sentence true or false? When ionic compounds form, the ions come together in a way that balances out the charges on the ions. _____

12. In the chemical formula for magnesium chloride ($MgCl_2$), what is the number "2" called, and what does it tell you?

_____

_____

_____

13. Is the following sentence true or false? For an ionic compound, the name of the negative ion comes first. _____

14. When does the end of a name of a negative ion end in *-ide*?

_____

_____

_____

Properties of Ionic Compounds

15. What are three characteristic properties of ionic compounds?

a. _____

b. _____

c. _____

16. An orderly, three-dimensional arrangement formed by ions is called a(n) _____.

17. In an ionic compound, which ions are attracted to each other?

_____

_____

_____

© Pearson Education, Inc., publishing as Pearson Prentice Hall. All rights reserved.

Atoms and Bonding ▪ *Guided Reading and Study*

Ionic Bonds *(continued)*

18. Why do ionic compounds have high melting points?

_____

_____

_____

_____

19. At room temperature, ionic bonds are strong enough to cause all ionic compounds to be _____.

20. Why do ionic compounds conduct electricity well when they are dissolved in water?

_____

_____

_____

_____

_____

_____

© Pearson Education, Inc., publishing as Pearson Prentice Hall. All rights reserved.

Atoms and Bonding • *Review and Reinforce*

Ionic Bonds

Understanding Main Ideas

Answer the following questions on a separate sheet of paper.

1. How does an atom become a positive ion? How does an atom become a negative ion?
2. How do ions form electrically neutral compounds?
3. What characteristics do solid ionic compounds share?
4. Why does the electrical conductivity of ionic compounds change when they are dissolved in water?

Ions and Their Charges		
Name	**Charge**	**Symbol/Formula**
Ammonium	1+	NH_4^+
Potassium	1+	K^+
Calcium	2+	Ca^{2+}
Magnesium	2+	Mg^{2+}
Chloride	1–	Cl^-
Oxide	2–	O^{2-}
Sulfide	2–	S^{2-}
Phosphate	3–	PO_4^{3-}

Use the chart above to answer the following on a separate sheet of paper.

5. How many potassium ions are needed to balance the charge of one sulfide ion? Explain.
6. Predict the formulas for calcium chloride and potassium phosphate.
7. Name the following compounds: MgS, NH_4Cl, and K_2O.
8. Which ions in the table are polyatomic ions?

Building Vocabulary

Answer the following questions on a separate sheet of paper.

9. What is an ion?
10. What is an ionic bond?
11. What is the arrangement of ions in a crystal?

© Pearson Education, Inc., publishing as Pearson Prentice Hall. All rights reserved.

Name _____ Date _____ Class _____

Pulling Away Electrons

You know that the metals in Group 1 and 2 are quite reactive. They combine easily with certain other elements to form compounds by losing electrons. Atoms from Group 1 lose one electron; atoms from Group 2 lose two electrons. It takes energy to remove an electron from an atom. Some atoms hold their electrons tighter than others do. Also, an individual atom holds some of its electrons tighter than others of its electrons.

The size of an atom's radius affects how tightly it holds its electrons. The larger the radius of an atom, the farther away from the nucleus some of its electrons are. The electron held the least tightly is easiest to remove. To remove yet another electron requires more energy than was needed to remove the first. The figure below compares the atomic radii of the Group 1 and 2 elements. The number underneath each element represents the atomic radius measured in picometers (pm).

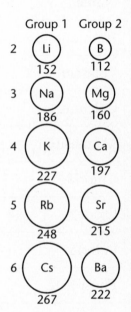

Answer the following questions on a separate sheet of paper.

1. What do you notice about atomic radius as you move down a group? As you move across a period from Group 1 to Group 2?

2. Which element would you expect to be the most reactive in Group 1? In Group 2? Explain your answer.

3. Within each period, which element of the two elements would you expect to be more reactive? Explain your answer.

4. As you go across the periodic table, atomic radius continues to decrease. How does this fact help explain why the atoms of noble gases don't react easily with other atoms?

© Pearson Education, Inc., publishing as Pearson Prentice Hall. All rights reserved.

Atoms and Bonding ▪ *Skills Lab*

Shedding Light on Ions

Problem

What kinds of compounds produce ions in solution?

Skills Focus

controlling variables, interpreting data, inferring

Materials

2 dry cells, 1.5-V

small light bulb and socket

4 lengths of wire with alligator chips on both ends

2 copper strips

distilled water

small beaker

small plastic spoon

sodium chloride

graduated cylinder, 100-mL

additional materials supplied by your teacher

or conductivity probe

or a conductivity probe

Procedure 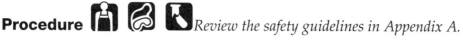 *Review the safety guidelines in Appendix A.*

1. Make a conductivity tester as described below or, if you are using a conductivity probe, see your teacher for instructions.

Making a Conductivity Tester
A. Use wire with alligator clips to connect the positive terminal of a dry cell to a lamp socket. CAUTION: The bulb is fragile and can break.
B. Similarly connect another wire between the negative terminal of the cell and the positive terminal of the second cell.
C. Connect one end of a third wire to the negative terminal of the second dry cell.
D. Connect one end of a fourth wire to the other terminal of the lamp socket.

© Pearson Education, Inc., publishing as Pearson Prentice Hall. All rights reserved.

Atoms and Bonding ▪ *Skills Lab*

Shedding Light on Ions *(continued)*

2. Pour about 50 mL of tap water into a small beaker. Place the copper strips in the beaker. Be sure the strips are not touching each other. Attach the alligator clip of the free end of one wire to a copper strip. Do the same with the other wire and the other copper strip. Record your observations in the data table.

3. Disconnect the wires from the copper strips. Take the strips out of the beaker, and pour out the tap water. Dry the inside of the beaker and the copper strips with a paper towel.

4. Pour 50 mL of distilled water into the beaker. Reconnect the conductivity tester and test the water as in Step 2. Keep the copper strips about the same distance apart as in Step 2. Record your observations in the data table.

5. Use 3 spoonfuls of sodium chloride to make a small pile on a clean piece of paper. Dry off the copper strips of the conductivity tester and use it to test the conductivity of the sodium chloride. Record your observations.

Data Table

Sample	Observations	Produced Ions in Solution? (yes/no)
Tap water		
Distilled water		
Sodium chloride		
Sodium chloride in water		

© Pearson Education, Inc., publishing as Pearson Prentice Hall. All rights reserved.

Atoms and Bonding · *Skills Lab*

6. Add 1 spoonful of sodium chloride to the distilled water in the beaker. Stir with the spoon until the salt dissolves. Repeat the conductivity test and record your observations.

7. Disconnect the conductivity tester and rinse the beaker, spoon, and copper strips with distilled water. Dry the beaker as in Step 3.

8. Test sucrose (table sugar) in the same ways that you tested sodium chloride in Steps 4 through 7. Test additional materials supplied by your teacher.

   ■ If the material is a solid, mix 1 spoonful of it with about 50 mL of distilled water and stir until the material dissolves. Test the resulting mixture.

   ■ If the substance is a liquid, simply pour about 50 mL into the beaker. Test it as you did the other mixtures.

Analyze and Conclude

Write your answers in the spaces provided.

1. **Controlling Variables** Why did you test both tap water and distilled water before testing the sodium chloride solution?

   _____

   _____

   _____

   _____

   _____

2. **Interpreting Data** Could you have used tap water in your tests instead of distilled water? Explain.

   _____

   _____

   _____

   _____

   _____

3. **Drawing Conclusions** Based on your observations, add a column to your data table indicating whether each substance produced ions in solution.

© Pearson Education, Inc., publishing as Pearson Prentice Hall. All rights reserved.

Atoms and Bonding · *Skills Lab*

Shedding Light on Ions *(continued)*

4. **Inferring** Sodium chloride is an ionic compound. How can you account for any observed differences in conductivity between dry and dissolved sodium chloride?

    _____

    _____

    _____

    _____

    _____

5. **Communicating** Based on your observations, decide whether or not you think sucrose (table sugar) is made up of ions. Explain how you reached your answer, using evidence from the experiment.

    _____

    _____

    _____

    _____

    _____

Design an Experiment

Design an experiment to test the effects of varying the spacing between the copper strips of the conductivity tester. *Obtain your teacher's permission before carrying out your investigation.*

© Pearson Education, Inc., publishing as Pearson Prentice Hall. All rights reserved.

Covalent Bonds

⏱ *2–3 periods, 1–1 1/2 blocks*

Ability Levels Key
- **L1** Basic to Average
- **L2** For All Students
- **L3** Average to Advanced

Objectives

L.1.4.1 State what holds covalently bonded atoms together.

L.1.4.2 Identify the properties of molecular compounds.

L.1.4.3 Explain how unequal sharing of electrons occurs and how it affects molecules.

Local Standards

Key Terms
- covalent bond • molecule • double bond
- triple bond • molecular compound
- polar bond • nonpolar bond

PRETEACH

Build Background Knowledge
Students recall that atoms can form bonds by sharing electrons.

 **Discover Activity** *Can Water and Oil Mix?* **L1**

Targeted Resources

❑ **All in One** **Teaching Resources**
  L2 Reading Strategy Transparency L9: Asking Questions
❑ 💿 **Presentation-Pro CD-ROM**

INSTRUCT

How Covalent Bonds Form Introduce covalent bonds by comparing and contrasting them with ionic bonds, with which students are already familiar.

Molecular Compounds Use a graphic organizer to summarize important points about molecular compounds and their properties.

Unequal Sharing of Electrons Use the familiar example of water to explain why some molecules are polar.

Targeted Resources

❑ **All in One** **Teaching Resources**
  L2 Guided Reading, pp. 75–77
  L2 Transparencies L10, L11, L12
❑ **www.SciLinks.org** Web Code: scn-1214
❑ 💿 **Student Edition on Audio CD**

ASSESS

Section Assessment Questions
🕒 Have students use their completed graphic organizers to answer the questions.

Reteach
Students define or describe and give examples of the key terms.

Targeted Resources

❑ **All in One** **Teaching Resources**
  Section Summary, p. 74
  L1 Review and Reinforce, p. 78
  L3 Enrich, p. 79

© Pearson Education, Inc., publishing as Pearson Prentice Hall. All rights reserved.

Atoms and Bonding · *Section Summary*

Covalent Bonds

Guide for Reading

■ What holds covalently bonded atoms together?

■ What are the properties of molecular compounds?

■ How does unequal sharing of electrons occur, and how does it affect molecules?

The chemical bond formed when two atoms share electrons is called a **covalent bond**. Covalent bonds usually form between atoms of nonmetals. Except for the noble gases, nonmetals can bond to other nonmetals by sharing electrons. **The force that holds atoms together in a covalent bond is the attraction of each atom's nucleus for the shared pair of electrons.** A neutral group of atoms joined by covalent bonds is called a **molecule**. The number of covalent bonds a nonmetal atom can form equals the number of valence electrons needed to make a total of eight. Some atoms share two pairs of electrons, forming a **double bond**. Some atoms even form **triple bonds** in which their atoms share three pairs of electrons.

A **molecular compound** is a compound that is composed of molecules. The molecules of a molecular compound often contain atoms that are covalently bonded. Molecular compounds have very different properties than ionic compounds. **Compared to ionic compounds, molecular compounds have lower melting points and boiling points, and they do not conduct electricity when dissolved in water.**

Atoms of some elements pull more strongly on shared electrons than do atoms of other elements. As a result, the electrons are pulled more toward one atom, causing the bonded atoms to have slight electrical charges. These charges are not as strong as the charges on ions. A covalent bond in which electrons are shared unequally is a **polar bond**. If two atoms pull equally on the shared electrons, neither atom becomes charged. When the valence electrons are shared equally, the bond is **nonpolar**.

A molecule is nonpolar if it contains only nonpolar bonds, or if it has polar bonds that cancel each other out. For example, in carbon dioxide (CO_2), the oxygen atoms attract electrons more strongly than the carbon atom. However, the two oxygen atoms pull with equal strength in opposite directions, so the polar bonds cancel each other out.

Some molecules with polar covalent bonds are themselves polar. In a water molecule, the two hydrogen atoms are at one end, while the oxygen atom is at the other end. The oxygen atom attracts electrons more strongly than do the hydrogen atoms. As a result, the molecule has a slightly negative charge at the oxygen end and a slightly positive charge at the hydrogen end.

Molecules that are polar are more strongly attracted to each other than nonpolar molecules. This difference in the attraction between molecules leads to different properties in polar and nonpolar compounds. Polar and nonpolar molecules also do not mix. For example, water, which is polar, does not mix with oil, which is nonpolar. The nonpolar oil molecules have little attraction for the polar water molecules, while the water molecules are more strongly attracted to one another.

© Pearson Education, Inc., publishing as Pearson Prentice Hall. All rights reserved.

Name _____ Date _____ Class _____

Covalent Bonds

This section describes how chemical bonds form when two atoms share electrons. It also describes how electrons are shared unequally in some chemical bonds.

Use Target Reading Skills

Before you read, preview the red headings. In the graphic organizer below, ask a what or how question for each heading. As you read, answer your questions.

Covalent Bonds

Question	Answer
How do covalent bonds form?	Covalent bonds form when . . .

How Covalent Bonds Form

1. What is a covalent bond?

_____

_____

2. On the dot diagram below, draw a circle around the shared electrons that form a covalent bond between two fluorine atoms.

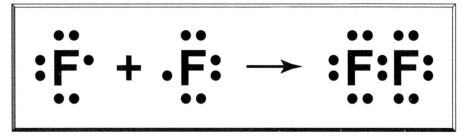

© Pearson Education, Inc., publishing as Pearson Prentice Hall. All rights reserved.

Atoms and Bonding · *Guided Reading and Study*

Covalent Bonds *(continued)*

3. The two bonded fluorine atoms form a(n) _____.

4. When two atoms share two pairs of electrons, a(n) _____ is formed.

5. Is the following sentence true or false? Atoms of some elements can share three pairs of electrons. _____

Molecular Compounds

6. What are molecular compounds composed of?

   _____

7. Circle the letter of each sentence that is true about molecular compounds.
   a. More heat is needed to separate their molecules than is needed to separate ions.
   b. They melt at much higher temperatures than do ionic compounds.
   c. They boil at much higher temperatures than do ionic compounds.
   d. Most are poor conductors of electricity when dissolved in water.

Unequal Sharing of Electrons

8. How do molecular compounds come to have a slight electrical charge?

   _____

   _____

   _____

   _____

9. In a(n) _____ covalent bond, electrons are shared unequally.

10. How are electrons shared in a nonpolar covalent bond?

    _____

11. How can a molecule be nonpolar overall and still contain polar bonds?

    _____

    _____

    _____

12. Is the following sentence true or false? Water molecules are polar.

    _____

© Pearson Education, Inc., publishing as Pearson Prentice Hall. All rights reserved.

Atoms and Bonding • *Guided Reading and Study*

13. Why do polar and nonpolar molecules have different properties?

_____

_____

_____

14. Why don't water and vegetable oil mix?

_____

_____

_____

_____

_____

_____

15. When you do laundry, what causes nonpolar oil or greasy dirt to mix with the polar water?

_____

_____

_____

_____

_____

© Pearson Education, Inc., publishing as Pearson Prentice Hall. All rights reserved.

Atoms and Bonding · *Review and Reinforce*

Covalent Bonds

Understanding Main Ideas

Answer the following questions in the spaces provided.

$(+)$ H:F: $(-)$:O::O:

:N:::N: :F:F:

1. Circle all the covalent bonds in the electron dot diagrams.

2. Which bond(s) shown are double bonds?

_____

3. Which bond(s) shown are triple bonds?

_____

4. What makes the bond in HF a polar bond?

_____

_____

_____

5. Which molecule(s) shown have nonpolar bonds?

_____

6. How do the melting points, boiling points, and conductivity of molecular compounds compare to those of ionic compounds?

_____

_____

_____

Building Vocabulary

From the list below, choose the term that best completes each sentence. Each term may be used more than once.

nonpolar

polar

7. A covalent bond is considered _____ if the two atoms share the electrons equally.

8. A water molecule is a(n) _____ molecule because the oxygen atom pulls electrons closer to it than the hydrogen atoms do, forming a molecule that is slightly more positive at one end than at the other.

9. A covalent bond is considered _____ if the electrons are shared unequally.

10. A carbon dioxide molecule is a(n) _____ molecule because the oxygen atoms are pulling on the shared electrons with equal strength in opposite directions and cancel each other out.

© Pearson Education, Inc., publishing as Pearson Prentice Hall. All rights reserved.

Atoms and Bonding • *Enrich*

Oil Spills

Each year over 907,000 metric tons of crude oil are spilled in Earth's oceans. This is enough oil to fill 100 school gymnasiums! It is important to clean up crude oil as soon after a spill as possible, because spilled crude oil has negative effects on the environment. Oil on ocean surfaces is harmful to ocean life because it blocks sunlight and reduces the level of dissolved oxygen in the water. In addition, many birds and fish die from contact with crude oil because the oil damages feathers and gills.

Two methods used to clean up oil spills are:

1. A floating barrier is placed around the spill to keep it from spreading. Because oil floats on water, the oil can be skimmed off the top of the water. Skimming the top of the water using a net with extremely small holes allows the water to escape but not the oil.

Figure 1
Detergent Molecule

Nonpolar end   Polar end

2. Chemicals that act like detergents are sprayed onto the surface of the spill. These chemicals break up the oil into tiny droplets. The small particles of oil spread over a large area have less effect on marine life than larger particles.

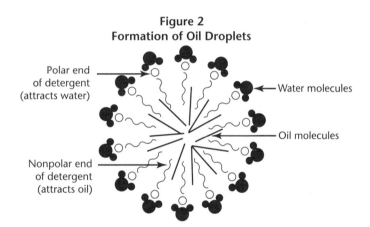

Figure 2
Formation of Oil Droplets

Polar end of detergent (attracts water)

Water molecules

Oil molecules

Nonpolar end of detergent (attracts oil)

Both of these methods work because of the chemical properties of oil molecules. Oil molecules are nonpolar, so they will not mix with polar water molecules. Detergents are long molecules that have a polar end and a nonpolar end, like the molecule shown in Figure 1. The polar end of the detergent attracts water molecules, and the nonpolar end attracts oil molecules. Figure 2 shows how detergent molecules cause the formation of droplets of water, detergent, and oil molecules.

Answer the following questions on a separate sheet of paper.

1. Explain how the nonpolar character of oil molecules helps when removing oil from water using nets and floating barriers.
2. The long "tail" on a detergent molecule is made up mostly of carbon atoms bonded to other carbon atoms. Why would you expect the tail to be nonpolar?
3. How does detergent sprayed on an oil spill break up the spill?
4. The action of waves can break up large sections of an oil spill. The oil looks like it has mixed with the water, but has it? Explain your answer.

© Pearson Education, Inc., publishing as Pearson Prentice Hall. All rights reserved.

Bonding in Metals

 1–2 periods, 1/2–1 block

Ability Levels Key
L1 Basic to Average
L2 For All Students
L3 Average to Advanced

Objectives

L.1.5.1 Describe how metal atoms are bonded in solid metal.

L.1.5.2 Explain how metallic bonding results in useful properties of metals.

Key Terms
• metallic bond • alloy • ductile • malleable

Local Standards

PRETEACH

Build Background Knowledge
Students name common objects containing metal and infer properties of metals based on the objects.

Discover Activity *What Do Metals Do?* **L1**

Targeted Resources

❏ **All in One Teaching Resources**
   L2 Reading Strategy Transparency L13: Relating Cause and Effect
❏ ⊙ **Presentation-Pro CD-ROM**

INSTRUCT

Metallic Bonding Use the figure in the textbook that shows metallic bonding to help students understand the nature of metallic bonds.
Metallic Properties Explain how the properties of metals depend on the nature of metallic bonds.

Targeted Resources

❏ **All in One Teaching Resources**
   L2 Guided Reading, pp. 82–83
   L2 Transparency L14
❏ **www.SciLinks.org** Web Code: scn-1215
❏ ⊙ **Student Edition on Audio CD**

ASSESS

Section Assessment Questions
⊙ Have students use their completed graphic organizers relating cause and effect to answer the questions.

Reteach
Students name properties of metals and describe an example of each property.

Targeted Resources

❏ **All in One Teaching Resources**
   Section Summary, p. 81
   L1 Review and Reinforce, p. 84
   L3 Enrich, p. 85

© Pearson Education, Inc., publishing as Pearson Prentice Hall. All rights reserved.

Atoms and Bonding • *Section Summary*

Bonding in Metals

Guide for Reading

■ How are metal atoms bonded in solid metal?

■ How does metallic bonding result in useful properties of metals?

The properties of solid metals can be explained by the structure of metal atoms and the bonding between those atoms. Recall that most metals have one, two, or three valence electrons. When metal atoms combine chemically with atoms of other elements, they usually lose valence electrons. As a result, they become positively charged ions. Metals lose electrons easily because their valence electrons are not strongly held.

Metals exist as crystals with atoms very close together in a specific arrangement. Because the electrons are not tightly held, they leave the atoms and mix with the valence electrons of all nearby atoms. **As a result, a metal crystal consists of positively charged metal ions embedded in a "sea" of valence electrons.** Each ion is held in the crystal by a metallic bond. A **metallic bond** is an attraction between a positive metal ion and the electrons surrounding it.

Metallic bonding explains many of the common physical properties of metals and their alloys. An **alloy** is a material made of two or more elements that has the properties of a metal. **The "sea of electrons" model of solid metals explains their ability to conduct heat and electricity, the ease with which they can be made to change shape, and their luster.**

Heat travels through materials as the increased motion of particles. Motion in the hotter parts of the material is passed along to the particles in the cooler parts. Metal ions and valence electrons are not rigidly held in a metal crystal. This makes it easy for particle motion to be passed along. Metals conduct electricity easily because the electrons in a metal crystal can move freely among the atoms.

Most metals are flexible and can be reshaped easily. This is because the metal ions in a crystal move easily. Metals are ductile. **Ductile** means easily bent and pulled into thin strands or wires. Metals are also malleable. **Malleable** means able to be rolled into thin sheets or beaten into complex shapes. In addition, polished metals have luster. Luster means shine. When light strikes the valence electrons of metals, the electrons absorb the light and then give it off again. This is what gives metals their luster.

© Pearson Education, Inc., publishing as Pearson Prentice Hall. All rights reserved.

Atoms and Bonding ▪ *Guided Reading and Study*

Bonding in Metals

This section describes how atoms of solid metals form bonds. It also explains how metallic bonds give metals their useful properties.

Use Target Reading Skills

As you read, identify the properties of metals that result from metallic bonding. Write the information in the graphic organizer below.

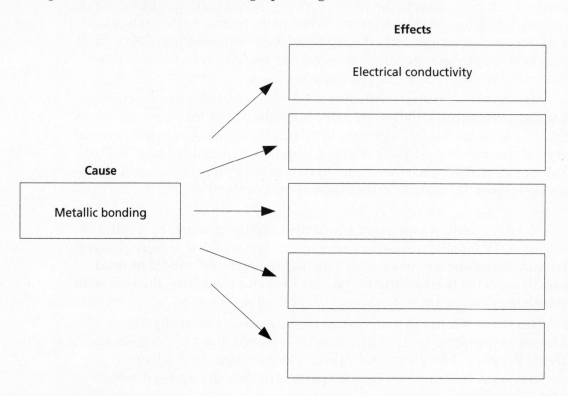

Effects

Electrical conductivity

Cause

Metallic bonding

Metallic Bonding

1. Circle the letter of each sentence that is true about metals and metallic bonding.
   a. Atoms of most metals have one, two, or three valence electrons.
   b. Metal atoms usually gain valence electrons when they combine chemically with other atoms.
   c. In chemical reactions, metal atoms usually become positively charged ions.
   d. Atoms of metals lose electrons easily.

2. What does a metal crystal consist of?

   _____

   _____

   _____

3. What is a metallic bond?

   _____

   _____

© Pearson Education, Inc., publishing as Pearson Prentice Hall. All rights reserved.

Atoms and Bonding · *Guided Reading and Study*

Metallic Properties

4. A(n) _____ is a material made of two or more elements that has the properties of a metal.

5. List four properties of metals.

_____

_____

_____

6. What explains the properties of metals?

_____

_____

7. Why do metals conduct electricity easily?

_____

_____

_____

8. Complete the table about the ability of metals to change shape.

Type of Ability	Definition	Example
Ductility	a.	Wire
b.	Ability to be rolled into thin sheets	Aluminum foil

9. Is the following sentence true or false? A metal's luster is due to its valence electrons. _____

© Pearson Education, Inc., publishing as Pearson Prentice Hall. All rights reserved.

Name _____ Date _____ Class _____

Bonding in Metals

Understanding Main Ideas

Use the diagram to answer questions 1–3 in the spaces provided.

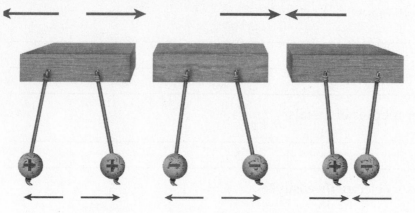

1. What model is represented by the diagram?

   _____

2. What do the large balls in the model represent? What do the small balls represent?

   _____

   _____

3. What type of bonds are shown in the model?

   _____

Answer questions 4 and 5 in the spaces provided.

4. What are the properties of metals?

   _____

   _____

5. How does metallic bonding result in these properties?

   _____

   _____

   _____

Building Vocabulary

Fill in the blank to complete each sentence.

6. An attraction between a positive metal ion and the electrons surrounding it is called a(n) _____.

7. _____ means able to be bent easily and pulled into thin strands.

8. _____ means able to be rolled into thin sheets or beaten into complex shapes.

© Pearson Education, Inc., publishing as Pearson Prentice Hall. All rights reserved.

Name _____ Date _____ Class _____

Atoms and Bonding • *Enrich*

How Hard Is Hard?

Some metals, such as copper and gold, are also minerals. A mineral is a naturally occurring solid that has a crystal structure and a definite chemical composition. Their crystal structure makes minerals hard. Nonetheless, there is considerable variation among minerals in hardness. Talc is the softest mineral, diamond is the hardest. Mohs Scale of Hardness, which is shown below, is used to classify minerals and other substances according to their hardnesses. An object on the scale will scratch anything with a lower number, but will be scratched by anything with a higher number. The table includes some everyday objects in parentheses for comparison.

Mineral (Object)	Hardness
talc	1
(asphalt)	1.3
gypsum	2
(fingernail)	2.5
calcite	3
(copper coin)	3
fluorite	4
apatite	5
(knife blade)	5.5
feldspar	6
(steel file)	6.5
quartz	7
topaz	8
corundum	9
diamond	10

Answer the following questions on a separate sheet of paper.

1. Which minerals will scratch quartz? How do you know?
2. According to the information in the table, do you think that you could scratch a copper coin with a knife blade? Explain your answer.
3. How could you determine the hardness rating for a mineral not listed on the scale?

© Pearson Education, Inc., publishing as Pearson Prentice Hall. All rights reserved.

Atoms and Bonding ▪ *Key Terms*

Key Terms

Answer the questions by writing the correct Key Terms in the blanks. Use the numbered letters in the terms to find the hidden Key Term. Then write a definition for the hidden Key Term.

Clues   **Key Terms**

What particles form a cloud around
the nucleus of an atom?   __ __ __ __ __ __ __ __ __
                                                                           1

What is a covalent bond called in
which electrons are shared unequally?   __ __ __ __ __
                                                                    2

_____ electrons
are involved in bonding.   __ __ __ __ __ __ __
                                                                3

What is an orderly, three-dimensional
arrangement formed by ions called?   __ __ __ __ __ __ __
                                                                                4

What is the core of an atom?   __ __ __ __ __ __ __
                                                                        5 6

What is an atom or group of atoms
that has become electrically charged?   __ __ __
                                                                      7

What is the neutral particle in an
atomic nucleus?   __ __ __ __ __ __
                                                                       8

What is the attraction between two
oppositely charged ions called?   __ __ __ __ __   __ __ __ __
                                                                                9

What is a bond in which electrons
are shared equally?   __ __ __ __ __ __ __ __
                                                                           10

What is the positive particle in an
atomic nucleus?   __ __ __ __ __ __
                                                                         11

What is a bond in which two pairs
of electrons are shared between atoms? __ __ __ __ __ __   __ __ __ __
                                                                 12

Key Term: __ __ __ __ __ __ __ __ __ __ __ __ __
                      1 2 3 4 5 6 7 8   9 10 11 12

Definition:

_____

_____

© Pearson Education, Inc., publishing as Pearson Prentice Hall. All rights reserved.

Atoms and Bonding ▪ *Connecting Concepts*

Connecting Concepts

Develop a concept map that uses the Key Concepts and Key Terms from this chapter. Keep in mind the big idea of this chapter: Atoms are the smallest particles of elements; they are represented by models that developed over time; and they can form bonds that are ionic, covalent, or metallic. The concept map shown is one way to organize how the information in this chapter is related. You may use an extra sheet of paper.

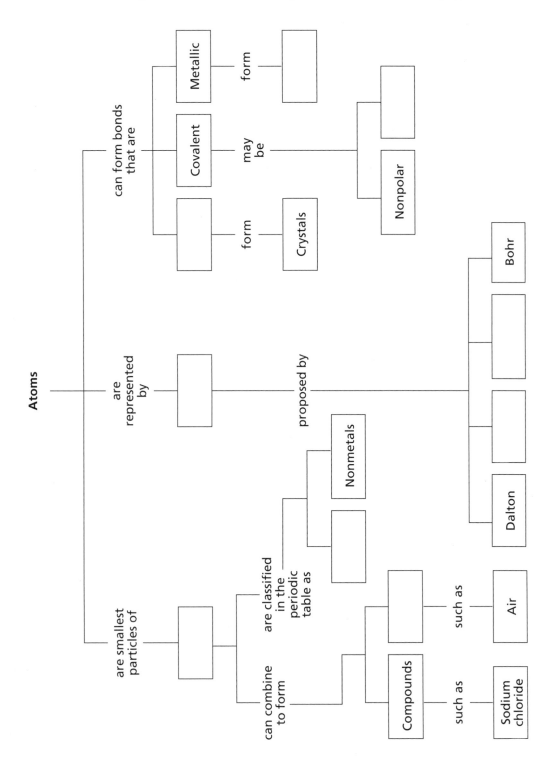

© Pearson Education, Inc., publishing as Pearson Prentice Hall. All rights reserved.

Testing for Hard Water

Key Concept

Hard water is a mixture of ions dissolved in water. The more ions present, the harder the water is.

Skills Focus

observing, predicting, classifying, designing experiments, controlling variables

Time

40 minutes

Materials *(per group)*

distilled water
tap water
3 or 4 test tubes
test-tube rack
graduated cylinder
plastic dropper
100-mL beaker
bar soap
liquid hand soap
standard sample of hard water

Teaching Tips

- You can make a standard sample of hard water by mixing 1 g of calcium chloride in 10 mL of distilled water. Prepare 200 mL of hard water for the lab.

- Have some students bring a sample of tap water from home and have others get tap water from school. You could also use bottled water for comparison.

  Get a supply of hand soap (liquid or bar) or soap flakes. If students use bar soap or soap flakes, a pea-sized piece will be enough for a 10-mL sample. One drop of liquid soap is enough for a 10 mL sample. If soap flakes are used, make sure that the product is soap and not detergent. Detergents should not be used for the investigation because they are formulated to compensate for hard water.

- If you are also testing bottled water, the procedure will require four test tubes, and students should adjust the data tables accordingly.

- Check that students are using the same amount of water and the same amount of soap for all tests. They should also have a consistent way to mix the sample with soap (for example, by shaking ten times.)

- Students can gauge hardness from the height of the suds in the test tube and the relative amount of cloudiness in the water. Letting the samples stand for 10 minutes accentuates the differences.

© Pearson Education, Inc., publishing as Pearson Prentice Hall. All rights reserved.

Atoms and Bonding • *Laboratory Investigation*

Testing for Hard Water

Pre-Lab Discussion

Hard water is a common problem for many households. It can form chemical deposits that clog water pipes and damage water heaters and boilers. What causes hard water? No natural water source is 100% pure water. All sources contain other chemicals, such as calcium and magnesium compounds. These compounds form ions in water. Ions are single atoms or groups of atoms that carry an electric charge. The total amount of ions present in water is a measure of the hardness of the water.

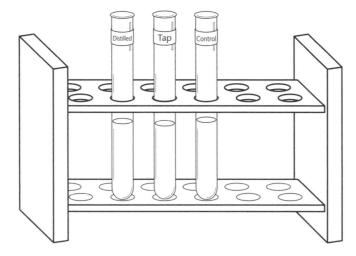

When you add soap to hard water, the ions combine with the soap and form scum. Because some soap is being used to produce scum, fewer suds form. Therefore, you need to use more soap when you shower or wash your clothes. You can tell from the amount of soap suds how hard the water is.

In this investigation, you will test water and rate its hardness.

1. How does soap make it possible for water and oil to mix?

_____

_____

_____

_____

2. Why are soap and the ions in hard water attracted to each other to form scum?

_____

_____

_____

_____

Problem

How can you determine if water is hard?

© Pearson Education, Inc., publishing as Pearson Prentice Hall. All rights reserved.

Atoms and Bonding · *Laboratory Investigation*

Testing for Hard Water *(continued)*

Possible Materials *(per group)*

distilled water

tap water

3 or 4 test tubes

test-tube rack

graduated cylinder

plastic dropper

100-mL beaker

bar soap

liquid hand soap

standard sample of hard water

Safety *Review the safety guidelines in Appendix A.*
Always clean up spilled water to prevent falls.

Procedure

1. Read the entire lab before starting your investigation.

2. Working with a partner or group, plan how to test the hardness of water. Consider the following:

   ■ What water will you test?

   ■ What will you use as a control?

   ■ Use soap to test for hardness. What will you look for as evidence of hardness? Be sure to use the same amount of soap for each sample.

   ■ What observations will you record? You can either use the Data Table in Observations or develop your own data table on a separate sheet of paper.

3. Once you have decided what samples you will test, predict which sample will be the hardest and which the least hard. Give reasons for your predictions.

   _____

   _____

   _____

   _____

4. Write your procedure on a separate sheet of paper. Have the teacher approve your procedure before you carry out the investigation. Remember to wear your safety goggles and apron.

© Pearson Education, Inc., publishing as Pearson Prentice Hall. All rights reserved.

Name _____ Date _____ Class _____

Atoms and Bonding · *Laboratory Investigation*

Observations

Data Table

Water Type and Soap	Observations	
	Just After Mixing	**10 min After Mixing**
Distilled water		
Tap water		
Control		

Analyze and Conclude

1. How does the soap show that water is hard?

_____

_____

_____

2. List samples in order of hardness, from most to least.

_____

_____

3. How do your results differ from your prediction? Explain what your results mean.

_____

_____

_____

_____

© Pearson Education, Inc., publishing as Pearson Prentice Hall. All rights reserved.

Atoms and Bonding · *Laboratory Investigation*

Testing for Hard Water *(continued)*

Critical Thinking and Applications

1. Did suds form in all the test tubes? If not, why?

   _____
   _____
   _____
   _____

2. The control contained calcium chloride dissolved in distilled water. What ions are present in the control?

   _____
   _____

3. What are the disadvantages of using hard water to do laundry?

   _____
   _____
   _____
   _____

4. What do you have to do to turn hard water into soft water?

   _____
   _____
   _____
   _____

More to Explore

Check the labels of some laundry detergents and soaps and list the ingredients. Note any special directions about using the detergent. Use a chemical reference book to find out more about these chemicals. How does getting clothes clean in hard water differ from doing so in soft water? Write a procedure you could use to test your hypothesis. Have the teacher approve your procedure before you carry out your investigation. Remember to wear your safety goggles and apron.

© Pearson Education, Inc., publishing as Pearson Prentice Hall. All rights reserved.

Bonds and Compounds

Students are presented with the task of creating a poster that classifies compounds based on the types of bonds they contain. To complete this task, students will apply concepts they have learned about chemical formulas and ionic and covalent bonds.

Expected Outcome

Students' posters should include a data table with the following information for each compound: its name and formula, its electron dot structure with either ionic charges or covalent bonds indicated; whether the compound contains ionic or covalent bonds, and, if applicable, whether its bonds and molecules are polar or nonpolar. Students should also classify each compound into one of four groups based on the bonds it contains. The most likely groups are ionic compounds, nonpolar compounds containing only nonpolar covalent bonds, nonpolar compounds containing polar covalent bonds, and polar compounds.

Potassium iodide (KI), calcium chloride ($CaCl_2$), sodium oxide (Na_2O), and lithium nitride (Li_3N) are ionic compounds. Methyl alcohol (CH_3OH) and acetic acid (CH_3COOH) are polar compounds. Chlorine gas (Cl_2) is a nonpolar compound containing only nonpolar bonds. Hydrogen chloride (HCl) is a polar compound containing polar covalent bonds. Carbon dioxide (CO_2) and carbon tetrafluoride (CF_4) are nonpolar compounds containing polar covalent bonds.

Note that other classification systems are possible. For example, a student might use the following groups: ionic compounds containing a halogen (i.e., ions with a 1^- charge), ionic compounds that do not contain a halogen, polar compounds, and nonpolar compounds.

Content Assessed

The Performance Assessment tests students' understanding of chemical formulas, electron dot diagrams, and ionic and covalent bonds.

Skills Assessed

communicating, applying concepts

Materials

Provide students with materials for making their posters such as poster board and colored pens or pencils.

Either distribute photocopies of the periodic table or allow students to reference the periodic table in the Student Edition.

Time

40 minutes

Monitoring the Task

- You may want to write the following information on the board for students to use during this assessment.

Group Number	Number of Valence Electrons
1	1
2	2
14	4
15	5
16	6
17	7

- After students have completed the assessment, you may want pairs of students to compare their posters to see if they came up with the same classification system.

© Pearson Education, Inc., publishing as Pearson Prentice Hall. All rights reserved.

Bonds and Compounds

In assessing students' performance, use the following rubric.

	4	3	2	1
Completing Data Table and Classifying Compounds	Data table is complete for all compounds, and all entries are accurate. Electron dot diagrams are labeled with covalent bonds or ionic charges as appropriate. Student correctly classifies each compound into one of four groups based on the types of bonds it contains.	Data table is complete for all compounds, but one or two entries contain minor errors. One or two electron dot diagrams are incorrectly labeled with covalent bonds or ionic charges. Student creates four groups of compounds. Student incorrectly classifies one or two compounds.	Data table is complete for all compounds, but several entries contain minor errors. Several electron dot diagrams are incorrectly labeled with covalent bonds or ionic charges. Student creates four groups of compounds. Student incorrectly classifies three or four compounds.	Data table is incomplete, and most entries contain errors. Most electron dot diagrams are either unlabeled or incorrectly labeled with covalent bonds or ionic charges. Student creates four groups of compounds, but groups are not based on the types of bonds the compounds contain. Student incorrectly classifies more than four compounds.
Concept Understanding	Student demonstrates a mastery of concepts relating to chemical formulas, electron dot diagrams, and ionic and covalent bonds.	Student demonstrates an adequate understanding of concepts relating to chemical formulas, electron dot diagrams, and ionic and covalent bonds.	Student demonstrates a partial understanding of concepts relating to chemical formulas, electron dot diagrams, and ionic and covalent bonds.	Student demonstrates a minimal understanding of concepts relating to chemical formulas, electron dot diagrams, and ionic and covalent bonds.

© Pearson Education, Inc., publishing as Pearson Prentice Hall. All rights reserved.

Atoms and Bonding • *Performance Assessment*

Bonds and Compounds

Problem

Create a poster that will classify compounds by their bond type. How can you classify compounds by the type of bonds they contain?

Suggested Materials

periodic table

poster board

marking pens or pencils

Devise a Plan

1. On one half of your poster, make a data table like the one shown below. Give yourself plenty of room for writing inside the boxes.

Name	Formula	Electron dot diagram	Ionic or covalent bonds?	Polar or nonpolar bonds?	Polar or nonpolar molecules?

2. Complete the table for the following compounds: potassium iodide; carbon dioxide; sodium oxide; calcium chloride; hydrogen chloride; carbon tetrafluoride (CF_4); methyl alcohol (CH_3OH); acetic acid (CH_3COOH); lithium nitride (Li_3N); and chlorine gas (Cl_2). For each electron dot diagram, either label the charges on the ions or circle the covalent bonds. The electron dot diagrams for methyl alcohol and acetic acid are provided below. The last two columns of the table will not need to be completed for ionic compounds. (*Hint:* Fluorine, oxygen, and chlorine strongly attract electrons.)

3. On the other half of your poster, classify these compounds into four groups based on the bonds they contain. Give each group an appropriate title.

Analyze and Conclude

After following the plan you devised, answer the following questions on a separate sheet of paper.

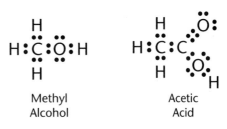

Methyl Alcohol

Acetic Acid

1. Why didn't you need to fill in the last two columns of the table for ionic compounds?

2. Name four compounds in your table that are solids at room temperature. How do you know these compounds are solids?

3. Why do you think there aren't any compounds in the table containing noble gases?

© Pearson Education, Inc., publishing as Pearson Prentice Hall. All rights reserved.

Atoms and Bonding · *Chapter Test*

Atoms and Bonding

Multiple Choice

Write the letter of the correct answer on the line at the left.

_____ 1. The positively charged particles in the nucleus of an atom are called

      a. electrons.   **b.** ions.

      c. neutrons.   **d.** protons.

_____ 2. The columns in the periodic table are referred to as

      a. groups.   **b.** sections.

      c. periods.   **d.** rows.

_____ 3. A(n) _____ is an atom or group of atoms that has an electrical charge.

      a. compound   **b.** ion

      c. crystal   **d.** neutron

_____ 4. A covalent bond is called _____ if the atoms equally share one or more pairs of electrons.

      a. double   **b.** ionic

      c. nonpolar   **d.** polar

_____ 5. An attraction between a positive metal ion and the electrons surrounding it is a(n) _____.

      a. covalent bond   **b.** metallic bond

      c. nonpolar bond   **d.** triple bond

_____ 6. Which of the following does NOT apply to valence electrons?

      a. farthest from the nucleus

      b. shown on electron dot diagrams

      c. transferred or shared in bonding

      d. make up most of the atom's mass

_____ 7. The _____ increases one at a time from left to right across the periodic table.

      a. atomic mass   **b.** atomic number

      c. number of possible bonds   **d.** total number of neutrons

_____ 8. Elements in Group 17, the halogen family, are very reactive because their atoms have _____ valence electrons.

      a. zero   **b.** one

      c. seven   **d.** eight

© Pearson Education, Inc., publishing as Pearson Prentice Hall. All rights reserved.

Name _____ Date _____ Class _____

Atoms and Bonding ▪ *Chapter Test*

____ 9. _____ ions are composed of more than one atom.

a. Covalent   b. Molecular

c. Polar   d. Polyatomic

____ 10. In a double bond, _____ electrons are shared.

a. 2   b. 4

c. 6   d. 8

Completion

Fill in the line to complete each statement.

11. A(n) _____ is material made of two or more elements that has the properties of a metal.

12. Most atoms become less reactive after a change to a total number of _____ valence electrons.

13. A row of the periodic table is called a(n) _____.

14. A(n) _____ ion is formed when an atom loses an electron.

15. In a reaction, atoms with _____ valence electrons will probably gain two electrons or share two covalent bonds.

True or False

If the statement is true, write true. *If it is false, change the underlined word or words to make the statement true.*

_____ 16. The particles in an atom's nucleus that carry no electrical charge are called <u>neutrons</u>.

_____ 17. The most stable elements in the periodic table are found in the family of <u>alkali metals</u>.

_____ 18. Ions form electrically <u>negative</u> compounds.

_____ 19. Atoms in a <u>nonpolar</u> covalent bond carry slight electrical charges.

_____ 20. A <u>family</u> of elements shares the same number of valence electrons.

Atoms and Bonding

© Pearson Education, Inc., publishing as Pearson Prentice Hall. All rights reserved.

97

Name _____ Date _____ Class _____

Atoms and Bonding · *Chapter Test*

Using Science Skills

Use the electron dot diagrams to answer the following.

$\cdot Na \quad \cdot Mg \quad \cdot \dot{Al}\cdot \quad \cdot \dot{Si}\cdot \quad \cdot \dot{P}{:} \quad \cdot \ddot{S}{:} \quad \cdot \ddot{Cl}{:} \quad {:}\ddot{Ar}{:}$

Sodium Magnesium Aluminum Silicon Phosphorus Sulfur Chlorine Argon

21. Applying Concepts Predict the formula for the compound, if any, that would form from the elements listed below. If a compound is unlikely, explain the reason why.

a. magnesium and chlorine

_____

b. aluminum and sulfur

_____

c. sodium and argon

_____

22. Drawing Conclusions Based on the electron dot diagrams of the elements shown above, is it possible that these elements increase in atomic number from left to right across a period?

_____

_____

Essay

Write an answer for each of the following in the spaces provided.

23. How does the "sea of electrons" model of metallic bonding explain the shared characteristics of metals?

_____

_____

_____

24. Explain why a water molecule (H_2O) is considered polar, and a molecule of hydrogen (H_2) is nonpolar.

_____

_____

_____

_____

25. Compare and contrast ionic bonds and covalent bonds.

_____

_____

_____

_____

© Pearson Education, Inc., publishing as Pearson Prentice Hall. All rights reserved.

Atoms and Bonding ▪ *Chapter Test*

Using Science Skills

Use the portion of the periodic table below to answer the following questions.

	1	2	13	14	15	16	17	18
2	3 Li Lithium 6.941	4 Be Beryllium 9.012	5 B Boron 10.811	6 C Carbon 12.011	7 N Nitrogen 14.007	8 O Oxygen 15.999	9 F Fluorine 18.998	10 Ne Neon 20.180
8								

26. **Classifying** A new period of very heavy elements from outer space has been discovered by scientists. In which group does each element belong? Write the element in the appropriate square of period eight.

   Element A: bonds with lithium to form the compound Li_3A

   Element D: has the lowest atomic number of the elements in period eight

   Element E: exists as a nonpolar molecule of two identical atoms with a double bond

   Element G: forms an ion with a 3+ charge when reacting with nitrogen

   Element J: nonreactive, discovered as a pure element

   Element L: explosively reactive when combined with lithium

   Element M: bonds with fluorine to form the compound MF_2

   Element Q: QO_2 is a covalent molecule with two double bonds

27. **Inferring** How many covalent bonds can element A form? Explain your answer.

   _____

   _____

   _____

Essay

Answer the following on a separate piece of paper.

28. Explain why the alkali metals in Group 1 are always found in nature combined with other elements.

29. An unknown solid does not conduct electricity. What could you do to determine whether the solid is an ionic compound or a molecular solid?

30. Explain why the polar structure of water molecules causes water to have a higher boiling point than carbon dioxide.

© Pearson Education, Inc., publishing as Pearson Prentice Hall. All rights reserved.

Chapter Project
Worksheet 1

1. Answers will vary. Sample answers: different fruits, gumdrops, various balls. Examples for covalent bonds are toothpicks, pipe cleaners, and small springs.

2. Answers will vary. Choices for nuclei should be something that will distinguish between different kinds of nuclei, such as different fruits or different colored gumdrops. The choice for covalent bonds must adequately connect nuclei, and the material must differentiate between single, double, and triple bonds.

3. Answers will vary. Sample answers: writing on the surface of the nucleus, small blobs of clay stuck to the nucleus

4. The first column of this table should read as follows: carbon 4, chlorine 7, fluorine 7, hydrogen 1, iodine 7, magnesium 2, nitrogen 5, oxygen 6, sodium 1, and sulfur 6. Students' answers in the second column will depend on the materials that they choose. Make sure that they have thought of a way to distinguish between the different types of elements.

Worksheet 2

Compounds Containing Ionic Bonds

The charges of the given ions are as follows: sodium (1+), chloride (1−), potassium (1+), and oxide (2−). Other compounds and their ions will vary. Be sure students have selected compounds with ionic bonds, not covalent bonds. They should give the charge of the compound's ions and briefly describe their model plans for these compounds.

Molecules Containing Covalent Bonds

Water contains single bonds. Carbon dioxide contains double bonds. Chlorine (Cl_2) and hydrogen (H_2) both contain single bonds. Some compounds that students choose will contain more than one kind of bond. Be sure students have selected compounds with covalent bonds, not ionic bonds. Students should briefly describe their model plans for these compounds.

Elements and Atoms
Guided Reading and Study

Use Target Reading Skills

I. The building blocks of matter
   A. Elements, compounds, and mixtures
   B. Particle of elements
II. Atomic theory and models
   A. Dalton's atomic theory
   B. Thomson and smaller parts of atoms
   C. Rutherford and the nucleus
   D. Bohr's model
   E. A cloud of electrons
   F. The modern atomic model

1. elements
2. Because all matter is composed of one element or a combination of two or more elements
3. **a.** Elements
   b. Mixture
   c. No
4. True
5. a, b, c
6. atom
7. Atoms are too small to be observed directly, and models help people understand what they cannot observe directly.
8. a, c, d
9. True
10. J. J. Thomson
11. Gold foil experiment
12. protons
13. Niels Bohr
14. energy level
15. Neutron
16. False
17. b

© Pearson Education, Inc., publishing as Pearson Prentice Hall. All rights reserved.

Elements and Atoms
Review and Reinforce

1. Rutherford
2. Dalton
3. Bohr
4. Thomson
5. d
6. j
7. g
8. a
9. e
10. c
11. i
12. b
13. f
14. h

Elements and Atoms
Enrich

1. Answers will vary. Sample: An electric current was passed through the tube. The current entered one end and traveled to the other end, showing that the ray was made up of particles that flowed from one place to another.

2. The experiment showed that electrons have a negative charge because the ray was deflected away from the negative electric plate and toward the positive plate.

3. The electric field showed whether or not the particles in the ray were charged, and if so, the type of charge. Light would be unaffected by the electric field.

4. Electrons are all the same, no matter what kind of atoms they come from.

Atoms, Bonding, and
the Periodic Table
Guided Reading and Study

Use Target Reading Skills
Sample definitions:

1. valence electrons: electrons that are in the highest energy level and held most loosely

2. electron dot diagram: diagram of an atom that includes the symbol for the element surrounded by dots that stand for valence electrons

3. chemical bond: the force of attraction that holds two atoms together as a result of the rearrangement of electrons between them

4. symbol: one or two letters that represent each element

5. atomic number: the number of protons in the nucleus of an atom

6. period: row of elements in the periodic table

7. group: column of elements in the periodic table; same as family

8. family: column of elements in the periodic table; same as group

9. noble gas: any element in Group 18, which consists of elements with eight valence electrons except for helium, which has two

10. halogen: any element in Group 17, which consists of elements with seven valence electrons

11. alkali metal: any element in Group 1, which consists of elements with one valence electron

Students' definitions may vary. Check that they have included all major concepts. Answers continue on next page.

© Pearson Education, Inc., publishing as Pearson Prentice Hall. All rights reserved.

1. Valence electrons
2. True
3. **a.** Hydrogen, 1 valence electron
   b. Carbon, 4 valence electrons
   c. Oxygen, 6 valence electrons
4. d
5. True
6. By a symbol consisting of one or two letters
7. atomic number
8. A period
9. It increases one at a time across a period.
10. A group, or family
11. valence electrons
12. **a.** Alkali metals
    b. High
    c. Halogens
    d. High
    e. Noble gases
    f. Low
13. Four or more valence electrons
14. Nonmetals can combine with metals by gaining electrons, or they can combine with other nonmetals by sharing electrons.
15. Metalloids can behave as nonmetals as well as metals.
16. False

Atoms, Bonding, and the Periodic Table
Review and Reinforce

1. 7
2. 7
3. 5
4. It is reactive because it needs three valence electrons to become stable.
5. Nonmetal
6. valence electrons
7. chemical bond
8. symbol
9. atomic number
10. period
11. group, or family

Atoms, Bonding, and the Periodic Table
Enrich

1. Groups 1 and 2; because they are very reactive
2. The noble gases; because they do not react easily
3. You need one fuse to ignite the gunpowder that sends the rocket into the air, and other fuses to ignite the chemical compounds that produce the light and noise once the rocket has reached its maximum height.
4. The element in solution might burn as it does in a firework rocket, giving off a color. The results could be used to tell the solutions apart.

Comparing Atom Sizes
Skills Lab

For answers, see the Teacher's Edition.

Ionic Bonds
Guided Reading and Study

Use Target Reading Skills
Sample questions and answers:
Formation of an Ionic Bond
Q. What is an ionic bond?
A. An ionic bond is the attraction between two oppositely charged ions.
Q. What is the overall charge on an ionic compound?
A. Overall, an ionic compound is electrically neutral.

1. ion
2. It loses a negative charge and becomes a positive ion.
3. It gains a negative charge and becomes a negative ion.
4. polyatomic ions
5. **a.** 1+ **b.** Na^+ **c.** 2+ **d.** Mg^{2+} **e.** 1– **f.** Cl^- **g.** 2– **h.** SO_4^{2-}
6. two more electrons than protons; its charge is 2–

© Pearson Education, Inc., publishing as Pearson Prentice Hall. All rights reserved.

7. A sodium atom becomes a positive ion, and a chlorine atom becomes a negative ion.

8. An ionic bond is the attraction between two oppositely charged ions.

9. Ionic bonds form as a result of the attraction between positive and negative ions.

10. chemical formula

11. True

12. The number "2" is called a subscript. It tells you that there are two chloride ions for each magnesium ion in the compound.

13. False

14. When the negative ion is a single element

15. crystal structures, high melting points, ability to conduct electricity in solution or when melted

16. crystal

17. Every ion is attracted to ions of opposite charge that surround it.

18. Because ionic bonds are strong, and a lot of energy is needed to break them

19. solids

20. The ions in solid crystals are tightly bound to each other, so no energy can flow. When ionic compounds are dissolved in water, the bonds between ions are broken, allowing the ions to move freely and conduct electricity.

Ionic Bonds
Review and Reinforce

1. An atom becomes a positive ion by losing an electron. An atom becomes a negative ion by gaining an electron.

2. Oppositely charged ions are attracted to each other. When ionic bonds form, the ions come together in a way that balances out the charges on the ions.

3. Solid ionic compounds typically have crystalline shapes and high melting points. They conduct electricity well when dissolved in water or melted.

4. As solids, the ions are tightly bound in ionic bonds. The ions are free to move when the compound is dissolved in water. Then electricity can flow.

5. Two. A sulfide ion has a charge of 2–. Since potassium ions only have a charge of 1+, two potassium ions are needed to balance the charge.

6. $CaCl_2$, K_3PO_4

7. Magnesium sulfide, ammonium chloride, and potassium oxide

8. Ammonium and phosphate are polyatomic.

9. An atom or group of atoms that has an electrical charge

10. The attraction between oppositely charged ions

11. In a crystal, positive and negative ions alternate, forming an orderly three-dimensional arrangement.

Ionic Bonds
Enrich

1. Atomic radius increases from top to bottom; atomic radius decreases from left to right.

2. Cesium; barium; These two should be the most reactive of their groups because each has the largest atomic radius in its group. The element with the largest atomic radius holds some of its electrons less tightly, so the electrons are easier to remove.

3. The Group 1 element is more reactive in each case because the atomic radius of the Group 1 element is larger than the atomic radius of the corresponding Group 2 element. This means the Group 1 element holds onto some of its electrons less tightly, so the electrons require less energy to remove. Also, two electrons must be removed from Group 2 atoms, which would require more energy than needed to remove one electron from Group 1 atoms.

4. Across a period, the noble gas elements would have the smallest atomic radii of any group, which means that their electrons would be held onto the tightest. To remove an electron and get these elements to react would require large amounts of energy.

Shedding Light on Ions
Skills Lab

For answers, see the Teacher's Edition.

Covalent Bonds
Guided Reading and Study

Use Target Reading Skills
    Possible questions and answers:

How do covalent bonds form? (*Covalent bonds form when two atoms share electrons.*)

What are molecular compounds? (*Molecular compounds are compounds that contain molecules bonded with covalent bonds.*)

How does unequal sharing of electrons affect the atoms in molecular compounds? (*Unequal sharing of electrons causes the bonded atoms to have slight electrical charges.*)

© Pearson Education, Inc., publishing as Pearson Prentice Hall. All rights reserved.

1. A chemical bond formed when two atoms share electrons

2. Students should circle the two electrons between the two "F's" on the right.

3. molecule, or covalent bond

4. double bond

5. True

6. Molecules

7. d

8. Atoms of some elements in a molecular compound pull more strongly on shared electrons than do atoms of other elements. As a result, the electrons are pulled more toward one atom, causing the bonded atoms to have slight electrical charges.

9. polar

10. equally

11. If two atoms pull on shared electrons with equal strength in opposite directions, the polar bonds cancel each other out.

12. True

13. Because polar molecules attract each other much more than nonpolar molecules do

14. Oil molecules are nonpolar, so they are not attracted to the polar water molecules, which are attracted more strongly to each other than to the molecules of oil.

15. Detergent causes the dirt and water to mix, because detergent molecules have a nonpolar end that is attracted to oil molecules and a polar end that is attracted to water molecules.

Covalent Bonds
Review and Reinforce

1. Students should have drawn one circle around the shared electrons in each diagram (two electron pairs shared in O_2 and three pairs in N_2).

2. The bond in O_2

3. The bond in N_2

4. The polar bond is a result of the fluorine atom pulling more strongly on the shared electrons than the hydrogen atom.

5. N_2, O_2, and F_2 have nonpolar bonds.

6. Compared to ionic compounds, molecular compounds have lower melting and boiling points. Most molecular compounds are poor conductors of electricity when melted or dissolved.

7. nonpolar

8. polar

9. polar

10. nonpolar

Covalent Bonds
Enrich

1. Because oil is nonpolar, it will not mix with polar water. It will only float on the water's surface. This allows floating barriers to keep oil contained until it can be removed with nets. If oil mixed with water, it could not be separated from water as easily.

2. Because the bonds are made up of two of the same kind of atom bonded together, they both would have an equal pull on the electrons involved in the bond. That means that the valence electrons are shared equally and the bonds are nonpolar.

3. One end of a detergent molecule attracts a water molecule, while the other end attracts an oil molecule. This attraction pulls apart a large oil spill bit by bit.

4. No. No matter how small the oil particles are, they will never mix with the water, because oil is nonpolar and water is polar. Even if they look like they are mixed, the oil and water will eventually separate.

Bonding in Metals
Guided Reading and Study

Use Target Reading Skills
Graphic organizers should show that metallic bonding causes the properties of metals, which include electrical conductivity, heat conductivity, ductility, malleability, and luster.

1. a, c, d

2. Positively charged metal ions embedded in a "sea" of valence electrons

3. In a metallic bond, the positive metal ions are attracted to the "sea" of electrons around them.

© Pearson Education, Inc., publishing as Pearson Prentice Hall. All rights reserved.

4. alloy

5. Ability to conduct heat, ability to conduct electricity, ability to change shape easily, luster

6. The "sea of electrons" model

7. Because the electrons in a metal crystal can move freely among the atoms

8. a. Ability to be bent easily and pulled into thin strands **b.** Malleability

9. True

Bonding in Metals
Review and Reinforce

1. "Sea of electrons" model

2. The large balls represent positive metal ions; the small balls represent valence electrons.

3. Metallic bonds

4. Ability to conduct heat and electricity, ability to change shape easily, and luster

5. Metal ions and valence electrons are not rigidly held in a metal crystal. This allows metals to conduct heat and electricity and to change shape. The valence electrons also absorb and then give off light, which gives metals their luster.

6. metallic bond

7. Ductility

8. Malleability

Bonding in Metals
Enrich

1. Topaz, corundum, and diamond; they have a higher rating on the Mohs scale.

2. Yes, according to the table you could scratch a copper coin with a knife blade because the knife blade has a higher rating on the Mohs scale.

3. You would find the mineral on the scale with the highest hardness rating that the unlisted one will scratch. Then find the mineral on the scale with the lowest hardness rating that will scratch the unlisted one. The hardness of the unlisted mineral would be a number between those two hardness ratings.

Key Terms

Key Terms: electrons, polar, valence, crystal, nucleus, ion, neutron, ionic bond, nonpolar, proton, double bond
Hidden Key Term: covalent bond
Definition: A chemical bond formed when two atoms share electrons

© Pearson Education, Inc., publishing as Pearson Prentice Hall. All rights reserved.

Connecting Concepts

Atoms are the smallest particles of elements; they are represented by models that developed over time; and they can form bonds that are ionic, covalent, or metallic. This concept map is only one way to represent the main ideas and relationships in this chapter. Accept other logical answer from students.

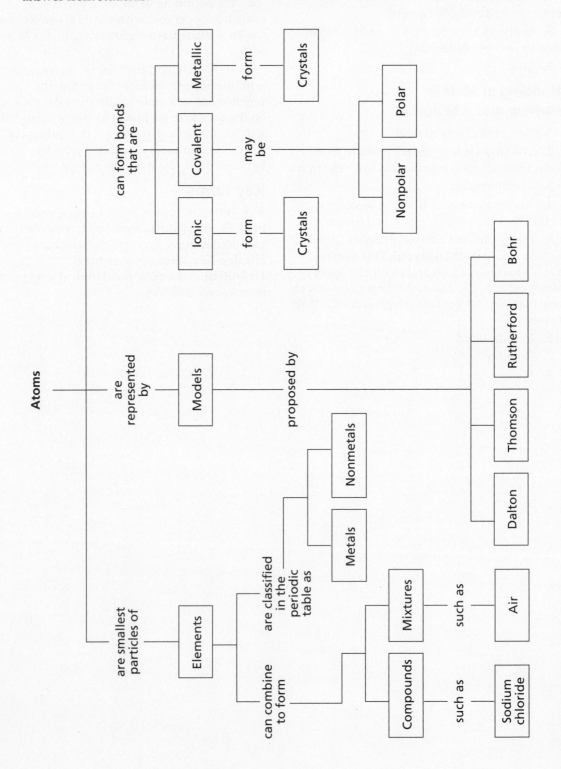

© Pearson Education, Inc., publishing as Pearson Prentice Hall. All rights reserved.

Laboratory Investigation

Testing for Hard Water
Pre-Lab Discussion

1. A soap molecule has a polar end and a non-polar end, so it attracts water (polar) and mixes with oil (nonpolar).

2. The polar ends of soap molecules attract the charged ions. These ions combine with soap to form a new compound (scum).

Procedure

3. Students' predictions may vary. They may be based on their experience with using different kinds of water, such as how sudsy water becomes when they wash their hands.

Sample Data Table

Data Table

Water Type and Soap	Observations	
	Just After Mixing	10 min After Mixing
Distilled water	Lots of suds fill the test tube; Water is clear.	Suds fill test tube and water is clear. Suds take a long time to dissipate.
Tap water	If the water is very hard, few suds will form and the water will be cloudy. If the water is not very hard, more suds will form and the water will be clearer.	If no suds were present before, none will be now. If suds were present, there will be fewer now. Cloudiness depends on amount of scum formed.
Control	Few suds; cloudy water	Few, if any, suds; cloudy water; Suds easily dissipate.

Analyze and Conclude

1. Because soap suds will not form in hard water, the absence of suds indicates hard water.

2. The order may vary. Distilled water is always the softest. Answers should reflect students' data.

3. Answers may vary. Students should describe how the results differ from the prediction. Some students may be knowledgeable about water hardness if their local water supply is very hard.

Critical Thinking and Applications

1. Answers will vary. Some samples, such as the control, may have many ions in them, so they are very hard. Soap cannot make suds in very hard water.

2. Calcium ions and chloride ions are present.

3. Hard water prevents the soap from dispersing in the water, so it cannot work on the dirt in the clothes. Also, scum forms in hard water and may collect in places around the inside walls of the washing machine and stick to clothes.

4. You have to remove the dissolved calcium and magnesium ions from the hard water to make it soft.

More to Explore

Detergents are designed to be active in all water conditions. They contain synthetic, soaplike molecules made from alkene benzene sulfonic acid or phosphates. These compounds do not form scum in hard water, so they work better than soap in hard water. Students may design a procedure to compare how much detergent is necessary for getting clothes clean in different types of water. Or they might compare the effectiveness of soap versus detergents. Warn students to keep laundry detergent off their skin; it is very harsh.

© Pearson Education, Inc., publishing as Pearson Prentice Hall. All rights reserved.

Performance Assessment

1. The terms *polar* and *nonpolar* refer to covalent bonds. Some students may add that ionic compounds exist as crystals rather than as individual molecules.

2. Potassium iodide, sodium oxide, calcium chloride, lithium nitride; these compounds are ionic. All ionic compounds exist as solids at room temperature.

3. Noble gases don't react very easily with other atoms, so they are rarely found in compounds.

Chapter Test

1. d

2. a

3. b

4. c

5. b

6. d

7. b

8. c

9. d

10. b

11. alloy

12. eight

13. period

14. positive

15. six

16. True

17. noble gases

18. neutral

19. polar

20. True

21. a. $MgCl_2$
　　b. Al_2S_3
　　c. None; an atom of argon already has eight electrons and does not react easily.

22. Yes, the number of valence electrons increases from left to right.

23. The positive ions and valence electrons in metals can move freely, allowing metals to conduct heat and electricity, to give off light (luster), and to readily change their shape.

24. In the H_2O molecule, the atoms do not share the electrons equally. The electrons are closer to one atom than the other, creating a slight positive charge on one end and a slight negative charge on the other end of the molecule. In the H_2 molecule, both hydrogen atoms pull the electrons with the same strength. They are shared equally, so the molecule is nonpolar.

25. Both ionic and covalent bonds involve electrons. Both kinds of bonds hold atoms together. In an ionic bond, the atoms have lost or gained electrons. Bonds form between oppositely charged ions. In a covalent bond, atoms share pairs of electrons.

26. A, Group 15; D, Group 1; E, Group 16; G, Group 13; J, Group 18; L, Group 17; M, Group 2; Q, Group 14

27. Element A can form three covalent bonds because it has five valence electrons and needs three more to have a total of eight.

28. The alkali metals have only one valence electron, which is easily lost. As a result, alkali metals are very reactive and will easily combine with other elements to form compounds.

29. Try dissolving the solid in water, or melting the solid. Then test again to see if the solution or the liquid will conduct electricity.

30. The opposite ends of polar water molecules are attracted to each other. This means that a higher temperature is required to provide enough energy for the molecules to separate from one another. Carbon dioxide is composed of nonpolar molecules, so there is less attraction between these molecules and less energy is needed to separate molecules from each other, allowing them to become a gas.

© Pearson Education, Inc., publishing as Pearson Prentice Hall. All rights reserved.

Chemical Reactions

© Pearson Education, Inc., publishing as Pearson Prentice Hall. All rights reserved.

Lab zone Chapter Project Design and Build a Closed Reaction Chamber

The following steps will walk you through the Chapter Project. Use the hints and detailed directions as you guide your students through design, construction, and presentation.

Chapter Project Overview

In this chapter, students will design and build a closed reaction chamber. They will use the reaction chamber to confirm that matter is not created or destroyed in a chemical reaction.

Introduce the project by asking students to identify reactants and products in an open chemical reaction with which they are familiar. A good example is logs burning in a camp fire or fireplace. Lead a discussion of how the masses of some of the reactants and products (logs, ashes) could easily be measured, whereas others (oxygen, carbon dioxide, water vapor) could not be measured in the open system. Conclude the discussion by telling students they will design and build a chamber that can contain all the reactants and products of a reaction so they can be measure.

Explain to students that they will use their closed chambers to burn sugar. On the board, write the equation for the combustion of sugar:

$$C_{12}H_{22}O_{11} + heat \rightarrow 12\ C + 11\ H_2O$$

Point out that using their closed reaction chambers will allow them to determine the mass of the reactant and products of the reaction. Explain the law of conservation of mass. Then, challenge students to predict how the mass of the products should compare to the mass of the reactants if their chambers function well. Ask them how they could determine whether matter is created or destroyed in the reaction.

Distribute the Chapter Project Overview. Review the project's rules. You may also want to hand out the Chapter Project Scoring Rubric so students will understand what is expected of them.

Organize the class into groups. Instruct the groups to brainstorm how they could build a closed reaction chamber in which they could burn sugar. Give them a list of suggested materials, and challenge them to think of how they could be combined to produce the chamber. After the groups have had their brainstorming session, encourage the class as a whole to share ideas about constructing the chamber. You may want to have students work in their groups to complete the project.

Set a deadline for the project presentation and some interim dates for the Keep Students on Track at the ends of Sections 1, 2, 3, and 4. Have students copy the dates in their Project Time Line.

Distribute Chapter Project Worksheet 1. Tell students that Worksheet 1 will help them design their reaction chambers. Then, hand out Chapter Project Worksheet 2 and tell students that Worksheet 2 will help them record and analyze their data when the use their chambers to burn sugar.

Materials and Preparation

Review the use of the triple beam balance before students need to use it. Remind students that the triple beam balance measures mass in grams.

Reaction chambers can be constructed from empty metal food cans, plastic bottles, and balloons. You may want to have each student bring in one can and one bottle with similar diameters.

To construct the chamber, students may need rulers, scissors, hot glue guns, and duct tape. To use the chamber for the combustion of sucrose, students will need a heat source (candle or Bunsen burner) and a way of holding the reaction chamber steady over the heat (ring stand or metal tongs).

© Pearson Education, Inc., publishing as Pearson Prentice Hall. All rights reserved.

Keep Students on Track— Section 1

The diameter of the bottle should be just large enough that the bottle slips over the can. If students have difficulty measuring the diameters, they can compare the sizes of bottles and cans by wrapping a string around the circumference and measuring the length of the string with a ruler.

The most likely set up of the materials is shown in Worksheet 1. Make sure that students have completed Worksheet 1 before they construct their chambers. Remind students to check their completed chamber for leaks before topping the bottle with the balloon.

Keep Students on Track— Section 2

Once students have constructed and tested their reaction chambers, they can add a small, measured mass of table sugar to the container, seal the container with the balloon, and find the mass of the sealed container. Then, they can light the heat source and heat the reaction chamber. During the reaction, students should record all observations and draw a picture of the experimental setup. Once the sugar has blackened, students should remove the chamber from the heat source and measure the mass of the vessel again. Remind students to record their observations and measurements in the Student Data Table in Worksheet 2.

Keep Students on Track— Section 3

Check that students have conducted the sucrose combustion reaction correctly and recorded the measurements of initial and final mass on Worksheet 2. List the measurements from all the students or groups of students on the board, and tell the class to copy them into the Class Data Table on Worksheet 2. Have students use the class values to find the average change in mass for the class. Then, ask students the following questions to guide them in interpreting the data. How does the final mass of the reaction vessel compare with the initial mass? From this, what can you conclude about the masses of the reactant and products in the chemical reaction? What happens to the reactants in the sucrose combustion reaction? How do they change? Why is it important for the reaction vessel to remain closed during the reaction? How would the experiment differ if the reaction chamber were not closed?

Keep Students on Track— Section 4

Remind students to prepare posters or other visual displays of their work. Tell them to include in their presentations a description of the design and construction of their closed reaction chambers. They also should include the results of the chemical reactions and their conclusions about the results.

Chapter Project Performance Assessment

Have students take turns presenting their work to the class while other students ask questions. You might want to make it a requirement that each student ask at least one question during the presentations. Challenge students to try to explain any differences in the results. Ask them what might have caused the discrepancies.

Extension

Let students use their closed reaction chambers to carry out other simple chemical reactions. For each reaction, students can identify the reactants and products and observe the reactants change into other substances. They also can gather additional mass data and relate it to conservation of mass.

© Pearson Education, Inc., publishing as Pearson Prentice Hall. All rights reserved.

Chemical Reactions · *Chapter Project*   **Overview**

Lab zone Chapter Project Design and Build a Closed Reaction Chamber

The principle of conservation of mass states that matter is neither created nor destroyed in a chemical reaction. The mass of reactant atoms is always equal to the mass of product atoms. This project focuses on a simple chemical reaction, the combustion, or burning, of sucrose (table sugar). When heat is added to sucrose, hydrogen and oxygen atoms are converted to water vapor, leaving solid carbon behind.

How can you measure the mass of these products? For this and many other chemical reactions, it is difficult to gather evidence to support the law of conservation of mass. In this chapter project, you will try to solve the problem of containing the reactants and products of a chemical reaction. By measuring the masses of reactants and products, you will also determine if mass is changed or remains the same after the chemical reaction.

Project Rules

- Design a solution for the problem of containing reactants and products in the combustion of sucrose. You must use the materials your teacher provides or approves. Your design must be approved as well.

- Using your design, build a closed reaction chamber.

- Evaluate your chamber, test it for leaks, and modify it as needed.

- Carry out the combustion of sucrose in your completed reaction chamber. Observe, measure, and record the results of the experiment.

- Interpret your data and the pooled class data to determine whether mass is conserved in the reaction.

- Present your findings in a visual display and oral presentation. In your presentation, you should include a description of the chamber you designed and the design process, as well as your experimental results and conclusions.

© Pearson Education, Inc., publishing as Pearson Prentice Hall. All rights reserved.

Name _____ Date _____ Class _____

Chemical Reactions • *Chapter Project*   **Overview**

Project Hints

■ As you begin to design your reaction chamber, complete Chapter Project Worksheet 1. It will guide you in designing and building an effective closed reaction chamber that is suitable for the sucrose combustion experiment.

■ At the beginning of the sucrose experiment, add a small amount of sucrose of known mass to the can through the open bottle top. Record the mass of the sugar in the space provided in the Student Data Table on Chapter Project Worksheet 2.

■ After adding the sucrose, cover the bottle top with a balloon, and then find the mass of the chamber plus sucrose. Record this value in the space provided in the Student Data Table.

■ When you burn the sucrose in the chamber, make sure the flame is centered beneath the can. Otherwise, the adhesive between the can and the bottle may melt. Make sure the flame is not too high for the same reason.

■ Always use proper safety precautions when using a flame. Safety goggles and lab aprons should be worn at all times.

■ Heat the sucrose until it turns black. Use tongs to handle the heated can or let the can cool before handling. Measure the mass of the reaction chamber. Record the final mass in the Student Data Table on Worksheet 2.

■ Use the Class Data Table on Worksheet 2 to pool data from the entire class. Use a calculator to find the class average. Also calculate the amount by which your change in mass differs from the class average. Record the results of your calculations in the spaces provided in the Student Data Table.

■ Use the data tables, or graphs made from the data tables, in your class presentation. Prepare for your presentation by writing note cards that summarize how you designed your closed reaction chamber and any problems you had to resolve; how you carried out the experiment and what the results were; and the conclusions you drew about conservation of mass based on your data and the pooled class data.

Project Timeline
Task   Due Date

1. Complete Worksheet 1 and design chamber.   _____
2. Build, test, and modify chamber.   _____
3. Complete sucrose combustion experiment.   _____
4. Complete Worksheet 2 and draw conclusions.   _____
5. Make presentation to the class.   _____

© Pearson Education, Inc., publishing as Pearson Prentice Hall. All rights reserved.

Name _____ Date _____ Class _____

Closed Reaction Chamber

This worksheet will walk you through the steps involved in making one type of closed reaction chamber suitable for burning sucrose. The reaction chamber is shown below. Use the figure as a guide.

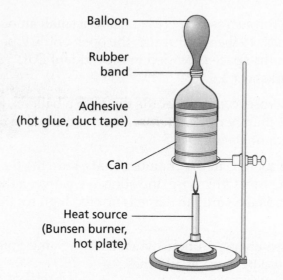

1. Obtain an empty metal food can. Also obtain an empty plastic water or soda bottle with about the same diameter as the can. Wash the can and bottle, and remove all the labels.

2. Cut off the top third of the bottle with scissors. Slide the bottle over the open end of the can as in the figure. Fasten the bottle to the can in this position using glue or tape.

3. Test the seal between the can and bottle by blowing into the top of the bottle and listening for escaping air. Find and seal any leaks.

4. Before adding the balloon to the bottle, add the sugar for the sucrose combustion experiment. Make sure you use the triple beam balance to measure the mass of the sugar first. Don't forget to record the mass in the Student Data Table on Worksheet 2.

5. After adding the sugar, put the balloon over the mouth of the bottle. An inadequate seal between the balloon and mouth of the bottle may result in a leaky chamber and loss of mass. This can be avoided by placing a tight rubber band over the balloon around the neck of the bottle.

6. Measure with the balance and record on Worksheet 2 the mass of the chamber plus sugar.

7. Set up the heat source as shown in the figure, and obtain your teacher's permission to carry out the experiment.

© Pearson Education, Inc., publishing as Pearson Prentice Hall. All rights reserved.

Chemical Reactions • *Chapter Project*   **Worksheet 2**

Data Tables for Sucrose Combustion Experiment

This worksheet consists of data tables to record your data and the data from the rest of the class. The tables also have spaces for you to record individual changes in mass, the class average change in mass, and how your data differ from the class average.

Student Data Table

Data source	Mass of sugar (g)	Initial mass of chamber with reactions (g)	Final mass of chamber with products (g)	Change in mass (g)
Your data				
Class average				
Deviation from class average				

Class Data Table

Data source	Mass of sugar (g)	Initial mass of chamber with reactions (g)	Final mass of chamber with products (g)	Change in mass (g)
Student 1				
Student 2				
Etc.				

Student Data Table

Data source	Mass of sugar (g)	Initial mass of chamber with reactions (g)	Final mass of chamber with products (g)	Change in mass (g)
Your data				
Class average				
Deviation from class average				

Class Data Table

Data source	Mass of sugar (g)	Initial mass of chamber with reactions (g)	Final mass of chamber with products (g)	Change in mass (g)
Student 1				
Student 2				
Etc.				

© Pearson Education, Inc., publishing as Pearson Prentice Hall. All rights reserved.

Chemical Reactions ▪ *Chapter Project* **Scoring Rubric**

Lab zone Chapter Project — Design and Build a Closed Reaction Chamber

In evaluating how well you complete the Chapter Project, your teacher will judge your work in four categories. In each, a score of 4 is the best rating.

	4	3	2	1
Constructing Reaction Chamber	The student correctly constructed a closed reaction chamber according to the instructions in Worksheet 1. The reaction chamber remained tightly closed throughout the experiment.	The student constructed an adequate reaction chamber, but the reaction chamber may have leaked slightly during the experiment.	The student constructed a reaction chamber, but the reaction chamber leaked significantly during the experiment.	The student attempted but failed to construct a useable reaction chamber.
Conducting Experiment	The student precisely conducted a valid experiment and accurately recorded all relevant observations and measurements in the data tables.	The student correctly conducted the experiment and recorded most relevant observations and measurements.	The student conducted the experiment but made some errors; the student recorded some relevant observations and measurements.	The student may have tried to conduct an experiment but did it incorrectly or failed to complete it; the student recorded few if any relevant observations or measurements.
Interpreting Data	The student accurately interpreted the data on change in mass and correctly related it to the principle of conservation of mass.	The student interpreted the data on change in mass and related it to the principle of conservation of mass, but the student made one or two minor omissions or errors.	The student attempted to interpret the data on change in mass and relate it to the principle of conservation of mass, but the student made several omissions and/or errors.	The student attempted to interpret the data on change in mass and relate it to the principle of conservation of mass, but the student made several omissions and/or errors.
Presenting Findings	The student made a thorough, well-organized presentation using an interesting and highly appropriate visual display.	The student made a satisfactory presentation using a suitable visual display.	The student made a presentation using a visual display, but the presentation was disorganized or too brief, and/or the visual display was flawed or inappropriate.	The student may not have made a presentation and/or visual display; if a presentation or visual display was made, it was seriously flawed.

© Pearson Education, Inc., publishing as Pearson Prentice Hall. All rights reserved.

Observing Chemical Change

⏱ *3–4 periods, 1 1/2–2 blocks*

Ability Levels Key
- **L1** Basic to Average
- **L2** For All Students
- **L3** Average to Advanced

Objectives

L.2.1.1 State how matter and changes in matter can be described.

L.2.1.2 Explain how you can tell when a chemical reaction occurs.

Key Terms

- matter • chemistry • physical property
- chemical property • physical change
- chemical reaction • precipitate
- endothermic reaction • exothermic reaction

Local Standards

PRETEACH

Build Background Knowledge
Students name familiar changes in matter as an introduction to the physical and chemical changes they will read about in the section.

 **Discover Activity** *What Happens When Chemicals React?* **L1**

Targeted Resources

☐ **All in One** **Teaching Resources**
  L2 Reading Strategy Transparency L16: Asking Questions
☐ 💿 **Presentation-Pro CD-ROM**

INSTRUCT

Properties and Changes of Matter Introduce physical and chemical properties of matter by discussing several examples.

Evidence for Chemical Reactions Describe the two main types of observable chemical change, and have students identify them in the reaction between magnesium and oxygen.

 Skills Lab *Where's the Evidence?* **L2**

Targeted Resources

☐ **All in One** **Teaching Resources**
  L2 Guided Reading, pp. 119–121
  L2 Transparencies L17, L18
  L2 Lab: *Where's the Evidence?*, pp. 124–127
☐ 📼 **Lab Activity Video/DVD**
  Skills Lab: *Where's the Evidence?*
☐ **www.SciLinks.org** Web Code: scn-1221
☐ 💿 **Student Edition on Audio CD**

ASSESS

Section Assessment Questions
🔄 Have students use their completed graphic organizers to answer the questions.

Reteach
Students answer questions based on the boldface sentences in the section.

Targeted Resources

☐ **All in One** **Teaching Resources**
  Section Summary, p. 118
  L1 Review and Reinforce, p. 122
  L3 Enrich, p. 123

© Pearson Education, Inc., publishing as Pearson Prentice Hall. All rights reserved.

Chemical Reactions

Chemical Reactions · *Section Summary*

Observing Chemical Change

Guide for Reading

■ How can matter and changes in matter be described?

■ How can you tell when a chemical reaction occurs?

Matter is anything that has mass and takes up space. The study of matter and how matter changes is called **chemistry**. **Matter can be described in terms of two kinds of properties—physical properties and chemical properties. Changes in matter can be described in terms of physical changes and chemical changes.**

A **physical property** is a characteristic of a substance that can be observed without changing the substance into another substance. The temperature at which a solid melts is a phyical property. Color, hardness, and texture are other physical properties.

A **chemical property** property is a characteristic of a substance that describes its ability to change into other substances. To observe the chemical properties of a substance, you must change it into another substance. For example, to observe the chemical reactivity of magnesium, you can let magnesium combine with oxygen to form a new substance called magnesium oxide.

A **physical change** is any change that alters the form or appearance of a substance but that does not make the substance into another substance. Examples of physical changes are bending and cutting.

A change in matter that produces one or more new substances is a chemical change, or **chemical reaction**. The burning of gasoline in a car's engine is a chemical change. **Chemical changes occur when bonds form between atoms, or when bonds break and new bonds form.** As a result, new substances are produced.

One way to detect chemical reactions is to observe changes in the properties of the materials involved. **Chemical reactions involve two main kinds of changes you can observe—formation of new substances and changes in energy.** Changes in properties result when new substances form. A change in color may signal that a new substance has formed. Another indicator might be the formation of a solid when two solutions are mixed. A solid that forms from solution during a chemical reaction is called a **precipitate**. A third indicator is the formation of a gas when solids or liquids react. These and other kinds of observable changes in properties may indicate that a chemical reaction has occurred.

As matter changes in a chemical reaction, it can either absorb or release energy. One indication that energy has been absorbed or released is a change in temperature. An **endothermic reaction** is a reaction in which energy is absorbed. A reaction that releases energy in the form of heat is called an **exothermic reaction**.

© Pearson Education, Inc., publishing as Pearson Prentice Hall. All rights reserved.

Observing Chemical Change

This section describes how matter can change physically or chemically. It also describes how you can tell when a chemical change in matter has occurred.

Use Target Reading Skills

Before you read, preview the red headings. In the graphic organizer below, ask a what *or* how *question for each heading. As you read, write the answers to your questions.*

Properties and Changes of Matter

Question	Answer
What are physical properties of matter?	Physical properties are . . .

Introduction

1. What is matter?

   _____

   _____

2. The study of matter and how matter changes is called _____.

Properties and Changes of Matter

3. Complete the following table about physical and chemical properties of matter.

Type of Property	How It Can Be Observed	Example
a.	Without changing one substance into another	Color
Chemical	b.	Ability to burn

© Pearson Education, Inc., publishing as Pearson Prentice Hall. All rights reserved.

Observing Chemical Change *(continued)*

4. Is the following sentence true or false? A physical change never alters the form or appearance of a substance. _____

5. Circle the letter of each choice that is a physical change in matter.

   a. bending a straw   **b.** boiling water
   c. burning wood   **d.** braiding hair

6. A change in matter that produces one or more new substances is a(n)

   _____.

7. What happens to the bonds between atoms when chemical changes occur?

   _____

   _____

   _____

Evidence for Chemical Reactions

8. List the two main kinds of changes that you can observe when chemical reactions occur.

   _____

   _____

9. If you detect a change in the color of a material, why does this indicate that a chemical reaction might have occurred?

   _____

   _____

   _____

   _____

10. A solid that forms during a chemical reaction is called a(n)

    _____.

11. Suppose you mix two clear liquids together to form a new substance and bubbles form. What type of reaction might this indicate? Explain your answer.

    _____

    _____

    _____

    _____

    _____

© Pearson Education, Inc., publishing as Pearson Prentice Hall. All rights reserved.

Name _____ Date _____ Class _____

12. Is the following sentence true or false? A change in energy occurs during a chemical reaction. _____

13. Why does a change in temperature indicate that a chemical reaction may have occurred?

_____

_____

_____

_____

14. Is the following sentence true or false? Endothermic reactions always result in a decrease in temperature. _____

15. Complete the table about changes in energy in chemical reactions.

Type of Reaction	Energy Change	Example
Endothermic	a.	Frying an egg
b.	Energy is released	Burning wood

© Pearson Education, Inc., publishing as Pearson Prentice Hall. All rights reserved.

Chemical Reactions   ·   *Review and Reinforce*

Observing Chemical Change

Understanding Main Ideas

Complete the following table. Describe changes in properties that you might notice during each process and state whether the changes are chemical or physical.

Changes in Matter		
Event	Observable Changes	Type of Change
Baking a cake	1.	2.
Burning a log	3.	4.
Freezing water	5.	6.

Building Vocabulary

From the list below, choose the term that best completes each sentence.

matter   physical change

chemical reaction   endothermic reaction

chemistry   exothermic reaction

precipitate

7. Any change that alters a substance without changing it into another substance is a(n) _____.

8. _____ is anything that has mass and takes up space.

9. A reaction that releases energy in the form of heat is called a(n) _____.

10. A(n) _____ is a reaction in which energy is absorbed.

11. A chemical change is also referred to as a(n) _____.

12. A(n) _____ is a solid formed from a solution during a chemical reaction.

13. _____ is the study of the properties of matter and how matter changes.

© Pearson Education, Inc., publishing as Pearson Prentice Hall. All rights reserved.

Name _____ Date _____ Class _____

Separation Science

A mixture is a combination of two or more pure substances, and the substances do not combine to form new material. Therefore, you should be able to separate a mixture into the substances that make it. There are several ways to separate mixtures. Figure 1 shows a mixture of sand and water being separated by *filtration*. The salt in a solution of salt water can be separated by *evaporation*, shown in Figure 2. When you let the sand particles in a mixture of sand and water settle to the bottom of a container, then carefully pour the water off into another container, you are using a method called *decanting*, shown in Figure 3.

Study the following illustrations, then answer the questions below on a separate sheet of paper.

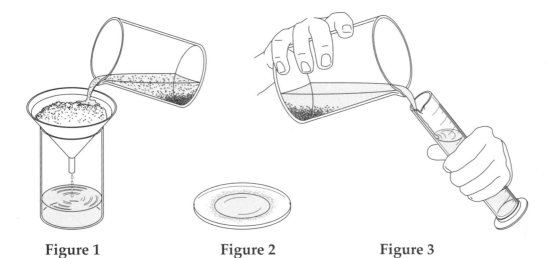

Figure 1   **Figure 2**   **Figure 3**

1. Using Figure 1, explain the process of filtration. Give another example of filtration used to separate a mixture.
2. Discuss a use for evaporation.
3. What types of mixtures could be separated by decanting? Is laboratory equipment necessary for decanting a mixture? Why or why not?
4. Would a separation of the types described above cause a chemical change or a physical change? Explain your answer.

© Pearson Education, Inc., publishing as Pearson Prentice Hall. All rights reserved.

Chemical Reactions

Chemical Reactions · *Skills Lab*

Where's the Evidence?

Problem

What are some signs that a chemical reaction has taken place?

Skills Focus

observing, predicting, drawing conclusions

Materials

4 small plastic cups

2 plastic spoons

tongs

matches

birthday candles

sugar

clay

sodium carbonate (powdered solid)

graduated cylinder, 10 mL

aluminum foil, about 10-cm square

dilute hydrochloric acid in a dropper bottle

copper sulfate solution

sodium carbonate solution

Procedure   *Review the safety guidelines in Appendix A.*

Preview the steps for each reaction. Be sure to record your data in the data table.

Part 1

1. Put a pea-sized pile of sodium carbonate into a clean plastic cup. Record the appearance of the sodium carbonate in the data table.

2. Observe a dropper containing hydrochloric acid. Record the appearance of the acid in the data table. **CAUTION:***Hydrochloric acid can burn you or anything else it touches. Wash spills with water.*

3. Make a prediction about how you think the acid and the sodium carbonate will react when mixed. Record your prediction in the data table.

4. Add about 10 drops of hydrochloric acid to the sodium carbonate. Swirl to mix the contents of the cup. Record your observations in the data table.

© Pearson Education, Inc., publishing as Pearson Prentice Hall. All rights reserved.

Chemical Reactions ▪ *Skills Lab*

Part 2

5. Fold up the sides of the aluminum foil square to make a small tray.

6. Use a plastic spoon to place a pea-sized pile of sugar into the tray.

7. Carefully describe the appearance of the sugar in your data table.

8. Secure a small candle on your desktop in a lump of clay. Carefully light the candle with a match only after being instructed to do so by your teacher. **CAUTION:***Tie back long hair and loose clothing.*

9. Predict what you think will happen if you heat the sugar. Record your prediction in the data table.

10. Use tongs to hold the aluminum tray. Heat the sugar slowly by moving the tray gently back and forth over the flame. Make observations while the sugar is heating.

11. When you think there is no longer a chemical reaction occurring, blow out the candle.

12. Allow the tray to cool for a few seconds and set it down on your desk. Record your observations of the material left in the tray.

Part 3

13. Put about 2 mL of copper sulfate solution in one cup. **CAUTION:** *Copper sulfate is poisonous and can stain your skin and clothes. Do not touch it or get it in your mouth.* Put an equal amount of sodium carbonate solution in another cup. Record the appearance of both liquids in the data table.

14. Write a prediction of what you think will happen when the two solutions are mixed. Record your prediction in the data table.

15. Combine the two solutions and record your observations. **CAUTION:** *Dispose of the solutions as directed by your teacher.*

16. Wash your hands when you have finished working.

Chemical Reactions

© Pearson Education, Inc., publishing as Pearson Prentice Hall. All rights reserved.

Chemical Reactions · *Skills Lab*

Where's the Evidence? *(continued)*

Data Table

Reaction	Observations Before Reaction	Predictions	Observations During Reaction	Observations After Reaction
1. Sodium carbonate (powder) + hydrochloric acid				
2. Sugar + heat				
3. Copper sulfate + sodium carbonate solutions				

Analyze and Conclude

Write your answers in the spaces provided.

1. **Predicting** How do the results of each reaction compare with your predictions?

   _____

   _____

   _____

   _____

2. **Observing** How did you know when the reaction in Part1 was over?

   _____

   _____

3. **Interpreting Data** What was the evidence of a chemical reaction in Part 1? In Part 2?

   _____

   _____

   _____

© Pearson Education, Inc., publishing as Pearson Prentice Hall. All rights reserved.

Chemical Reactions · *Skills Lab*

4. **Drawing Conclusions** Was the reaction in Part 2 endothermic or exothermic? Explain.

_____

_____

_____

5. **Observing** Was the product of the reaction in Part 3 a solid, a liquid, or a gas? How do you know?

_____

_____

_____

6. **Drawing Conclusions** How do you know if new substances were formed in each reaction?

_____

_____

_____

7. **Communicating** Make a table or chart in the space below briefly describing each chemical change in this lab, followed by the evidence for the chemical change.

More to Explore

Use your observation skills to find evidence of chemical reactions involving foods in your kitchen. Look for production of gases, color changes, and formation of precipitates. Share your findings with your classmates.

© Pearson Education, Inc., publishing as Pearson Prentice Hall. All rights reserved.

Chemical Reactions

Describing Chemical Reactions

Ability Levels Key
L1 Basic to Average
L2 For All Students
L3 Average to Advanced

🕐 *2–3 periods, 1–1 1/2 blocks*

Objectives

L.2.2.1 Identify what information a chemical equation contains.
L.2.2.2 State the principle of the conservation of mass.
L.2.2.3 Explain what a balanced chemical equation must show.
L.2.2.4 Name three categories of chemical reactions.

Key Terms

• chemical equation • reactant • product
• conservation of mass • open system
• closed system • coefficient • synthesis
• decomposition • replacement

Local Standards

PRETEACH

Build Background Knowledge

Students brainstorm familiar symbols and explain how symbols are helpful, as an introduction to the use of symbols to describe chemical reactions.

 **Discover Activity** *Do You Lose Anything?* **L1**

Targeted Resources

❏ **All in One** Teaching Resources
  L2 Reading Strategy: Building Vocabulary
❏ 💿 **Presentation-Pro CD-ROM**

INSTRUCT

What Are Chemical Equations? Show students the general plan of all chemical equations.
Conservation of Mass Ask questions about the figure showing the reaction of iron and sulfur to guide students in understanding the principle of conservation of mass.
Balancing Chemical Equations Explain why chemical equations must be balanced, and show students how to balance a sample equation.
Classifying Chemical Reactions Have students read about categories of chemical reactions and then apply the concepts by classifying several sample chemical reactions.

Targeted Resources

❏ **All in One** Teaching Resources
  L2 Guided Reading, pp. 130–134
  L2 Transparencies L19, L20, L21
❏ **PHSchool.com** Web Code: cgp-2022
❏ **PHSchool.com** Web Code: cgh-2020
❏ 💿 **Student Edition on Audio CD**

ASSESS

Section Assessment Questions

🔾 Have students use their completed sentences using key terms to answer the questions.

Reteach

Students help make a table comparing and contrasting synthesis, degradation, and replacement reactions.

Targeted Resources

❏ **All in One** Teaching Resources
  Section Summary, p. 129
  L1 Review and Reinforce, p. 135
  L3 Enrich, p. 136

© Pearson Education, Inc., publishing as Pearson Prentice Hall. All rights reserved.

Name _____ Date _____ Class _____

Describing Chemical Reactions

Guide for Reading

- What information does a chemical equation contain?
- What does the principle of conservation of mass state?
- What must a balanced chemical equation show?
- What are three categories of chemical reactions?

A **chemical equation** is a short, easy way to show a chemical reaction. **Chemical equations use chemical formulas and other symbols instead of words to summarize a reaction.** All chemical equations have a common structure. A chemical equation tells you the substances you start with in a reaction and the substances you get at the end. The substances you have at the beginning are called the **reactants**. When the reaction is complete, you have new substances called the **products**. The formulas for the reactants are written on the left side of the equation, followed by an arrow ($\rightarrow$). You read the arrow as "yields." The formulas for the products are written on the right side of the equation. When there are two or more reactants or products, they are separated by plus signs.

The principle called **conservation of mass** was first demonstrated in the late 1700s. **The principle of conservation of mass states that in a chemical reaction, the total mass of the reactants must equal the total mass of the products.** In an **open system**, matter can enter from or escape to the surroundings. A match burning in the air is an example of an open system. You cannot measure the mass of all the reactants and products in an open system. A **closed system** is a system in which matter cannot enter from or escape to the surroundings. A sealed plastic bag is an example of a closed system. A closed system allows you to measure the mass of all reactants and products in a reaction.

To describe a reaction accurately, a chemical equation must show the same number of each type of atom on both sides of the equation. An equation is balanced when it accurately represents conservation of mass. To balance a chemical equation, you may have to use coefficients. A **coefficient** is a number placed in front of a chemical formula in an equation. It tells you how many atoms or molecules of a reactant or a product take part in the reaction.

Many chemical reactions can be classified in one of three categories: synthesis, decomposition, or replacement. When two or more elements or compounds combine to make a more complex substance, the reaction is called a **synthesis** reaction. The reaction of hydrogen and oxygen to make water is a synthesis reaction. A reaction called a **decomposition** reaction breaks down compounds into simpler products. For example, hydrogen peroxide decomposes into water and oxygen gas. When one element replaces another in a compound, or when two elements in different compounds trade places, the reaction is called a **replacement** reaction.

© Pearson Education, Inc., publishing as Pearson Prentice Hall. All rights reserved.

Chemical Reactions ▪ *Guided Reading and Study*

Describing Chemical Reactions

This section explains how to show chemical reactions with symbols. It also states the principle of conservation of mass, and identifies three categories of chemical reactions.

Use Target Reading Skills

After you read the section, reread the paragraphs that contain definitions of Key Terms. Use all of the information you have learned to write a meaningful sentence using each Key Term.

a. chemical equation: _____

_____

b. reactant: _____

_____

c. product: _____

_____

d. conservation of mass: _____

_____

e. open system: _____

_____

f. closed system: _____

_____

g. coefficient: _____

_____

h. synthesis: _____

_____

i. decomposition: _____

_____

j. replacement: _____

_____

© Pearson Education, Inc., publishing as Pearson Prentice Hall. All rights reserved.

Chemical Reactions · *Guided Reading and Study*

What Are Chemical Equations?

1. What is a chemical equation?

_____

_____

2. Is the following sentence true or false? Chemical equations use symbols instead of words to summarize chemical reactions.

_____

3. If a molecule of carbon dioxide is involved in a chemical reaction, how is it represented in the chemical equation for the reaction?

_____

4. The substances you have at the beginning of a chemical reaction are called the _____.

5. The substances you have when a chemical reaction is complete are called the _____.

6. What do you read the arrow in a chemical equation as meaning?

_____

7. Label each formula in the chemical equation below as either a reactant or a product.

   $Fe + S \rightarrow FeS$

   a. Fe _____   b. S _____

   c. FeS _____

8. Circle the letter of each statement that is true about chemical equations.

   a. Chemical equations have no real structure.
   b. A chemical equation summarizes a reaction.
   c. The formulas for the reactants are written on the right.
   d. Symbols in the equation show the reactants and the products.

Conservation of Mass

9. Is the following sentence true or false? All the atoms present at the start of a reaction are present at the end. _____

10. At the end of a chemical reaction, what is the total mass of the reactants compared to the total mass of the products?

_____

_____

_____

© Pearson Education, Inc., publishing as Pearson Prentice Hall. All rights reserved.

Chemical Reactions

Chemical Reactions • *Guided Reading and Study*

Describing Chemical Reactions *(continued)*

11. What is the principle called the conservation of mass?

_____

_____

_____

12. Describe an open system.

_____

_____

_____

13. What is an example of a closed system?

_____

_____

Balancing Chemical Equations

14. When is a chemical equation balanced?

_____

_____

_____

_____

_____

15. How many atoms of oxygen are there on each side of the following chemical equation: $2\,Mg + O_2 \rightarrow 2\,MgO$?

_____

_____

16. Circle the letter of each chemical equation that is balanced.

   a. $H_2 + O_2 \rightarrow H_2O$ **b.** $Mg + O_2 \rightarrow MgO$

   c. $Na + O_2 \rightarrow Na_2O$ **d.** $2\,H_2O_2 \rightarrow 2\,H_2O + O_2$

17. A number placed in front of a chemical formula in a chemical equation is called a(n) _____.

18. What does a coefficient tell you?

_____

_____

_____

© Pearson Education, Inc., publishing as Pearson Prentice Hall. All rights reserved.

19. Tell why this chemical equation is not balanced:

$H_2 + O_2 \rightarrow H_2O$.

_____

_____

_____

20. Write a balanced equation for this reaction: Oxygen reacts with hydrogen to yield water.

_____

Classifying Chemical Reactions

21. In what three categories can chemical reactions be classified?

_____

_____

_____

22. Which category of chemical reactions comes from a term that means "to put things together"?

_____

23. Complete the table about the three categories of chemical reactions.

Categories of Chemical Reactions		
Category	Description	Example Chemical Equation
a.	Two or more substances combine to make a more complex compound.	$2 SO_2 + O_2 + 2 H_2O \rightarrow H_2SO_4$
Decomposition	**b.**	$2 H_2O_2 \rightarrow 2 H_2O + O_2$
c.	One element replaces another in a compound, or two elements in different compounds trade places.	$2 CuO + C \rightarrow 2 Cu + CO_2$

© Pearson Education, Inc., publishing as Pearson Prentice Hall. All rights reserved.

Chemical Reactions · *Guided Reading and Study*

Describing Chemical Reactions *(continued)*

Classify each of the following equations as synthesis, decomposition, or replacement.

24. **a.** $CaCO_3 \rightarrow CaO + CO_2$_____

   b. $2\,Na + Cl_2 \rightarrow 2\,NaCl$ _____

   c. $Mg + CuSO_4 \rightarrow MgSO_4 + Cu$ _____

© Pearson Education, Inc., publishing as Pearson Prentice Hall. All rights reserved.

Describing Chemical Reactions

Understanding Main Ideas

Balance the equations on the lines below. State whether the reaction is a synthesis, decomposition, or replacement reaction.

Given Equation	Balanced Equation	Type of Reaction
1. $FeS + HCl \rightarrow FeCl_2 + H_2S$	a.	b.
2. $Na + F_2 \rightarrow NaF$	a.	b.
3. $HgO \rightarrow Hg + O_2$	a.	b.

Answer questions 4 and 5 on a separate sheet of paper.

4. Describe in words the chemical composition of the molecules involved and the reaction represented by the equation: $2H_2 + O_2 \rightarrow 2\,H_2O$

5. Use the principle of conservation of mass to explain why the equation in question 4 is balanced.

Building Vocabulary

Match each term with its definition by writing the letter of the correct definition in the right column on the line beside the term in the left column.

____ **6.** chemical equation

____ **7.** decomposition reaction

____ **8.** coefficient

____ **9.** product

____ **10.** reactant

____ **11.** conservation of mass

____ **12.** synthesis reaction

____ **13.** replacement reaction

a. substance present after a reaction

b. reaction in which substances combine to form a more complex compound

c. uses symbols and formulas to show chemical reactions

d. reaction in which one element replaces another in a compound

e. substance present before a reaction

f. number telling how many molecules of a substance are involved in a chemical reaction

g. reaction in which compounds are broken down into simpler products

h. principle that states that matter is not created or destroyed during a chemical reaction

© Pearson Education, Inc., publishing as Pearson Prentice Hall. All rights reserved.

The Decomposition of Water

You learned in Section 2 that hydrogen gas and oxygen gas can react to produce water. The reverse of this reaction can also occur. In other words, water can be broken down to make hydrogen gas and oxygen gas. The breakdown of water is a decomposition reaction. The unbalanced equation for this reaction is shown below.

$$H_2O \quad \rightarrow \quad H_2 \quad + \quad O_2$$

Water   Hydrogen gas   Oxygen gas

For this reaction to occur, there must be an electric current through the water as shown in the figure below. Two wires are connected to a battery, and the free ends of the wires are put into a beaker of water that contains a small amount of sulfuric acid. The sulfuric acid helps to increase the flow of current through the water.

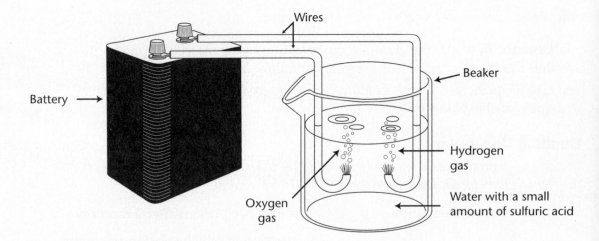

Answer the following questions on a separate sheet of paper.

1. Write a balanced equation for the decomposition of water.

2. How many atoms of hydrogen are on the left side of the balanced equation? How many oxygen atoms? How many hydrogen atoms are on the right side of the balanced equation? How many oxygen atoms?

3. The water in a beaker has a mass of 18 g. An electric current is turned on in the water for two hours. Afterward the water has a mass of only 16 g. What happened to the missing mass?

4. Water decomposes to make 4 g of hydrogen gas and 32 g of oxygen gas. What mass of water decomposed? How do you know?

5. Look at the figure above. How can you tell that a reaction is occurring?

© Pearson Education, Inc., publishing as Pearson Prentice Hall. All rights reserved.

Controlling Chemical Reactions

Ability Levels Key
L1 Basic to Average
L2 For All Students
L3 Average to Advanced

3–4 periods, 1 1/2–2 blocks

Objectives

L.2.3.1 Explain how activation energy is related to chemical reactions.

L.2.3.2 Identify factors that affect the rate of a chemical reaction.

Key Terms
- activation energy • concentration • catalyst
- enzyme • inhibitor

PRETEACH

Build Background Knowledge
Students infer from a familiar example how temperature affects the rate of chemical reactions.

 Discover Activity *Can You Speed Up or Slow Down a Reaction?* **L1**

Targeted Resources
❑ **All in One** **Teaching Resources**
  L2 Reading Strategy Transparency L22: Relating Cause and Effect
❑ ⊙ **Presentation-Pro CD-ROM**

INSTRUCT

Energy and Reactions Use a questioning strategy to define and explain activation energy.
Rates of Chemical Reactions List and discuss four factors that affect rates of chemical reactions.

 Skills Lab *Temperature and Enzyme Activity* **L3**

Targeted Resources
❑ **All in One** **Teaching Resources**
  L2 Guided Reading, pp. 139–142
  L2 Transparencies L23, L24, L25
  L3 Lab: *Temperature and Enzyme Activity*, pp. 145–147
❑ ▭ **Lab Activity Video/DVD**
  Skills Lab: *Temperature and Enzyme Activity*
❑ **PHSchool.com** Web Code: cgd-2023
❑ ⊙ **Student Edition on Audio CD**

ASSESS

Section Assessment Questions
⟳ Have students use their completed graphic organizers of cause and effect to answer the questions.

Reteach
Students define the key terms.

Targeted Resources
❑ **All in One** **Teaching Resources**
  Section Summary, p. 138
  L1 Review and Reinforce, p. 143
  L3 Enrich, p. 144

© Pearson Education, Inc., publishing as Pearson Prentice Hall. All rights reserved.

Chemical Reactions

Chemical Reactions • *Section Summary*

Controlling Chemical Reactions

Guide for Reading

■ How is activation energy related to chemical reactions?

■ What factors affect the rate of a chemical reaction?

Activation energy is the minimum amount of energy needed to start a chemical reaction. **All chemical reactions need a certain amount of activation energy to get them started.** Even exothermic reactions need activation energy to get started. Once a few molecules react, the rest will quickly follow, because the first few reactions provide the activation energy for more molecules to react. Endothermic reactions not only need activation to get started. They also need additional energy from the environment to keep going.

Chemical reactions don't all occur at the same rate. How fast a reaction happens depends on how often and with how much energy the particles of the reactants come together. **Chemists can control rates of reactions by changing factors such as surface area, temperature, and concentration, and by using substances called catalysts and inhibitors.**

A third way to increase the rate of a reaction is to increase the concentration of the reactants. The **concentration** is the amount of a substance in a given volume. Increasing the concentration of reactants makes more particles available to react.

When a solid reacts with a liquid or a gas, only the particles on the surface of the solid come in contact with the other reactant. To increase the rate of reaction, you can break the solid into smaller pieces that have more surface area. More material is exposed, so the reaction happens faster.

Another way to increase the rate of a reaction is to increase its temperature. When you heat something, its particles move faster. Faster-moving particles come into contact more often, which means there are more opportunities for a reaction to occur. Faster-moving particles also have more energy. This energy helps the reactants get over the activation energy "hump."

Another way to control the rate of a reaction is to change the activation energy needed. If you decrease the activation energy, the reaction happens faster. A **catalyst** is a material that increases the rate of a reaction by lowering the activation energy. Catalysts affect the reaction rate, but they are not considered reactants. The cells in your body contain biological catalysts, called **enzymes**. Enzymes increase the reaction rates of chemical reactions necessary for life.

Sometimes a reaction is more useful when it can be slowed down rather than speeded up. A material used to decrease the rate of a reaction is called an **inhibitor**. Most inhibitors work by preventing reactants from coming together.

© Pearson Education, Inc., publishing as Pearson Prentice Hall. All rights reserved.

Chemical Reactions · *Guided Reading and Study*

Controlling Chemical Reactions

This section explains how energy is related to chemical reactions. It also describes how the rates of chemical reactions can be controlled.

Use Target Reading Skills

As you read, identify the factors that can cause the rate of a chemical reaction to increase. Write the information in the graphic organizer below.

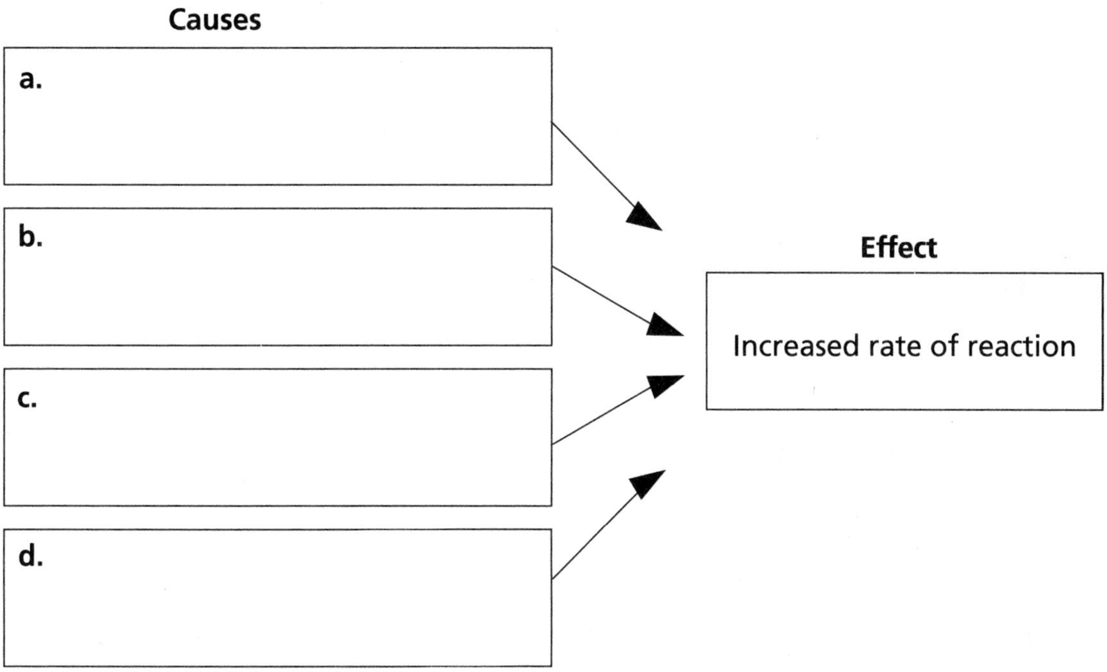

Causes

a.

b.

c.

d.

Effect

Increased rate of reaction

Energy and Reactions

1. The _____ is the minimum amount of energy needed to start a chemical reaction.

2. Is the following sentence true or false? All chemical reactions need a certain amount of activation energy to get started.

   _____

3. In a reaction that makes water from hydrogen gas and oxygen gas, where does the activation energy come from?

   _____

   _____

4. A reaction that releases energy is called a(n) _____.

5. A reaction that absorbs energy is called a (n)

   _____.

© Pearson Education, Inc., publishing as Pearson Prentice Hall. All rights reserved.

Chemical Reactions ▪ *Guided Reading and Study*

Controlling Chemical Reactions *(continued)*

6. Why does an exothermic reaction need activation energy?

_____

_____

_____

_____

_____

7. On the graph below, how does the energy of the products compare with the energy of the reactants?

_____

_____

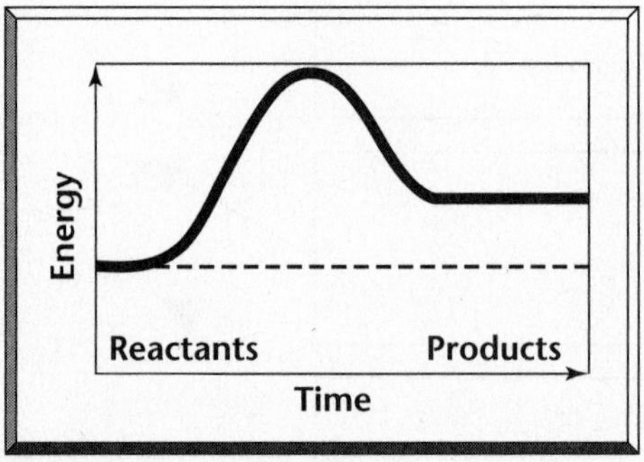

8. Label the graph above as either an exothermic or endothermic reaction.

9. What part of the graph in question 7 represents the activation energy for the reaction?

_____

_____

Rates of Chemical Reactions

10. What are five factors that affect the rate of a chemical reaction?

_____

_____

_____

11. Why does surface area of a reactant influence the rate of the reaction?

_____

_____

_____

© Pearson Education, Inc., publishing as Pearson Prentice Hall. All rights reserved.

Name _____ Date _____ Class _____

Chemical Reactions ▪ *Guided Reading and Study*

12. In what way is temperature related to chemical reaction rates?

_____

_____

13. Circle the letter of each of the following that would increase the rate of a reaction.

    a. Add heat.   **b.** Decrease the surface area.

    c. Increase the surface area.   **d.** Reduce heat.

14. The amount of substance in a given volume is called _____.

15. To increase the rate of a reaction, why would you increase the concentration of the reactants?

_____

_____

_____

16. Is the following sentence true or false? Another way to control the rate of a reaction is to change the activation energy needed.

_____

17. What is a catalyst?

_____

_____

_____

18. Is the following sentence true or false? Catalysts are always permanently changed in a reaction. _____

19. A biological catalyst is called a(n) _____.

20. Why must living things rely on thousands of catalysts for chemical reactions necessary for life?

_____

_____

_____

_____

Chemical Reactions

Chemical Reactions ▪ *Guided Reading and Study*

Controlling Chemical Reactions *(continued)*

21. What is an inhibitor?

_____

_____

_____

22. How do most inhibitors work?

_____

_____

© Pearson Education, Inc., publishing as Pearson Prentice Hall. All rights reserved.

Chemical Reactions · *Review and Reinforce*

Controlling Chemical Reactions

Understanding Main Ideas

Use the figures to answer questions 1–3. Write your answers on a separate sheet of paper.

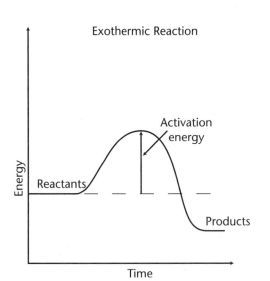

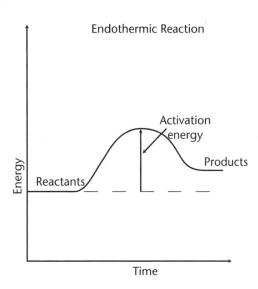

1. Use what you know about endothermic and exothermic reactions to explain the differences in the graphs above.
2. Why is the activation energy pictured as a hill in the two diagrams?
3. Explain how adding heat to the reactions shown in the diagram would change the rate of these chemical reactions. Name two other ways to change the rate of a chemical reaction.

Building Vocabulary

Write a definition for each of the following terms on the lines below.

4. concentration _____

_____

5. enzyme _____

_____

6. inhibitor _____

_____

© Pearson Education, Inc., publishing as Pearson Prentice Hall. All rights reserved.

Chemical Reactions • *Enrich*

Flameless Ration Heaters

Suppose that you are a soldier on patrol far from your base camp. The weather is very cold and you wish you had something warm to eat. However, you aren't carrying a camp stove and it would be too dangerous to light a fire because its smoke would reveal your position. Luckily, you have a *Meal Ready to Eat* (MRE) and a *Flameless Ration Heater* (FRH) in your backpack. (A ration is a portion of food.)

An MRE is a meal, such as beef stew, inside a special pouch made of aluminum foil and plastic. To heat your MRE, you slide it into an FRH. An FRH is a kind of plastic envelope that contains certain chemicals. When you add water to the FRH, an exothermic reaction occurs. The heat produced by this reaction warms up your meal in about 15 minutes.

The chemicals inside an FRH include magnesium (Mg), iron (Fe), and sodium chloride (NaCl). The reaction that takes place when water is added to an FRH is as follows.

$$Mg \quad + \quad 2H_2O \quad \rightarrow \quad Mg(OH)_2 \quad + \quad H_2$$

Magnesium   Water   Magnesium hydroxide   Hydrogen gas

The reaction of magnesium and water is normally very slow. As a result, it gives off heat very slowly. In an FRH, however, this reaction occurs much faster and so it gives off heat much faster as well.

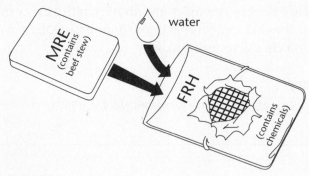

Answer the following questions on a separate sheet of paper.

1. Iron and sodium chloride are present in an FRH, but they are not reactants in the equation shown above. Why do you think they are included in an FRH?

2. Why do you think an FRH doesn't come with water already in it?

3. Do you think there are small pieces or large pieces of magnesium metal in an FRH? Explain.

4. Why is it important that the reaction in an FRH be fast?

© Pearson Education, Inc., publishing as Pearson Prentice Hall. All rights reserved.

Chemical Reactions ▪ *Skills Lab*

Temperature and Enzyme Activity

Problem

Catalase is an enzyme that speeds up the breakdown of hydrogen peroxide into water and oxygen gas. Hydrogen peroxide is a poisonous waste product of reactions in living things. How does temperature affect the action of an enzyme?

Skills Focus

calculating, interpreting data, drawing conclusions

Materials

forceps

stopwatch

test tube with a one-hole stopper

0.1% hydrogen peroxide solution

filter paper disks soaked in liver preparation (catalese enzyme) and kept at
   four different temperatures (room temperature, 0–4°C, 37°C, and 100°C)

container to hold water (beaker or bowl)

Procedure   *Review the safety guidelines in Appendix A.*

1. Form a hypothesis that predicts how the action of the catalase enzyme will differ at the different temperatures to be tested.

2. Fill a container with water. Then fill a test tube with 0.1% hydrogen peroxide solution until the test tube is overflowing. Do this over a sink or the container of water.

3. Use the data table on the next page.

4. Moisten the small end of a one-hole stopper with water.

5. Using forceps, remove a filter paper disk soaked in liver preparation (catalase enzyme) that has been kept at room temperature. Stick it to the moistened end of the one-hole stopper.

6. Your partner should be ready with the stopwatch for the next step.

7. Place the stopper firmly into the test tube, hold your thumb over the hole, and quickly invert the test tube. Start the stopwatch. Put the inverted end of the test tube into the container of water, as shown in the photograph in your textbook, and remove your thumb.

© Pearson Education, Inc., publishing as Pearson Prentice Hall. All rights reserved.

Chemical Reactions • *Skills Lab*

Temperature and Enzyme Activity *(continued)*

8. Observe what happens to the filter paper inside the test tube. Record the time it takes for the disk to rise to the top in the data table below. If the disk does not rise within 2 minutes, record "no reaction" and go on to Step 9.

9. Rinse the test tube and repeat the procedure with catalase enzyme disks kept at 0°C, 37°C, and 100°C. **CAUTION:***When you remove the disk kept in the hot water bath, do not use your bare hands. Avoid spilling the hot water.*

Data Table

Temperature (°C)	Time (s)	Average Time for Class (s)

Analyze and Conclude

Write your answers in the spaces provided.

1. **Observing** What makes the disk float to the top of the inverted test tube?

   _____

   _____

2. **Calculating** Calculate the average time for each temperature based on the results of the entire class. Enter the results in your data table.

3. **Graphing** Make a line graph of the data you collected. Label the horizontal axis (*x*-axis) "Temperature" with a scale from 0°C to 100°C. Label the vertical axis (*y*-axis) "Time" with a scale from 0 to 30 seconds. Plot the class average time for each temperature.

4. **Interpreting Data** What evidence do you have that your hypothesis from Step 1 is either supported or not supported?

   _____

   _____

   _____

© Pearson Education, Inc., publishing as Pearson Prentice Hall. All rights reserved.

Chemical Reactions ▪ *Skills Lab*

5. **Interpreting Data** How is the time it takes the disk to rise to the top of the inverted tube related to the rate of the reaction?

_____

_____

_____

6. **Drawing Conclusions** What can you conclude about the activity of the enzyme at the various temperatures you tested? (*Hint:* Enzyme activity is greater when the rate of reaction is faster.)

_____

_____

_____

7. **Predicting** Make a prediction about how active the enzyme would be at 10°C, 60°C, and 75°C. Give reasons to support your prediction.

_____

_____

_____

8. **Communicating** A buildup of hydrogen peroxide in living things can damage cells. The normal human body temperature is 37°C. Write a paragraph relating your results to the body's temperature and its need to break down hydrogen peroxide.

_____

_____

_____

_____

Design an Experiment

The activity of an enzyme also depends upon the concentration of the enzyme. Design an experiment that explores the relationship between enzyme activity and enzyme concentration. (Your teacher can give you disks soaked with different enzyme concentrations.) *Obtain your teacher's permission before carrying out your investigation.*

© Pearson Education, Inc., publishing as Pearson Prentice Hall. All rights reserved.

Fire and Fire Safety

Ability Levels Key
L1 Basic to Average
L2 For All Students
L3 Average to Advanced

🕐 *1–2 periods, 1/2–1 block*

Objectives
L.2.4.1 List the three things necessary to maintain a fire.
L.2.4.2 Explain why you should know about the causes of fire and how to prevent a fire.

Key Terms
• combustion • fuel

Local Standards

PRETEACH

Build Background Knowledge
Students share experiences they have had with fire and recall fire safety rules they have learned.

 **Discover Activity** *How Does Baking Soda Affect a Fire?* **L1**

Targeted Resources

❑ **All in One** **Teaching Resources**
    L2 Reading Strategy Transparency L26: Using Prior Knowledge
❑ 💿 **Presentation-Pro CD-ROM**

INSTRUCT

Understanding Fire Use the fire triangle to show students what every fire needs to burn.
Home Fire Safety Review methods for fighting fires and how to prevent injuries and deaths from fires.

Targeted Resources

❑ **All in One** **Teaching Resources**
    L2 Guided Reading, pp. 150–151
    L2 Transparencies L27, L28
❑ **www.SciLinks.org** Web Code: scn-1224
❑ 💿 **Student Edition on Audio CD**

ASSESS

Section Assessment Questions
🔄 Have students use their completed graphic organizers of what they know and what they learned to answer the questions.

Reteach
Students name fire-prevention and fire safety features of a fire-safe house.

Targeted Resources

❑ **All in One** **Teaching Resources**
    Section Summary, p. 149
    L1 Review and Reinforce, p. 152
    L3 Enrich, p. 153

© Pearson Education, Inc., publishing as Pearson Prentice Hall. All rights reserved.

Chemical Reactions • *Section Summary*

Fire and Fire Safety

Guide for Reading

- What are the three things necessary to maintain a fire?

- Why should you know about the causes of fire and how to prevent a fire?

Fire is the result of **combustion**, a rapid reaction between oxygen and a substance called a fuel. A **fuel** is a material that releases energy when it burns. Some fuels include oil, coal, wood, gasoline, and paper. Combustion of these types of fuel always produces carbon dioxide and water. When fuels don's burn completely, products such as smoke and poisonous gases may be produced.

The following three things are necessary to start and maintain a fire—fuel, oxygen, and heat. Oxygen comes from the air. About 20 percent of the air around you is composed of oxygen gas. A large fire creates a draft and draws oxygen toward it. Fuel and oxygen can be together, but they won't react until something provides enough activation energy to start combustion. This energy can come from a lighted match, an electric spark, or the heat from a stove. Once combustion starts, the heat released supplies more activation energy to keep the reaction going.

You can control a fire by removing one part of the fire triangle. You can control a fire if you can get the fuel away from the flames, keep oxygen from getting to the fuel, or cool the combustion reaction. Firefighters use large hoses to spray huge amounts of water on the flaming parts of a building. Water removes two parts of the fire triangle. Water covers the fuel, which keeps it from coming into contact with oxygen. Evaporation of the water uses a large amount of heat, causing the fire to cool.

Every year, fire claims thousands of lives in the United States. **If you know how to prevent fires in your home and what to do if fire starts, you are better prepared to take action.** The most common sources of home fires are small heaters and faulty electrical wiring.

You can put out a small fire on the stove by covering it with baking soda. Baking soda decomposes when heated and releases carbon dioxide gas. The carbon dioxide gas prevents contact between the fuel and the oxygen in the air.

A small fire is easy to control. You can cool a match enough to stop combustion just by blowing on it. A small fire in a trashcan may be put out with a pan of water. One of the most effective ways to fight a small fire is with a fire extinguisher. But a fire that is growing as you fight it is out of control. The only safe thing to do is to get away from the fire and call the fire department. Remember, the best form of fire safety is fire prevention.

© Pearson Education, Inc., publishing as Pearson Prentice Hall. All rights reserved.

Chemical Reactions · *Guided Reading and Study*

Fire and Fire Safety

This section describes the three things necessary to maintain a fire. It also explains how to prevent fires in the home.

Use Target Reading Skills

Before you read, write what you know about fire safety in the graphic organizer below. As you read, continue to write in what you learn.

What You Know
1.
2.
3.

What You Learned
1.
2.
3.

Understanding Fire

1. What is combustion?

   _____

   _____

   _____

2. A material that releases energy when it burns is called a(n)

   _____.

© Pearson Education, Inc., publishing as Pearson Prentice Hall. All rights reserved.

Chemical Reactions • *Guided Reading and Study*

3. What are the three things necessary to start and maintain a fire?

_____

_____

4. Circle the letter of the source of oxygen for a fire.

    a. air   **b.** fuel

    c. reactants   **d.** products

5. Is the following sentence true or false? An electric spark can provide the activation energy needed to start a combustion reaction.

_____

6. How does water remove two parts of the fire triangle?

_____

_____

_____

_____

Home Fire Safety

7. What are the three most common sources of home fires?

_____

_____

8. Covering a small fire on the stove with _____ may put the fire out.

9. Circle the letter of each of the following that is a safety aid in a fire-safe home.

    a. smoke detectors   **b.** gasoline can in the basement

    c. fire extinguisher   **d.** box of baking soda in the kitchen

© Pearson Education, Inc., publishing as Pearson Prentice Hall. All rights reserved.

Chemical Reactions • *Review and Reinforce*

Fire and Fire Safety

Understanding Main Ideas

Use the illustration to answer questions 1 and 2 in the spaces provided.

1. What are the three points of the fire triangle shown in the illustration?

   _____

   _____

   _____

   _____

2. Name one way you can stop this small stove fire safely. Also explain how this method would remove a part of the fire triangle.

   _____

   _____

   _____

   _____

   _____

Write your answers to questions 3 and 4 in the spaces provided.

3. Name two fire safety tips you should practice in your kitchen.

   _____

   _____

   _____

4. What should you do when a fire continues to grow while you are fighting it?

   _____

   _____

Building Vocabulary

Answer the following questions in the spaces provided.

5. What is combustion?

   _____

   _____

6. What is a fuel? What are some examples of fuels?

   _____

   _____

   _____

© Pearson Education, Inc., publishing as Pearson Prentice Hall. All rights reserved.

Chemical Reactions · *Enrich*

Fighting Forest Fires

Each year thousands of forest fires occur throughout the United States. There are many methods used to control forest fires, but all rely on breaking the fire triangle of heat, fuel, and oxygen.

Some methods of fire control begin long before a forest fire starts. For example, firebreaks can be used to divide a forest into smaller sections. A *firebreak* is a strip of land that has been cleared of trees and other plants. Firebreaks are wide enough that a fire in one section of the forest usually cannot "jump" across them to other sections.

Another method of prevention used before a forest fire starts involves setting fires on purpose. Firefighters set small fires in areas of a forest where large amounts of fuel such as fallen branches and leaves have built up on the forest floor. These fires are called *controlled burns.* Firefighters closely watch controlled burns so that they can put the fires out before they grow too large. By reducing the amount of fuel available, controlled burns actually help to protect the forest.

In addition, firefighters sometimes set small fires during a forest fire to help bring a large forest fire under control. These fires, called *backfires,* are set in between a firebreak and an approaching forest fire. Backfires help to control a forest fire by reducing the amount of fuel in its path.

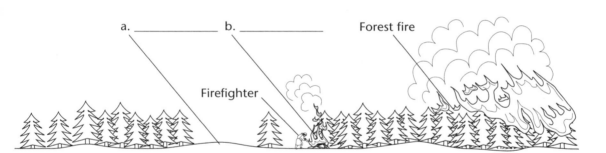

Answer the following questions on a separate sheet of paper.

1. Label the type of fire control pictured in the diagram above by filling in the blanks.
2. What keeps a forest fire from "jumping" across a firebreak?
3. Firefighters sometimes add chemicals called wetting agents to the water that they spray on forest fires. *Wetting agents* increase the ability of water to penetrate or seep into wood. Why do you think this helps to control a fire?
4. In remote areas, firefighters may have only a limited water supply available to spray on fires. In these cases, firefighters may shovel dirt onto the flames. How do you think dirt helps to put out a fire?

© Pearson Education, Inc., publishing as Pearson Prentice Hall. All rights reserved.

Key Terms

Complete the sentences by using one of the scrambled terms below.

mocpsoinoited	dcsutrop	emtrsyhci	msubocniot	ysisehtns
neefiticcof	ntreactonionc	etaptiicrpe	tyltsaac	ctatsnaer
nioatvicat	rtiohbiin	eaeeplcmnrt		

1. A material that increases the rate of a reaction by lowering the activation energy is called a(n) _____.

2. A chemical reaction that breaks down compounds into simpler products is called a(n) _____ reaction.

3. A solid that forms from solution during a chemical reaction is called a(n) _____.

4. The materials you have at the beginning of a chemical reaction are called _____.

5. A chemical reaction in which two or more substances combine to make a more complex compound is called a(n) _____ reaction.

6. The amount of one material in a given volume of another material is called _____.

7. A material used to decrease the rate of a reaction is called a(n) _____.

8. A rapid reaction between oxygen and a fuel is called _____.

9. The minimum amount of energy needed to start a chemical reaction is called the _____ energy.

10. A chemical reaction in which one element replaces another in a compound, or in which two elements in different compounds trade places, is called a(n) _____ reaction.

11. The substances formed as a result of a chemical reaction are called _____.

12. A number placed in front of a chemical formula in a chemical equation is called a(n) _____.

13. The study of the properties of matter and how matter changes is called _____.

© Pearson Education, Inc., publishing as Pearson Prentice Hall. All rights reserved.

Chemical Reactions · *Math Skills*

Math Skills

Balance the chemical equations below by adding coefficients. Write the balanced equations on the lines provided.

Balancing Chemical Equations

1. $H_2O \rightarrow H_2 + O_2$

   _____

2. $N_2 + H_2 \rightarrow NH_3$

   _____

3. $C_3H_8 + O_2 \rightarrow CO_2 + H_2O$

   _____

4. $K + H_2O \rightarrow H_2 + KOH$

   _____

5. $Li + O_2 \rightarrow Li_2O$

   _____

6. $Fe + O_2 \rightarrow Fe_2O_3$

   _____

7. $Ag + N_2 \rightarrow Ag_3N$

   _____

8. $C_2H_5OH + O_2 \rightarrow CO_2 + H_2O$

   _____

© Pearson Education, Inc., publishing as Pearson Prentice Hall. All rights reserved.

Chemical Reactions · *Connecting Concepts*

Connecting Concepts

Develop a concept map that uses the Key Concepts and Key Terms from this
chapter. Keep in mind the big idea of this chapter. Chemical reactions,
including fire, are a way that matter can change. The concept map shown is
one way to organize how the information in this chapter is related. You may
use an extra sheet of paper.

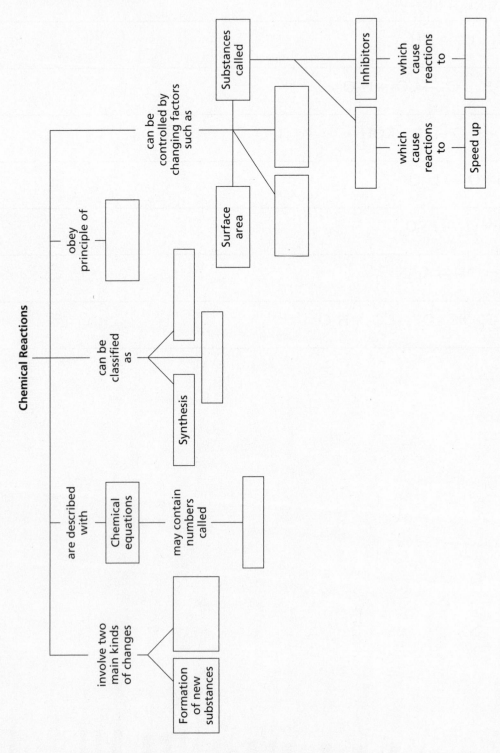

© Pearson Education, Inc., publishing as Pearson Prentice Hall. All rights reserved.

The Law of Definite Proportions

Key Concept

The law of definite proportions states that the elements in a compound always occur in the same ratio by mass. Compounds containing the same elements will differ in properties, depending on the ratios of the elements involved.

Skills Focus

observing, inferring, measuring, developing hypotheses

Time

40 minutes

Materials *(per group)*

2 test tubes

test-tube rack

glass marker

graduated cylinder, 10 mL

hydrogen peroxide, 3% solution

manganese dioxide

2 wood splints

matches

tongs

Teaching Tips

- If graduated cylinders are not available, have students fill the test tubes to equal levels. The quantity used is not critical as long as the amounts are the same.

- Caution students not to taste either liquid.

- Point out that manganese dioxide is a catalyst, not a reactant.

© Pearson Education, Inc., publishing as Pearson Prentice Hall. All rights reserved.

Chemical Reactions • *Laboratory Investigation*

The Law of Definite Proportions

Pre-Lab Discussion

Many compounds made of exactly the same elements have different physical and chemical properties. For example, carbon dioxide (CO_2) and carbon monoxide (CO) are both gases made of carbon and oxygen. Yet CO_2 is a virtually harmless gas found in the body and in the atmosphere, while CO is deadly when inhaled in sufficient amounts.

The law of definite proportions explains the differences between these two carbon-oxygen compounds. This law states that the elements in a compound always occur in the same ratio by mass. In other words, a CO molecule consists of only one carbon atom and one oxygen atom. A CO_2 molecule consists of one carbon atom and two oxygen atoms. The different numbers of oxygen atoms make these two compounds different from each other.

In this investigation, you will compare the physical and chemical properties of water and hydrogen peroxide, both of which consist of hydrogen and oxygen.

1. What is a ratio?

_____

_____

_____

2. What are some signs of a chemical reaction?

_____

_____

_____

_____

3. How does a catalyst affect a chemical reaction?

_____

_____

4. What happens during a decomposition reaction?

_____

_____

_____

© Pearson Education, Inc., publishing as Pearson Prentice Hall. All rights reserved.

Chemical Reactions ▪ *Laboratory Investigation*

Problem

How can two compounds consist of the same elements yet have different properties?

Materials *(per group)*

2 test tubes

test-tube rack

glass marker

graduated cylinder, 10 mL

hydrogen peroxide, 3% solution

manganese dioxide

2 wood splints

matches

tongs

Safety 🦺 🥽 🔥 ☠️ 🧤 *Review the safety guidelines in Appendix A.*
Hydrogen peroxide and manganese dioxide are both poisonous. Keep them away from your face, and wash your hands thoroughly after using these compounds. Wear safety goggles and lab aprons throughout the activity.

Procedure

1. **CAUTION:** *Put on your safety goggles and lab apron. Hydrogen peroxide is a poison. Keep it away from your face.* Label one test tube H_2O (water) and the other H_2O_2 (hydrogen peroxide). Measure 5 mL of each liquid and pour it into the appropriate test tube.

2. Observe the physical properties of each compound and record your observations in the Data Table provided on the next page.

3. **CAUTION:** *Tie back long hair and loose clothing, in case you need to use a flame. Manganese dioxide is a poison.* Put a small amount of manganese dioxide on the tip of a wood splint and add a little of this chemical to each test tube. If you see evidence of a chemical reaction, light the unused wood splint with a match. Blow out the flame, so that the wood is glowing at the edges. Using tongs, insert the glowing splint into the test tube(s) in which a chemical reaction is occurring. Record your observations in the Data Table.

4. Wash your hands when you're finished with the lab.

© Pearson Education, Inc., publishing as Pearson Prentice Hall. All rights reserved.

Chemical Reactions · *Laboratory Investigation*

The Law of Definite Proportions *(continued)*

Observations

Data Table

Compound	Physical Properties	Evidence of Chemical Reaction to Manganese Dioxide
Water (H_2O)		
Hydrogen peroxide (H_2O_2)		

Analyze and Conclude

1. Compare the physical properties of water and the hydrogen peroxide solution.

   _____

   _____

2. Compare and contrast the molecular formulas for the two compounds.

   _____

   _____

3. State a hypothesis to explain why water and hydrogen peroxide have different chemical properties.

   _____

   _____

Critical Thinking and Applications

1. Hydrogen gas burns. Oxygen gas does not burn but supports the burning of other materials. What seemed to burn in the splint test? What gas did the chemical reaction in this activity produce? How do you know?

   _____

   _____

2. In this activity, manganese dioxide is a catalyst and is not permanently changed by any chemical reaction in which it is involved. Consider your observations and the role that manganese dioxide plays in a reaction. State a hypothesis about what happened during any chemical reaction that took place.

   _____

   _____

© Pearson Education, Inc., publishing as Pearson Prentice Hall. All rights reserved.

Chemical Reactions • *Laboratory Investigation*

3. The atomic mass number of hydrogen is 1.0. The atomic mass number of oxygen is 16.0. What is the ratio by mass of hydrogen to oxygen in water? In hydrogen peroxide?

_____

4. How does the law of definite proportions explain why water and hydrogen peroxide have different properties, although they consist of the same elements?

_____

_____

_____

More to Explore

Do hydrogen peroxide and water react differently in bleach? Do the activity to find out. You will need hydrogen peroxide, water, bleach, 2 test tubes, a test tube holder, and a medicine dropper. Wear safety goggles and aprons. Bleach can damage your clothes. It is also a poison, so keep it away from your face. Wash up after the experiment is done. Put a test tube in a holder. Put a few drops of bleach in the test tube. Hold the test tube away from you and add a few drops of hydrogen peroxide. Make sure the tube is not pointed at anyone. Record your observations below. Predict what will happen if you repeat this investigation using water instead of hydrogen peroxide. Test your prediction, then write your observations and answers in the spaces provided below.

Hydrogen peroxide and bleach:

Water and bleach:

1. Why do you think hydrogen peroxide and bleach reacted as they did?

_____

_____

_____

2. How could you find out if bleach is used up in the reaction with hydrogen peroxide or if it is a catalyst?

_____

_____

_____

_____

© Pearson Education, Inc., publishing as Pearson Prentice Hall. All rights reserved.

Chemical Reactions

Students are asked to decide if the chemical reaction which takes place as the iron in steel wool rusts to form iron oxide is exothermic or endothermic. To answer this question, students must design an experiment and apply concepts from the chapter.

Expected Outcome

Students write a hypothesis that answers the question, "Is the chemical reaction that causes the iron in a piece of steel wool to form iron oxide (rust) when it is soaked in salt water exothermic or endothermic?" They must then devise an experiment with a control to test their hypothesis. One possibility is to use two identical thermometers (one is a control) and two large jars. The jars provide a convenient place to hold the thermometers during the experiment. After recording the initial temperature of both thermometers, wrap salt water-soaked steel wool around one thermometer, place each in a separate jar, and store the jars in a safe place away from direct sunlight. After 10 or 20 minutes, record the temperature again. Expect the second reading with the thermometer in the steel wool to be higher than the first, indicating that iron rusting is an exothermic chemical reaction.

Content Assessed

This activity evaluates students' understanding of energy flow in chemical reactions as described in the chapter.

Skills Assessed

developing hypotheses, designing experiments, drawing conclusions, applying concepts, making predictions

Materials

Provide each group with two Celsius thermometers and two small jars of approximately the same size.

Place a glass bowl of steel wool submerged in salt water in a central location. There must be enough to allow each group a small handful.

Advance Preparation

Obtain jars, thermometers, steel wool, and salt water.

Divide the class into as many groups as there are jars and thermometers.

Place the steel wool in salt water at the start of the activity.

Time

40 minutes

Safety

Use thermometers that contain alcohol rather than mercury. Instruct students to wear safety goggles and disposable gloves during this activity. Also caution them to handle glass jars and thermometers carefully. Broken glass and steel wool can cause puncture wounds and become embedded in the eye.

Monitoring the Task

Before beginning, encourage students to reread the paragraphs on exothermic and endothermic reactions as well as those on synthesis, decomposition, and replacement reactions. Also, review the use of a control in an experiment.

Advise students to keep jars away from direct sunlight. Stress that an initial temperature reading is mandatory when testing something that might affect temperature. Note, too, that excess liquid should be squeezed out of the steel wool.

© Pearson Education, Inc., publishing as Pearson Prentice Hall. All rights reserved.

Chemical Reactions

In assessing students' performance, use the following rubric.

	4	3	2	1
Developing a Hypothesis	Student's hypothesis is logical and clearly stated as a possible answer to the question.	Student's hypothesis is general, but does address the question.	Student's hypothesis is vague, but demonstrates some understanding of the question.	Student's hypothesis does not demonstrate an understanding of the question.
Designing an Experiment	Student's experimental design positively tests the hypothesis.	Student's experimental design adequately tests the hypothesis.	Student's experimental design partially tests the hypothesis.	Student's experimental design does not test the hypothesis.
Applying Concepts	Student demonstrates mastery of the underlying concepts, including energy flow in chemical reactions.	Student demonstrates good understanding of the underlying concepts, including energy flow in chemical reactions.	Student demonstrates some understanding of the underlying concepts, including energy flow in chemical reactions.	Student demonstrates minimal understanding of the underlying chapter concepts.
Drawing Conclusions	Student's conclusion naturally follows from observed results.	Student's conclusion is well related to observed results.	Student's conclusion is somewhat related to observed results with evidence of conjecture.	Student's conclusion is minimally related to observed results with evidence of conjecture.

© Pearson Education, Inc., publishing as Pearson Prentice Hall. All rights reserved.

Name _____ Date _____ Class _____

Chemical Reactions · *Performance Assessment*

Chemical Reactions

You learned that chemical reactions produce new substances. One sign that a chemical reaction has occurred is a change in temperature. If a reaction gives off heat energy, it is an exothermic reaction. In this activity, you will observe that salt water reacts chemically with the iron in steel wool to form iron oxide (rust). You must form a hypothesis to answer the question: "Is the chemical reaction that causes the iron in a piece of steel wool to from iron oxide when it is soaked in salt water exothermic?" Devise a plan to test your hypothesis using the materials your teacher has provided.

Problem

Is the chemical reaction that causes the iron in a piece of steel wool to form iron oxide when it is soaked in salt water exothermic or endothermic?

Suggested Materials

jars with a covers

thermometers that fit in the jars

steel wool soaked in salt water

paper

pen or pencil

Safety 🖐️ ✂️ 🔥 *Exercise caution when handling glass thermometers, jars, and steel wool. Wash your hands after the activity.*

Devise a Plan

1. Form a hypothesis and record it on a separate sheet of paper.
2. Study the materials and decide how to use them to test your hypothesis.
3. Record the step-by-step procedure you will follow on the paper.
4. Predict what you expect to happen and record your prediction on the paper.

Analyze and Conclude

After carrying out the plan you devised, answer the following questions on a separate sheet of paper.

1. Was your prediction correct? Explain your answer.
2. What can you conclude from your results?
3. Name two ways that you could increase the rate of this chemical reaction.
4. Iron combines with oxygen to form iron oxide, as illustrated in the following chemical equation: $4Fe + 3O_2 \rightarrow 2Fe_2O_3$. Is this an example of a synthesis reaction, a decomposition reaction, or a replacement reaction? Explain your answer.

© Pearson Education, Inc., publishing as Pearson Prentice Hall. All rights reserved.

Chemical Reactions

Multiple Choice

Write the letter of the correct answer on the line at the left.

_____ 1. A change in matter that produces new substances is called a

    a. chemical reaction.   **b.** physical change.
    c. mixture.   **d.** solution.

_____ 2. Which of the following cannot be used to put out a small fire?

    a. water   **b.** carbon dioxide
    c. baking soda   **d.** oxygen

_____ 3. Which of the following is an example of a physical property?

    a. chemical composition   **b.** ability to burn
    c. freezing point   **d.** ability to react with metals

_____ 4. A chemical reaction in which energy is absorbed in the form of heat is called

    a. synthetic.   **b.** exothermic.
    c. combustion.   **d.** endothermic.

_____ 5. Chemical equations must be balanced because chemical reactions obey the principle of

    a. activation.   **b.** conservation of mass.
    c. decomposition.   **d.** mass coefficients.

_____ 6. Most inhibitors work by preventing

    a. reactants from coming together.
    b. enzymes from working.
    c. products from forming.
    d. combustion.

_____ 7. When two or more substances combine to form a more complex substance, the process is called a

    a. decomposition reaction.
    b. replacement reaction.
    c. synthesis reaction.
    d. physical change.

_____ 8. The number in front of a chemical formula that tells how many molecules or atoms of each reactant take part in a reaction is called a

    a. symbol.   **b.** subscript.
    c. coefficient.   **d.** concentration.

Chemical Reactions

© Pearson Education, Inc., publishing as Pearson Prentice Hall. All rights reserved.

_____ 9. Which of the following is an example of a chemical change?

     a. meat spoiling   **b.** water freezing

     c. mercury rising   **d.** butter softening

_____ 10. Which statement is true about an exothermic reaction?

     a. It releases energy.

     b. It absorbs energy.

     c. It requires no activation energy.

     d. The energy of the products is greater than the energy of the reactants.

Completion

Fill in the blank to complete each statement.

11. The energy required to start a chemical reaction is called

_____.

12. A(n) _____ is a material that slows down the rate of a chemical reaction.

13. Reactions that release energy are called _____.

14. A(n) _____ is a biological catalyst that can be found in the cells of your body.

15. In the fire triangle, coal is an example of a(n) _____.

True or False

If the statement is true, write true. *If it is false, change the underlined word or words to make the statement true.*

_____ **16.** A <u>chemical equation</u> shows a chemical reaction using symbols instead of words.

_____ **17.** Combustion is the rapid reaction between <u>carbon dioxide</u> and fuel.

_____ **18.** In a(n) <u>open system</u>, matter is not allowed to enter or leave.

_____ **19.** A <u>precipitate</u> is a solid formed from solution during a chemical reaction.

_____ **20.** The <u>reactants</u> are the new materials produced during a chemical reaction.

© Pearson Education, Inc., publishing as Pearson Prentice Hall. All rights reserved.

Name _____ Date _____ Class _____

Chemical Reactions • *Chapter Test*

Using Science Skills

Use the diagram below to answer questions 21 through 23. Write your answers on the diagram and in the spaces provided.

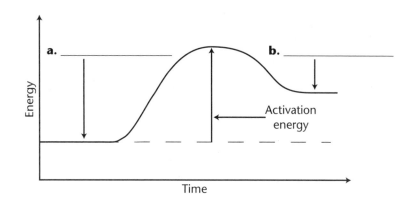

21. **Interpreting Diagrams** Label the reactants and products on lines **a** and **b** in the figure above.

22. **Drawing Conclusions** Is this reaction endothermic or exothermic? Explain your answer.

_____

_____

_____

_____

23. Would increasing the concentration of the reactants change the value of the activation energy on the graph? Explain.

_____

_____

_____

Essay

Write an answer for each of the following questions on a separate sheet of paper.

24. How is water able to stop the combustion of fuels?

25. Use the principle of conservation of mass to explain how you know the following equation is balanced. The symbol Fe represents iron and O represents oxygen. How many atoms of iron and oxygen are present as products and how many are present as reactants?

$$4Fe + 3O_2 \rightarrow 2Fe_2O_3$$

© Pearson Education, Inc., publishing as Pearson Prentice Hall. All rights reserved.

Chemical Reactions · *Chapter Test*

Using Science Skills

Use the table below to answer questions 26 and 27. Write your answers on a separate sheet of paper.

Compound name	Formula
hydrochloric acid	HCl
hydrogen iodide	HI
lithium chloride	LiCl

26. **Applying Concepts** Write and balance the following chemical reactions.
   a. Hydrogen (H_2) reacts with iodine (I_2) to form hydrogen iodide.
   b. Lithium (Li) and hydrochloric acid react to produce hydrogen (H_2) and lithium chloride.
   c. When you run an electrical current through water, you get hydrogen (H_2) and oxygen (O_2).

27. **Classifying** Identify each chemical reaction described above as synthesis, decomposition, or replacement reactions. Explain your choices.

Essay

Answer questions 28–30 on a separate sheet of paper.

28. When baking soda and vinegar are combined, gas bubbles form, the vinegar smell disappears, and the mixture gets colder. Has a chemical or physical change taken place? How do you know?

29. When a person gets hypothermia from exposure to cold temperatures, the enzymes in their body become less active. How does this change affect the body's chemical reactions?

30. When balancing a chemical equation, why can you change the coefficients but not the subscripts?

© Pearson Education, Inc., publishing as Pearson Prentice Hall. All rights reserved.

Chapter Project
Worksheet 1

1-6. Check that students follow the procedures outlined in Steps 1–6.

2. Students should obtain your approval before beginning Step 7.

Worksheet 2

Data in both tables should generally support the principle of conservation of mass. The initial and final mass of each chamber will be about the same, with a nearly zero change in mass, unless students make errors in measurement and/or the reaction chambers are not sealed.

Observing Chemical Change
Guided Reading and Study

Use Target Reading Skills

Sample questions and answers:

Question What are physical properties of matter?

Answer Physical properties are characteristics that can be observed without changing one substance into another.

Question What is the evidence for chemical reactions?

Answer The evidence for chemical reactions is the formation of new substances and changes in energy.

1. Matter is anything that has mass and takes up space.

2. chemistry

3. a. Physical

   b. Only by changing one substance into another

4. False

5. a, b, d

6. chemical reaction, or chemical change

7. They break and form new bonds, producing new substances.

8. Formation of new substances and changes in energy

9. The change in color is an indication of a change in properties, and a change in properties is a sign that a chemical reaction occurred.

10. precipitate

11. It might indicate a chemical reaction, because the bubbles are gas, and the presence of a gas indicates a new substance may have been formed.

12. True

13. A change in temperature reflects a change in energy.

14. False

15. a. Energy is absorbed

   b. Exothermic

Observing Chemical Change
Review and Reinforce

1. Answers may vary. Sample answer: Change in texture, from gooey liquid to dry and crumbly solid

2. Chemical change

3. Sample answer: Change in color, from brown log to black ashes

4. Chemical change

5. Sample answer: Change in state, from liquid water to solid ice

6. Physical change

7. physical change

8. Matter

9. exothermic reaction

10. endothermic reaction

11. chemical reaction

12. precipitate

13. Chemistry

Observing Chemical Change
Enrich

1. In filtration, a liquid-solid mixture is passed through a filter to remove solid particles from the mixture. Filters that you can install on your kitchen faucet or the type you buy and place inside a pitcher of drinking water use filtration to remove small particles.

2. Evaporation can be used to separate salt from sea water to produce fresh water and also salt for commercial purposes. This can be done by pumping the sea water into large, shallow holding tanks. When the water evaporates, the salt remains.

3. Mixtures that have solid particles large enough and heavy enough to settle out of the mixture on standing can be decanted. Decanting can be done almost anywhere because it does not require special equipment—only a container with a spout and another container to hold the separated liquid.

© Pearson Education, Inc., publishing as Pearson Prentice Hall. All rights reserved.

4. Separations of the types mentioned here cause physical changes because no new substances form. The individual substances you get after separation were present in the mixture at the start.

Where's the Evidence?
Skills Lab

For answers, see the Teachers' Edition.

Describing Chemical Reactions
Guided Reading and Study

Use Target Reading Skills

a. A *chemical equation* is a short, easy way to show a chemical reaction.

b. A substance you have at the beginning of a reaction is a *reactant*.

c. A new substance produced in a reaction is a *product*.

d. *Conservation of mass* means that during a chemical reaction, matter is not created or destroyed.

e. In an *open system*, matter can enter from or escape to the surroundings.

f. In a *closed system*, matter is not allowed to enter or leave.

g. A *coefficient* is a number in a chemical equation telling you how many atoms or molecules of a reactant or product take part in the reaction.

h. *Synthesis* means combining two or more elements or compounds to make a more complex substance.

i. *Decomposition* means breaking down compounds into simpler products.

j. Replacement is the process in which one element replaces another in a compound or two elements in different compounds trade places.

1. A short, easy way to show a chemical reaction

2. True

3. By its chemical formula, CO_2

4. reactants

5. products

6. Yields

7. a. Reactant
b. Reactant
c. Product

8. b, d

9. True

10. The total mass of the reactants is the same as the total mass of the products.

11. During a chemical reaction, matter is not created or destroyed.

12. Matter can enter from or escape to the surroundings.

13. Sample answer: a sealed plastic bag

14. When it accurately represents the conservation of mass by showing the same number of each type of atom on both sides of the equation

15. There are two atoms of oxygen on each side.

16. d

17. coefficient

18. It tells you how many atoms or molecules of each reactant or product take part in the reaction.

19. There are two oxygen atoms in the reactants, but only one oxygen atom in the product.

20. $2 H_2 + O_2 \rightarrow 2 H_2O$

21. Synthesis, decomposition, and replacement reactions

22. Synthesis

23. a. Synthesis
b. Compounds are broken down into simpler products
c. Replacement

24. a. Decomposition
b. Synthesis
c. Replacement

Describing Chemical Reactions
Review and Reinforce

1. a. $FeS + 2HCl \rightarrow FeCl_2 + H_2S$
b. Replacement

2. a. $2Na + F_2 \rightarrow 2NaF$
b. Synthesis

3. a. $2HgO \rightarrow 2Hg + O_2$
b. Decomposition

4. Two molecules of hydrogen combine with one molecule of oxygen to form 2 molecules of water. Each hydrogen molecule is formed by 2 hydrogen atoms, the oxygen molecule is formed by 2 atoms of oxygen, and each water molecule is made of 2 hydrogen atoms bonded with 1 oxygen atom.

5. The conservation of mass states that mass is neither created nor destroyed during a chemical reaction. The equation is balanced because both the reactants and the product contain the same number of atoms of each element: 4 hydrogen atoms and 2 oxygen atoms.

© Pearson Education, Inc., publishing as Pearson Prentice Hall. All rights reserved.

6. c
7. g
8. f
9. a
10. e
11. h
12. b
13. d

Describing Chemical Reactions
Enrich

1. $2H_2O \rightarrow 2H_2 + O_2$
2. There are 4 hydrogen atoms and 2 oxygen atoms on each side of the equation.
3. The missing mass is due to oxygen gas and hydrogen gas that have escaped from the beaker. These gases are produced by the decomposition of water.
4. 36 g; the total mass of the reactants must equal the total mass of the products.
5. Gas bubbles are being produced.

Controlling Chemical Reactions
Guided Reading and Study

Use Target Reading Skills
   a. Increase in surface area
   b. Increase in temperature
   c. Increase in concentration
   d. Use of a catalyst
1. activation energy
2. True
3. The activation energy can be a spark.
4. Exothermic reaction
5. Endothermic reaction
6. For the reaction to start, a tiny amount of activation energy is needed. Once a few molecules react, the rest will quickly follow because the first few reactions provide activation energy for more molecules to react.
7. The energy of the products is greater than the energy of the reactants.
8. Endothermic
9. The peak of the curve

10. Surface area, temperature, concentration, use of a catalyst, or use of an inhibitor
11. Increasing the surface area allows more particles of a substance to react, and this increases the rate of the reaction.
12. Reaction rates are faster at higher temperatures.
13. a, c
14. concentration
15. Increasing the concentration of the reactants supplies more particles to react.
16. True
17. A catalyst is a material that increases the rate of a reaction by lowering the activation energy.
18. False
19. enzyme
20. Many chemical reactions necessary for life happen at temperatures that would kill living things. Enzymes are necessary to allow these reactions to occur at body temperature.
21. An inhibitor is a material used to decrease the rate of a reaction.
22. Most inhibitors work by preventing reactants from coming together.

Controlling Chemical Reactions
Review and Reinforce

1. In the graph of the exothermic reaction, the products are at a lower level of energy than the reactants. This is because an exothermic reaction releases energy. The products in the endothermic reaction are at a higher level of energy than the reactants. This is because an endothermic reaction absorbs energy.
2. Activation energy is the amount of energy that has to be added to start a reaction. With enough energy, reactants can get "over the hump" and form products.
3. Increasing the temperature of a reaction makes the reacting particles move faster, increasing the rate of the reaction. Other ways to increase the rate of a chemical reaction are increase the concentration of a reactant, increase the surface area of a solid reactant, or add a catalyst.
4. The amount of substance in a given volume

© Pearson Education, Inc., publishing as Pearson Prentice Hall. All rights reserved.

5. A biological catalyst
6. A material used to decrease the rate of a reaction

Controlling Chemical Reactions
Enrich

1. They are catalysts for the reaction.
2. If an FRH came with water already in it, the exothermic reaction would already have taken place and no more heat would be given off.
3. The smaller the pieces of magnesium, the larger their surface area. As the surface area of a reactant increases, so does the rate of reaction. For this reason, the pieces of magnesium in an FRH are probably very small.
4. It is important that the reaction be fast so that a large amount of heat will be given off in a short period of time. In this way, the MRE can be quickly heated to a fairly warm temperature.

Temperature and Enzyme Activity
Skills Lab

For answers, see the Teacher's Edition.

Fire and Fire Safety
Guided Reading and Study

Use Target Reading Skills
Sample answers:
What You Know
  1. A fire needs fuel to burn.
  2. A fire needs oxygen to burn
  3. All homes should have smoke detectors.
What You Learned
  1. Fire is the result of a combustion reaction.
  2. The most deadly fires start with cigarettes.
  3. Baking soda can be used to put out small fires.

  1. Combustion is a rapid reaction between oxygen and a substance called a fuel.
  2. fuel
  3. Fuel, oxygen, and heat
  4. a
  5. True
  6. Water covers the fuel, which keeps the fuel from coming into contact with oxygen. The evaporation of water also uses up heat, which cools the fire.
  7. Small heaters, cooking, and faulty electrical wiring
  8. baking soda
  9. a, c, d

Fire and Fire Safety
Review and Reinforce

  1. Fuel (the food in the skillet), oxygen (in the air), and heat (from the stove)
  2. Answers should include one of the following. You can stop a small stove fire safely with baking soda. This smothers the fire and combines with the liquid in the food to produce carbon dioxide. The carbon dioxide prevents contact between the fuel and oxygen. You can also stop a small stove fire safely by putting the lid on the skillet. This keeps the fuel from coming into contact with oxygen. You can stop a small stove fire by using a fire extinguisher. This also keeps the fuel from coming into contact with oxygen.
  3. Answers may vary. Sample answers: Keep flammable things, like pot-holders, towels, and curtains, away from stove burners. Keep a box of baking soda in the kitchen to fight grease fires. Have at least one fire extinguisher in good working order and within easy reach in your home.
  4. You should get away from the fire and call the fire department.
  5. Combustion is a rapid reaction between oxygen and fuel. Fire is caused by combustion.
  6. A fuel is a material that releases energy when it burns. Examples of fuels are oil, coal, wood, gasoline, and paper.

Fire and Fire Safety
Enrich

  1. a. Firebreak
     b. Backfire
  2. Because there are no trees or large plants in a firebreak, there is virtually no fuel available and the fire cannot cross it.
  3. Wetting agents increase the ability of water to keep the wood from coming into contact with oxygen. Without oxygen, the wood cannot burn. Water also reduces the temperature of the fire.
  4. Throwing dirt on the flames covers up the fire's fuel, preventing oxygen from coming into contact with it.

© Pearson Education, Inc., publishing as Pearson Prentice Hall. All rights reserved.

Key Terms

1. catalyst
2. decomposition
3. precipitate
4. reactants
5. synthesis
6. concentration
7. inhibitor
8. combustion
9. activation
10. replacement
11. products
12. coefficient
13. chemistry

Math Skills

1. $2\,H_2O \rightarrow 2\,H_2 + O_2$
2. $N_2 + 3\,H_2 \rightarrow 2\,NH_3$
3. $C_3H_8 + 5\,O_2 \rightarrow 3\,CO_2 + 4\,H_2O$
4. $2\,K + 2\,H_2O \rightarrow H_2 + 2\,KOH$
5. $4\,Li + O_2 \rightarrow 2\,Li_2O$
6. $4\,Fe + 3\,O_2 \rightarrow 2\,Fe_2O_3$
7. $6\,Ag + N_2 \rightarrow 2\,Ag_3N$
8. $C_2H_5OH + 3\,O_2 \rightarrow 2\,CO_2 + 3\,H_2O$

© Pearson Education, Inc., publishing as Pearson Prentice Hall. All rights reserved.

Connecting Concepts

Chemical reactions, including fire, are a way that matter can change. This concept map is only one way to represent the main ideas and relationships in this chapter. Accept other logical answers from students.

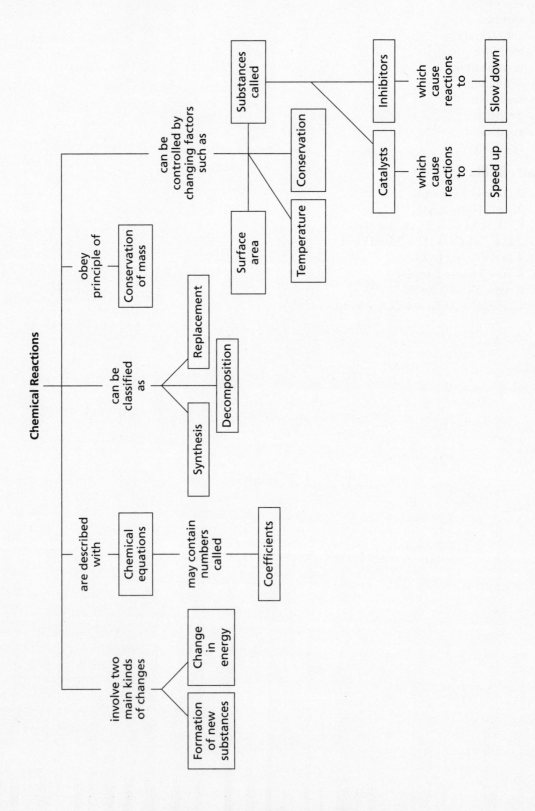

© Pearson Education, Inc., publishing as Pearson Prentice Hall. All rights reserved.

Laboratory Investigation

The Law of Definite Proportions
Pre-Lab Investigation

1. A comparison of two numbers expressed as a fraction, usually in lowest terms
2. Answers may include gas production (or bubbles), precipitates, temperature change, color change, and changes in other physical properties.
3. Speeds it up
4. A compound breaks down into simpler compounds or elements.

Observations

Physical Properties: Both water and hydrogen peroxide are clear, colorless, odorless liquids at room temperature. **Evidence of Chemical Reaction to Manganese Dioxide:** With water, none; with hydrogen peroxide, bubbles that support combustion

Analyze and Conclude

1. All the physical properties observed in this lab are the same. Both are clear, colorless, odorless liquids.
2. Both compounds consist of hydrogen and oxygen; the numbers of atoms of each differ.
3. Answers should include that different compositions result in different properties.

Critical Thinking and Applications

1. The splint starts to flame. Oxygen is the gas produced.
2. Hydrogen peroxide broke down into water and oxygen gas.
3. 2:16, or 1:8; 2:32, or 1:16
4. The elements are not in the same ratio in the two compounds, resulting in different chemical properties.

More to Explore

Students should observe considerable fizzing when they combine bleach and hydrogen peroxide. They should observe no evidence of a reaction for bleach and water.
1. Bleach is a catalyst that permits very rapid oxidation of hydrogen peroxide.
2. You can tell bleach is a catalyst because adding more hydrogen peroxide always gets the same reaction, which calms down rapidly when the peroxide has virtually all been oxidized.

Performance Assessment

1. Student's answer must demonstrate that he/she used observed results to evaluate his/her prediction.
2. Students can conclude that when iron combines with oxygen to form iron oxide, energy is released in the form of heat. This makes it an exothermic chemical reaction.
3. Answers may vary, but should include two of the following: increase the concentration of the salt in the salt water solution, warm the jar while the reaction is taking place, break up the steel wool into smaller pieces, add a catalyst.
4. It is a synthesis reaction because iron combines with oxygen to form iron oxide.

Chapter Test

1. a
2. d
3. c
4. d
5. b
6. a
7. c
8. c
9. a
10. a
11. activation energy
12. inhibitor
13. exothermic
14. enzyme
15. fuel
16. True
17. oxygen
18. closed system
19. True
20. products
21. a. Reactants
    b. Products
22. The reaction is an endothermic reaction, because the energy level of the products is higher than the energy level of the reactants. This indicates that the reaction took in energy.
23. No. Increasing the concentration of the reactants will increase the rate of reaction, but it will not change the activation energy.
24. Water stops combustion first by coating the fuel and separating it from the oxygen in the air. As the water evaporates, it also lowers the temperature and decreases the available heat.

© Pearson Education, Inc., publishing as Pearson Prentice Hall. All rights reserved.

25. Conservation of mass means that matter is neither created nor destroyed in a reaction. Therefore, there should be the same number of atoms of each element in the products and the reactants. There are 4 atoms of iron, and 6 atoms of oxygen before and after the reaction.

26. a. initial formula: $H_2 + I_2 \rightarrow HI$ Balanced formula: $H_2 + I_2 \rightarrow 2HI$ **b.** initial formula: $Li + HCl \rightarrow H_2 + LiCl$ balanced: $2Li + 2HCl \rightarrow H_2 + 2LiCl$ **c.** initial formula: $H_2O \rightarrow H_2 + O_2$ balanced: $2H_2O + 2H_2 + O_2$

27. a. Synthesis: The products are more complex than the reactants. **b.** Replacement: Lithium replaces the hydrogen in the compound. **c.** Decomposition: The products are simpler than the reactants.

28. Adding baking soda to vinegar produces a chemical reaction. The production of gas bubbles and the disappearance of the vinegar smell indicate that a gas was released and a different material formed.

29. Enzymes are biological catalysts that decrease the activation energy of chemical reactions. If a person's enzymes were not working properly, for example during hypothermia, the activation energy of the body's chemical reactions would be too high and the rate of chemical reactions in the body would decrease. Because these chemical reactions are necessary for life, a person could die of hypothermia.

30. To balance an equation you can change the coefficients to change the number of molecules in the reaction. However, if you were to change the subscripts, you would change the identities of the substances in the reactions.

© Pearson Education, Inc., publishing as Pearson Prentice Hall. All rights reserved.

Acids, Bases, and Solutions

© Pearson Education, Inc., publishing as Pearson Prentice Hall. All rights reserved.

Lab zone Chapter Project ► Make Your Own Indicator

The following steps will walk you through the Chapter Project. Use the hints as you guide your students through planning, indicator extraction, and pH testing.

Chapter Project Overview

In this project, students will make their own acid-base indicators from foods, plants, or other materials. They will use these indicators to test the pH of common household substances and compare their results with the results obtained with pH test papers.

Before introducing the project, do a class presentation in which you use tea as an acid-base indicator. Students should observe color change as you add a couple of drops of the tea to test tubes of vinegar and ammonia. Explain to students that they will be using colored materials, like the tea, to test the pH of various substances.

Decide on the number of indicators that students will extract and the number of substances students will test. Have students read the Chapter Project Overview. Review the project's rules and hand out the Chapter Scoring Rubric, you will use for scoring students' work. Discuss with students what will be expected of them.

Set a deadline for the project presentation and interim dates for the Keep Students on Track at the ends of Section 1, Section 2, and Section 4. Encourage students to copy the dates in the Project Timeline.

Group students. Have them brainstorm a list of naturally occurring substances they can use to obtain indicators. Go over their suggestions and discuss the advantages and drawbacks.

Review students' choice of materials and the procedures they intend to use for indicator extraction. Once students have your approval, they may begin extracting their indicators.

Distribute copies of Chapter Project Worksheet 1. Have them use this worksheet to organize their data. Chapter Project Worksheet 2, will help students analyze their data and prepare for the presentation. Distribute this worksheet once students have completed their data collection.

Remind students to refer to the hints in the Chapter Project Overview as they plan and carry out the project.

Materials and Preparation

Substances that would make good indicators include rose petals, day lilies, tea (flavored or unflavored), red cabbage, beets, radishes, rhubarb, red grapes, red onions, blueberries, blackberries, tomato skins, tomato leaves, grass, and greens (collards, spinach, mustard, and carrot). Or students may try other colored substances as indicators. In particular, they should look for bright, definite colors. (Some white flower petals, such as roses, also work.)

Some substances you might have students test include vinegar, milk, lemon juice, apple juice, carbonated drinks, soapy water, salt water (35 g NaCl to 1,000 mL H_2O), household ammonia, household bleach, household cleaners, and shampoo. Warn students not to mix ammonia and bleach together. Avoid testing water as it is sensitive to the pH of the indicator and will cause students to get inaccurate readings.

Students will need equipment such as electric blenders, mortars and pestles, cheesecloth, and strainers for extracting indicators. They will also need empty bottles with screw-top lids for storing their indicator juices once they have been made.

Keep Students on Track— Section 1

Check students' procedures for isolating indicator juices. Make sure they plan to use similar amounts of starting materials. Also, be sure they rinse all equipment after each round of indicator extraction.

If students want to use an electric blender to isolate their indicators, plan to run the blender for them for safety purposes. If students are using a mortar and pestle, have them add a little fine sand to the mortar. This will help them grind the sample.

Make sure students store their indicators in the refrigerator to prevent spoilage.

© Pearson Education, Inc., publishing as Pearson Prentice Hall. All rights reserved.

Keep Students on Track— Section 2

Set a minimum number (six, for example) of substances for students to test with their indicators. If students have used different materials to make their indicators, you may choose to have all students test the same substances so they can compare results.

Check students' data tables. Be sure students have separate columns for the indicator source, the substance tested, the color of the indicator before it was used, and the color of the solution after it is tested. They will need another column for the pH of the tested substance.

Keep Students on Track— Section 4

Check students' data tables for completeness. They should indicate actual pH values for tested substances.

Make sure students have listed all tested substances from low to high pH. They should begin to think about how the color changes relate to the actual pH values.

Chapter Project Performance Assessment

Tell students analyzing their data means looking at their observations, summarizing them, finding patterns, and deciding what these patterns tell about the indicators.

As students give their reports, ask their classmates to take notes, writing down observed color changes and actual pH values.

Extension

Consider organizing the class in groups for this project. If space and time are limited, you may want to have students use different indicators to test the same substances. Alternatively, you may have students use the same indicator to test different substances. This will provide a wider range of data.

Assign one particular indicator source to each student. Have the student determine the indicator's pH range by testing various substances. Alternatively, you can have each student test acidity and basicity of one substance using a variety of indicators. One way to do this would be to have pairs of students make one indicator, then distribute all indicators to the class.

Consider grouping students according to the indicators used and/or substances tested. Have them combine their data and summarize their results. Direct groups to discuss their results. Instruct each group to present its findings to the rest of the class.

Students could make indicator paper by soaking strips of filter paper in the indicator solutions and letting the strips dry. The strips could then be stored in an airtight container and used to test pH in other activities. Students should label the container with the source material used to make the indicator and its pH range.

© Pearson Education, Inc., publishing as Pearson Prentice Hall. All rights reserved.

Acids, Bases, and Solutions • *Chapter Project*   **Overview**

Make Your Own Indicator

Acidic and basic solutions can be detected using substances called acid-base indicators. Perhaps you are familiar with litmus paper, a common indicator. The active chemical in litmus is made from a natural substance found in lichens, which are living organisms. The litmus is applied to paper to make it more convenient to use.

There are many other naturally occurring substances that can also act as acid-base indicators. In this project, you will first select a few substances that you think might be good sources of indicators. Using these indicators, you will test a variety of acidic and basic substances such as vinegar and ammonia. You will then use standard pH test paper to assign pH values to the different colors of the indicators you have selected. Finally, you will rank the substances you have tested according to their pH value.

Project Rules

- You must write a procedure that you will use to obtain your indicators. Have your teacher approve your materials and procedures before you begin extraction.

- All indicators must come from naturally occurring substances. Do not use indicators produced in the lab.

- Your teacher will tell you how many substances to test with your indicators. All materials to be tested must be readily available substances commonly found in the home. You may not use acids and bases that are standard laboratory supplies.

- Do not taste the acids or bases from food sources.

- Once you have used your indicators to test your substances, use pH test paper to determine their actual pH values.

Suggested Materials

- Substances that might make good indicators include rose petals, day lilies, tea (flavored or unflavored), red cabbage, beets, radishes, rhubarb, red grapes, red onions, blueberries, blackberries, tomato skins, tomato leaves, grass, and greens (collards, kale, spinach, mustard, and carrot).

- Some substances you might test include vinegar, milk, lemon juice, apple juice, carbonated drinks, soapy water, salt water, household ammonia, household bleach, household cleaners, and shampoo.

- You will need equipment such as electric blenders, mortars and pestles, cheesecloth, and strainers for extracting indicators. You will also need empty bottles with screw-top lids for storing your indicator juices once they have been made.

© Pearson Education, Inc., publishing as Pearson Prentice Hall. All rights reserved.

Acids, Bases, and Solutions · *Chapter Project*   **Overview**

Project Hints

- Be creative when selecting your indicator sources. They may be recognized by bright, definite colors. Look for reds, blues, purples, or yellows.

- When designing your procedure for indicator extraction, plan to use similar amounts of starting materials. This will make the concentrations of your indicators similar.

- If using a mortar and pestle for indicator extraction, add a small amount of fine sand to your mortar. This will help you grind up your material.

- Your indicators should be liquids. Make sure that you get rid of all remaining solid materials before using each of your indicators.

- Store all extracted indicators in the refrigerator to prevent spoilage.

- Use small, equal volumes (1–2 mL) of both indicator and test substance for each test. This will reduce the amount of each indicator you will need to make and give definite color changes.

- Be sure to rinse test tubes and droppers between each test in order to avoid contamination between one test and the next.

Project Time Line

Task	Due Date
1. Materials selected.	_____
2. Extraction procedure written.	_____
3. Materials and procedure approved.	_____
4. Extraction completed.	_____
5. Substances tested with indicators.	_____
6. pH of substances determined with pH test paper.	_____
7. Data analysis and list of substances completed.	_____
8. Class presentation made.	_____

© Pearson Education, Inc., publishing as Pearson Prentice Hall. All rights reserved.

Acids, Bases, and Solutions · *Chapter Project*   **Worksheet 1**

Project Planning and Data Collection

Making Plans

Complete the following tasks using a separate sheet of paper. When the tasks have been completed, you are ready to get your teacher's approval and begin the Chapter Project.

1. List the naturally occurring substances that you plan to use for making your indicators.

2. Write the procedure that you plan to use for extraction. Make sure you include the amount of starting materials, how you intend to grind up these materials, and how you plan to separate the liquid indicator from the remaining solid materials. As you prepare your indicators, you may need to modify your extraction process in order to meet unexpected circumstances. For example, you may need to dilute a too-dark indicator, or not dilute a pale indicator at all.

3. List the household substances that you plan to test with your indicators.

4. Some indicators may stain skin and clothing. Wear a lab apron when preparing and using your indicators. Wash your hands throughly when finished.

Recording Observations

Record your observations in a data table organized like the one below. Include indicator source, the substance tested, the color of the indicator before it was used, and the color of the indicator after it was used. You will be completing the last column later in the project.

Indicator Source	Substance Tested	Indicator Color Before Use	Solution Color After Testing	pH of Substance

© Pearson Education, Inc., publishing as Pearson Prentice Hall. All rights reserved.

Analyzing and Presenting Your Data

Use a table similar to the one below to organize your tested substances by pH.
Include the colors that you observed for each of your indicators.

Tested Substance	pH of Substance	Color of Indicator #1	Color of Indicator #2	Color of Indicator #3

Complete the following tasks on a separate sheet of paper. When they have been
completed, you are ready to put together your presentation.

1. What qualities are required of a good indicator? Which of your indicators exhibited these qualities?

2. Did any of your indicators work poorly? Explain why you think they were not good indicators.

3. Write several sentences summarizing your research.

4. Write several sentences summarizing your observations from the data table. Did you notice patterns in the response of your indicators? For instance, did the indicators turn the same color in an acid? Did the indicators work equally well for all acids and for all bases?

5. Decide how you want to communicate what you have learned to your classmates. Make a list of the things you will need to make this presentation.

Acids, Bases, and Solutions

© Pearson Education, Inc., publishing as Pearson Prentice Hall. All rights reserved.

Acids, Bases, and Solutions ▪ *Chapter Project*   **Scoring Rubric**

Make Your Own Indicator

In evaluating how well you complete the Chapter Project, your teacher will judge your work in three categories. In each, a score of 4 is the best rating.

	4	3	2	1
Planning and Indicator Preparation	Written description of indicator preparation is thorough and complete, including details describing quantities and equipment used.	Written description of indicator preparation is good, including most details describing quantities and equipment used.	Written description of indicator preparation is adequate, including some details describing quantities and equipment used.	Written description of indicator preparation is minimal, including few details describing quantities and equipment used.
Following Rules and Organizing Data	Makes the required number of indicators and tests the required number of substances. Carefully follows safe lab practices. Makes complete and accurate written observations on color changes and actual pH values.	Makes the required number of indicators and tests the required number of substances. Follows safe lab practices. Makes fairly complete written observations on color changes and actual pH values.	Makes the required number of indicators and tests more than half of the required number of substances. Lab practices are fairly safe. Written observations on color changes and actual pH values are somewhat disorganized or incomplete.	Makes fewer than the required number of indicators and tests half or less than half of the required number of substances. Lab practices are unsafe. Written observations on color changes and actual pH values are disorganized and incomplete.
Analyzing and Presenting the Data	Makes a thorough, well-organized presentation. Clearly explains which indicators are useful for testing which ranges of pH. Prepares well-designed visual aids.	Makes an acceptable presentation. Explains which indicators are useful for testing which ranges of pH. Prepares useful visual aids.	Presentation is somewhat hard to follow. Explanation of which indicators are useful for testing which ranges of pH is unclear. Prepares one visual aid.	Presentation is brief and hard to follow. Explanation of which indicators are useful for testing which ranges of pH is unclear. Prepares no visual aids.

© Pearson Education, Inc., publishing as Pearson Prentice Hall. All rights reserved.

Understanding Solutions

 *3–4 periods, 1–2 blocks*

Ability Levels Key
L1 Basic to Average
L2 For All Students
L3 Average to Advanced

Objectives

L.3.1.1 State the characteristics of solutions, colloids, and suspensions.

L.3.1.2 Describe what happens to the particles of a solute when a solution forms.

L.3.1.3 Explain how solutes affect the freezing point and boiling point of a solvent.

Key Terms
• solution • solvent • solute • colloid
• suspension

Local Standards

PRETEACH

Build Background Knowledge
Students think of a way to distinguish a familiar solution from plain water.

 **Discover Activity** *What Makes a Mixture a Solution?* **L1**

Targeted Resources

❑ **All in One** **Teaching Resources**
  L2 Reading Strategy Transparency L30: Using Prior Knowledge
❑ 💿 **Presentation-Pro CD-ROM**

INSTRUCT

What Is a Solution? Explain what a solution is and which substance in a solution is the solute and which is the solvent.

Colloids and Suspensions Define colloids and suspensions, and challenge students to explain how they could separate a solute from a suspension.

Particles in a Solution Compare and contrast solutions of ionic compounds and molecular compounds.

Effects of Solutes on Solvents Use differences in taste to introduce the concept that solutes affect the properties of solvents.

Design Your Own Lab *Speedy Solutions* **L2**

Targeted Resources

❑ **All in One** **Teaching Resources**
  L2 Guided Reading, pp. 187–189
  L2 Transparency L31
  L2 Lab: *Speedy Solutions*, pp. 192–194
❑ 📼 **Lab Activity Video/DVD**
  Design Your Own Lab: *Speedy Solutions*
❑ **PHSchool.com** Web Code: cgp-2031
❑ 💿 **Student Edition on Audio CD**

ASSESS

Section Assessment Questions
↻ Have students use their completed graphic organizers answer the questions.

Reteach
Students fill in details in an outline of the section.

Targeted Resources

❑ **All in One** **Teaching Resources**
  Section Summary, p. 186
  L1 Review and Reinforce, p. 190
  L3 Enrich, p. 191

© Pearson Education, Inc., publishing as Pearson Prentice Hall. All rights reserved.

Name _____ Date _____ Class _____

Acids, Bases, and Solutions • *Section Summary*

Understanding Solutions

Guide for Reading

■ What are the characteristics of solutions, colloids, and suspensions?

■ What happens to the particles of a solute when a solution forms?

■ How do solutes affect the freezing point and boiling point of a solvent?

A **solution** is a well-mixed mixture that contains a solvent and at least one solute. The **solvent** is the part of a solution present in the largest amount. It dissolves the other substances. A substance that is present in a solution in a smaller amount and dissolved by the solvent is the **solute**. **A solution has the same properties throughout. It contains solute particles (molecules or ions) that are too small to see.**

In many common solutions, the solvent is water. Life depends on water solutions. Water is the solvent in sap—a solution that carries sugar to tree cells. Water is the solvent in blood, saliva, and tears.

Solutions can be made with solvents other than water too. A solution may be made of any combination of gases, liquids, or solids.

All mixtures are not solutions. Colloids and suspensions are mixtures that have different properties than solutions. A **colloid** is a mixture containing small, undissolved particles that do not settle out. **A colloid contains larger particles than a solution. The particles are still too small to be seen easily, but are large enough to scatter a light beam.** Fog, gelatin, mayonnaise, and shaving cream are colloids.

A **suspension** is a mixture in which particles can be seen and easily separated by settling or filtration. **Unlike a solution, a suspension does not have the same properties throughout. It contains visible particles that are larger than the particles in solutions or colloids.**

When a solution forms, particles of the solute leave each other and become surrounded by particles of the solvent. When an ionic solid mixes with water, water molecules surround and separate positive and negative ions as the ionic solid dissolves into the solution. A molecular solid breaks up into individual neutral molecules. Solutions of ionic compounds dissolved in water conduct electricity. Solutions of molecular compounds dissolved in water do not conduct electricity.

Solutes affect the boiling and freezing points of a solvent. **Solutes lower the freezing point and raise the boiling point of a solvent.** The freezing point is lowered because the solute particles get in the way, making it harder for the solvent to form crystals. Thus, the temperature must drop in order for the solvent to freeze. Solutes also raise the boiling point of a solvent. More energy is needed for the solvent particles to escape as a gas.

© Pearson Education, Inc., publishing as Pearson Prentice Hall. All rights reserved.

Acids, Bases, and Solutions • *Guided Reading and Study*

Understanding Solutions

This section explains what happens to particles of substances in solution. It also describes properties of solutions.

Use Target Reading Skills

As you read about solutions, complete the graphic organizer by filling in the details.

Main Idea

A solution consists of a solvent and at least one solute in a well mixed mixture.			

Detail	**Detail**	**Detail**	**Detail**
a.	b.	c.	d.

© Pearson Education, Inc., publishing as Pearson Prentice Hall. All rights reserved.

Acids, Bases, and Solutions

Acids, Bases, and Solutions • *Guided Reading and Study*

Understanding Solutions *(continued)*

What Is a Solution?

1. A well-mixed mixture that contains a solvent and at least one solute is called a(n) _____.

2. Complete the table about solvents and solutes.

Parts of a Solution		
Part	**Definition**	**Which Part of Sugar Water Solution?**
a.	The part of a solution present in the largest amount	**c.**
b.	A substance present in a solution in a smaller amount	**d.**

3. In a solution, the _____ is dissolved by the _____.

4. Why is water called the "universal solvent"?

_____

_____

5. Is the following sentence true or false? Solutions can only be made with liquid solvents. _____

Colloids and Suspensions

6. What is a colloid?

_____

_____

_____

7. A colloid contains _____ particles than a solution.

8. Circle the letter of each example of a colloid.

   a. fog   **b.** salt water
   c. milk   **d.** snow globe

9. What is a suspension?

_____

_____

© Pearson Education, Inc., publishing as Pearson Prentice Hall. All rights reserved.

Acids, Bases, and Solutions · *Guided Reading and Study*

10. How does a suspension differ from a solution?

_____

_____

_____

_____

Particles in a Solution

11. What happens to the solute's particles whenever a solution forms?

_____

_____

_____

12. Circle the letter of each sentence that is true about particles in a solution.

   a. When an ionic solid mixes with water, its ions repel water molecules.

   b. When a molecular solid mixes with water, the covalent bonds within molecules are broken.

   c. When an ionic solid mixes with water, water molecules surround each ion.

   d. When a molecular solid mixes with water, the solute breaks down into individual molecules.

13. Which solution will conduct electricity, a sugar solution or a salt solution?

_____

Effects of Solutes on Solutions

14. Circle the letter of each sentence that is true about the effects of solutes on solutions.

   a. Solutes raise the boiling point of a solvent.

   b. The temperature must drop lower than 0°C for water to freeze when a solute is dissolved in the water.

   c. Solutes raise the freezing point of a solvent.

   d. Antifreeze boils at a lower temperature than pure water.

Acids, Bases, and Solutions

© Pearson Education, Inc., publishing as Pearson Prentice Hall. All rights reserved.

Name _____ Date _____ Class _____

Understanding Solutions

Understanding Main Ideas

Study the three mixtures below. Identify each mixture as a solution, colloid, or suspension. Explain.

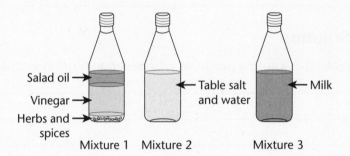

Salad oil →
Vinegar →
Herbs and →
spices

← Table salt
and water

← Milk

Mixture 1   Mixture 2   Mixture 3

1. _____

2. _____

3. _____

Answer the following questions on a separate sheet of paper.

4. Compare and contrast what happens to the particles of a ionic solid and a molecular solid when each mixes with water.

5. What are two ways that solutes affect the properties of solvents?

Building Vocabulary

From the list below, choose the term that best completes each sentence.

suspension   colloid

solute   solvent

solution

6. The part of a solution that is present in the smaller amount is the

   _____.

7. The part of a solution that is present in the larger amount is the

   _____.

8. A(n) _____ is a mixture containing small, undissolved particles that do not settle out, but are large enough to scatter light.

9. A mixture in which particles can be seen and easily separated by settling or filtration is called a(n) _____.

10. A well-mixed mixture that contains a solvent and at least one solute is called a(n) _____.

© Pearson Education, Inc., publishing as Pearson Prentice Hall. All rights reserved.

Acids, Bases, and Solutions • *Enrich*

The Chemistry of Ice Cream

A colloid is similar to a suspension in that its particles are larger than those of a solution. However, the particles of a colloid, like those of a solution, are small enough that they cannot be separated by settling or filtration. The particles in a colloid are said to be *dispersed*, rather than dissolved or suspended. Familiar colloids include shaving cream, whipped cream, fog, and smoke.

Ice cream is another familiar colloid. The particles in this colloid are solid fat, tiny crystals of ice, and droplets of water. A high concentration of sugars, salts, and proteins is dissolved in the water. Here, air acts something like a solvent. The particles of ice cream are dispersed in many tiny bubbles of air. Ice cream also contains other substances that allow "unlike" compounds to mix and stay mixed under the proper conditions. The unlike compounds in ice cream are water, which is polar, and fat, which is nonpolar.

The colloid formed by ice cream remains stable only at cold temperatures. When ice cream is warmed above freezing, its dispersed particles absorb energy and begin to move faster. When the fast-moving particles collide, they sometimes stick together. Eventually, the particles grow so large that they can no longer remain dispersed, and they settle out of the colloid.

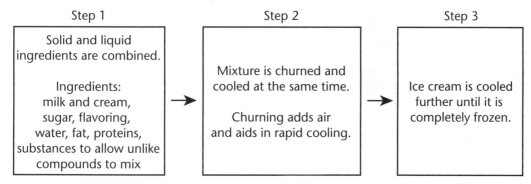

Step 1	Step 2	Step 3
Solid and liquid ingredients are combined. Ingredients: milk and cream, sugar, flavoring, water, fat, proteins, substances to allow unlike compounds to mix	Mixture is churned and cooled at the same time. Churning adds air and aids in rapid cooling.	Ice cream is cooled further until it is completely frozen.

Answer the following questions on a separate sheet of paper.

1. Suppose the liquid water in ice cream did not have solutes dissolved in it. What effect do you think this would have on ice cream? (*Hint:* Consider the temperature at which ice cream is kept.)

2. What do you think happens to the air in the colloid when ice cream melts?

3. Look at the diagram above. Why do you think air isn't added until Step 2 when the mixture is cooled?

4. Milk is also a colloid. It consists mainly of water, proteins, and fat. Which colloid is more stable, milk or ice cream? How do you know?

© Pearson Education, Inc., publishing as Pearson Prentice Hall. All rights reserved.

Acids, Bases, and Solutions

Acids, Bases, and Solutions · *Design Your Own Lab*

Speedy Solutions

Problem

How can you control the rate at which certain salts dissolve in water?

Skills Focus

controlling variables, drawing conclusions, designing experiments

Materials

spoon	solid stoppers, #4	thermometers
hot plate	balance	stirring rods
ice	timer or watch	test tube rack
test tubes, 25 × 150 mm	coarse, rock, and table salt	
graduated cylinders and beakers, various sizes		

Design a Plan   *Review the safety guidelines in Appendix A of your textbook.*

1. List on the lines below all the variables you can think of that could affect the speed with which salt dissolves in water.

   _____

   _____

2. Compare your list with your classmates' lists, and add other variables.
3. Choose one variable from your list to test.
4. Write a hypothesis on the lines below predicting the effect of your chosen variable on the speed of dissolving.

   _____

   _____

5. Decide how to work with your choice.

   - If you choose temperature, you might perform tests at 10°C, 20°C, 30°C, 40°C, and 50°C.
   - If you choose stirring, you might stir for various amounts of time.

6. Plan at least three tests for whichever variable you choose. Remember to control all other variables.
7. Write down on the back of this sheet a series of steps for your procedure and safety guidelines for your experiment. Be quite detailed in your plan.
8. As part of your procedure, prepare a data table like the one on the following page in which to record your results. Fill in the headings on your table that identify your manipulated variable and the responding variable. (*Hint:* Remember to include units.)
9. Have your teacher approve your procedure, safety guidelines, and data table.
10. Perform the experiment.

© Pearson Education, Inc., publishing as Pearson Prentice Hall. All rights reserved.

Name _____ Date _____ Class _____

Acids, Bases, and Solutions • *Design Your Own Lab*

Data Table

Manipulated Variable	Dissolving Time		
	Test 1	Test 2	Test 3

Analyze and Conclude

Write your answers in the spaces provided.

1. **Controlling Variables** Which is the manipulated variable in your experiment? Which is the responding variable? How do you know which is which?

   _____

   _____

2. **Controlling Variables** List three variables you held constant in your procedure. Explain why controlling these variables makes your data more meaningful.

   _____

   _____

   _____

3. **Graphing** Make a line graph of your data. Label the horizontal axis with the manipulated variable. Label the vertical axis with the responding variable. Use an appropriate scale for each axis and label the units.

4. **Drawing Conclusions** Study the shape of your graph. Write a conclusion about the effect of the variable you tested on the speed at which salt dissolves in water.

   _____

   _____

   _____

© Pearson Education, Inc., publishing as Pearson Prentice Hall. All rights reserved.

Acids, Bases, and Solutions • *Design Your Own Lab*

Speedy Solutions *(continued)*

5. **Drawing Conclusions** Does your conclusion support the hypothesis you wrote in Step 4 of your Plan? Explain.

   _____

   _____

   _____

6. **Designing Experiments** What advantage would there be in running your tests a second or third time?

   _____

   _____

7. **Predicting** If you switched procedures with another student who tested the same variable as you, do you think you would get the same results? Explain why or why not.

   _____

   _____

   _____

8. **Communicating** Write an e-mail to a friend explaining how your results relate to what you have learned about particles and solubility.

   _____

   _____

   _____

   _____

More to Explore

Choose another variable from the list you made in Steps 1 and 2 of your Plan. Repeat the process with that variable. Of the two variables you chose, which was easier to work with? Explain.

© Pearson Education, Inc., publishing as Pearson Prentice Hall. All rights reserved.

Concentration and Solubility

2–3 periods, 1–1 1/2 blocks

Objectives

L.3.2.1 Describe how concentration is measured.

L.3.2.2 Explain why solubility is useful in identifying substances.

L.3.2.3 Identify factors that affect the solubility of a substance.

Local Standards

Key Terms
- dilute solution • concentrated solution
- solubility • saturated solution
- unsaturated solution
- supersaturated solution

PRETEACH

Build Background Knowledge Students recall what they already know about concentration using a familiar example.

 **Discover Activity** *Does It Dissolve?* **L1**

Targeted Resources

- ❑ **All in One Teaching Resources**
  L2 Reading Strategy: Building Vocabulary
- ❑ 💿 **Presentation-Pro CD-ROM**

INSTRUCT

Concentration Define and discuss concentration.

Solubility Introduce and explain solubility.

Factors Affecting Solubility Describe how solubility may be affected by pressure, type of solvent, and temperature.

Targeted Resources

- ❑ **All in One Teaching Resources**
  L2 Guided Reading, pp. 197–198
  L2 Transparency L32
- ❑ **www.SciLinks.org** Web Code: scn-1232
- ❑ 💿 **Student Edition on Audio CD**

ASSESS

Section Assessment Questions

🔄 Have students use their completed sentences using key terms to answer the questions.

Reteach

Students fill in the blanks in sentences in which key terms are defined.

Targeted Resources

- ❑ **All in One Teaching Resources**
  Section Summary, p. 196
  L1 Review and Reinforce, p. 199
  L3 Enrich, p. 200

Acids, Bases, and Solutions

© Pearson Education, Inc., publishing as Pearson Prentice Hall. All rights reserved.

Acids, Bases, and Solutions • *Section Summary*

Concentration and Solubility

Guide for Reading

- How is concentration measured?

- Why is solubility useful in identifying substances?

- What factors affect the solubility of a substance?

Concentration is the amount of solute dissolved in a certain amount of solvent. A **dilute solution** has only a little solute dissolved in the solvent. A **concentrated solution** has a lot more solute dissolved in the solvent. You can change the concentration of a solution by adding more solute. You can also change the concentration by adding or removing solvent. **To measure concentration, you compare the amount of solute to the amount of solvent or to the total amount of solution.**

Solubility is a measure of how much solute can dissolve in a solvent at a given temperature. When you've added so much solute that no more dissolves, you have a **saturated solution**. If you can continue to dissolve more solute, you still have an **unsaturated solution**. The solubility of a substance tells you how much solute you can dissolve before a solution becomes saturated. **Solubility can be used to help identify a substance because it is a characteristic property of matter.**

The solubilities of solutes change when conditions change. **Factors that affect the solubility of a substance include pressure, the type of solvent, and temperature.** Pressure affects the solubility of gases. The higher the pressure of the gas over the solvent, the more gas can dissolve.

Sometimes you can't make a solution because the solute and solvent will not mix. Ionic and polar compounds dissolve in polar solvents. Nonpolar compounds do not dissolve in polar solvents.

Many solids dissolve better when the temperature of the solvent increases. Unlike most solids, gases become less soluble when the temperature goes up. When heated, a solution can dissolve more solute than it can at cooler temperatures. A **supersaturated solution** has more dissolved solute than is predicted by its solubility at the given temperature. Dropping a crystal of the solute in a supersaturated solution will cause the extra solute to come out of solution.

© Pearson Education, Inc., publishing as Pearson Prentice Hall. All rights reserved.

Concentration and Solubility

This section describes how concentration is measured. It also describes the usefulness of solubility and factors that affect it.

Use Target Reading Skills

After you read the section, for each Key Term write a meaningful sentence that incorporates that Key Term.

dilute solution

_____

_____

concentrated solution

_____

_____

solubility

_____

_____

saturated solution

_____

_____

unsaturated solution

_____

_____

supersaturated solution

_____

_____

Concentration

Match the term with its definition.

Term	Definition
____ **1.** dilute solution	**a.** A mixture that has a lot of solute dissolved in it.
____ **2.** concentrated solution	**b.** A mixture that has only a little solute dissolved in it.

© Pearson Education, Inc., publishing as Pearson Prentice Hall. All rights reserved.

Acids, Bases, and Solutions • *Guided Reading and Study*

Concentration and Solubility (continued)

3. What are two ways in which you can change the concentration of a solution?

   _____

   _____

   _____

4. How do you measure the concentration of a solution?

   _____

   _____

   _____

Solubility

5. What is solubility?

   _____

   _____

6. A mixture that has so much solute in it that no more will dissolve is called a(n)

   _____.

7. A mixture in which more solute can be dissolved is called a(n)

   _____.

8. Which is more soluble in water, baking soda or sugar? _____

9. Is the following sentence true or false? Solubility can be used to identify an unknown substance. _____

Factors Affecting Solubility

10. What are three factors that affect the solubility of a substance?

    a. _____ b. _____

    c. _____

11. The higher the pressure of the gas, the _____ gas can dissolve in a solvent.

12. Is the following sentence true or false? Nonpolar compounds dissolve in polar solvents. _____

13. Circle the letter of each sentence that is true about temperature and solubility.

    a. Most solids become more soluble as the temperature goes up.
    b. Most gases become less soluble as the temperature goes up.
    c. Sugar dissolves better in cold water than in hot water.
    d. Carbon dioxide dissolves better in cold water than in hot water.

© Pearson Education, Inc., publishing as Pearson Prentice Hall. All rights reserved.

Acids, Bases, and Solutions ▪ *Review and Reinforce*

Concentration and Solubility

Understanding Main Ideas

Answer the following questions on the lines below.

1. What amounts do you compare when measuring concentration?

   _____

   _____

2. How can you tell that a white powder is salt without tasting it?

   _____

   _____

3. Which solution will have more gas dissolved in it, a solution under high pressure or one under low pressure?

   _____

   _____

4. Explain the meaning of the expression "like dissolves like."

   _____

   _____

   _____

5. How does temperature affect the solubility of most solids?

   _____

   _____

Building Vocabulary

Match each term with its definition by writing the letter of the correct definition on the line beside the term in the left column.

_____ 6. dilute solution

_____ 7. concentrated solution

_____ 8. solubility

_____ 9. saturated solution

_____ 10. unsaturated solution

_____ 11. supersaturated solution

a. a measure of how much solute can dissolve in a solvent at a given temperature

b. a solution that has more dissolved solute than is predicted by its solubility

c. a solution that has so much solute that no more dissolves

d. a solution that has only a little solute

e. a solution in which more solute can be dissolved

f. a solution that has a lot of solute

Acids, Bases, and Solutions

© Pearson Education, Inc., publishing as Pearson Prentice Hall. All rights reserved.

Name _____ Date _____ Class _____

Temperature and Solubility

One of the factors that affects the solubility of a substance is temperature. The graph below shows how the solubilities of different solids change with the temperature of water.

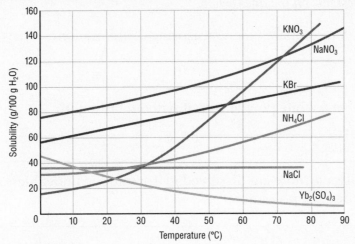

The next graph shows how the solubilities of different gases change with the temperature of water..

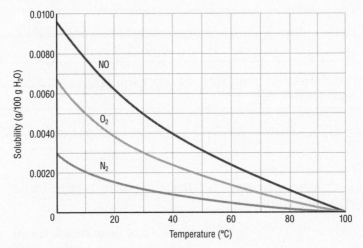

Answer the following questions on a separate sheet of paper.

1. What are the manipulated variables and the responding variables on each graph?
2. What are the general trends in solubility implied by the two graphs?
3. Do all of the solids in the first graph follow the trend? Explain.
4. Which solid shows the greatest change in solubility with temperature?
5. At higher temperatures, gas particles move faster. Use this behavior to explain the change in solubility of gases.

© Pearson Education, Inc., publishing as Pearson Prentice Hall. All rights reserved.

Describing Acids and Bases

2–3 periods, 1–1 1/2 blocks

Ability Levels Key
L1 Basic to Average
L2 For All Students
L3 Average to Advanced

Objectives

L.3.3.1 Name the properties of acids and bases.
L.3.3.2 Identify where acids and bases are commonly used.

Key Terms

• acid • corrosive • indicator • base

Local Standards

PRETEACH

Build Background Knowledge
Students identify sour taste as a common property of acids in lemons and vinegar.

 **Discover Activity** *What Colors Does Litmus Paper Turn?* **L1**

Targeted Resources

❏ **All in One** Teaching Resources
   L2 Reading Strategy Transparency L33: Asking Questions
❏ 💿 **Presentation-Pro CD-ROM**

INSTRUCT

Properties of Acids Introduce properties of acids, and give students examples of acids that demonstrate the properties.
Properties of Bases Guide students in inferring the properties of bases, based on the description of bases as the "opposite" of acids.
Uses of Acids and Bases Use Figures 15 and 16 to help students identify uses of specific acids and bases.

Targeted Resources

❏ **All in One** Teaching Resources
   L2 Guided Reading, pp. 203–204
❏ **www.SciLinks.org** Web Code: scn-1233
❏ 💿 **Student Edition on Audio CD**

ASSESS

Section Assessment Questions
🕑 Have students use their completed graphic organizers to answer the questions.

Reteach
Students help make a concept map showing the properties and uses of acids and bases.

Targeted Resources

❏ **All in One** Teaching Resources
   Section Summary, p. 202
   L1 Review and Reinforce, p. 205
   L3 Enrich, p. 206

Acids, Bases, and Solutions

© Pearson Education, Inc., publishing as Pearson Prentice Hall. All rights reserved.

Acids, Bases, and Solutions • *Section Summary*

Describing Acids and Bases

Guide for Reading

■ What are the properties of acids and bases?

■ Where are acids and bases commonly used?

Acids are compounds whose characteristic properties include the kinds of reactions they undergo. **An acid is a substance that tastes sour, reacts with metals and carbonates, and turns blue litmus paper red.** Acids react with certain metals to produce hydrogen gas. Acids are described as **corrosive**, meaning they "eat away" at other materials. Acids also react with carbonate ions in a characteristic way. Carbonate ions have carbon and oxygen atoms bonded together. When acids react with compounds made of carbonates, a carbon dioxide gas forms.

Litmus is an example of an **indicator**, a compound that changes color when in contact with an acid or a base. Sometimes chemists use other indicators to test for acids and bases, but litmus is one of the easiest to use.

Bases are another group of compounds that can be identified by their common properties. **A base is a substance that tastes bitter, feels slippery, and turns red litmus paper blue.** Bases are often described as the "opposites" of acids. Unlike acids, bases don't react with metals or carbonates. Bases do react with acids.

Acids and bases are found almost anywhere. Acids are found in many fruits and other foods. Many acids have important roles in the body. **Acids and bases have many uses around the home and in industry.** Many of the uses of bases take advantage of their ability to react with acids.

© Pearson Education, Inc., publishing as Pearson Prentice Hall. All rights reserved.

Acids, Bases, and Solutions • *Guided Reading and Study*

Describing Acids and Bases

This section describes properties of compounds called acids and bases.

Use Target Reading Skills

Before your read, preview the red headings. In the graphic organizer below, ask a what question for each heading. As you read, write the answers to your questions.

Describing Acids and Bases

Question	Answer
What is an acid?	An acid is . . .

Properties of Acids

1. What are three characteristic properties of an acid?

   a. _____

   b. _____

   c. _____

2. Why would you never use "sour taste" to identify a compound as acidic?

   _____

   _____

   _____

© Pearson Education, Inc., publishing as Pearson Prentice Hall. All rights reserved.

Acids, Bases, and Solutions

Name _____ Date _____ Class _____

Acids, Bases, and Solutions • *Guided Reading and Study*

Describing Acids and Bases (continued)

3. Why are acids often described as corrosive?

_____

_____

4. What happens when acids react with compounds made of carbonates?

_____

_____

5. A compound that changes color when in contact with an acid or a base
is called a(n) _____.

6. Why does lemon juice turn blue litmus paper red?

_____

_____

_____

Properties of Bases

7. What three properties are characteristic of a base?

a. _____

b. _____

c. _____

8. Is the following sentence true or false? A safe way to identify a base is to
feel it. _____

Uses of Acids and Bases

9. Is the following sentence true or false? Acids are found in many foods.

_____

10. Acids and bases have many uses around the _____
and in _____.

11. Many of the uses of bases take advantage of their ability to react with

_____

© Pearson Education, Inc., publishing as Pearson Prentice Hall. All rights reserved.

Acids, Bases, and Solutions ▪ *Review and Reinforce*

Describing Acids and Bases

Understanding Main Ideas

Complete the following table.

Characteristic	Acid	Base
When Found in Foods, What Does It Taste Like?	1.	2.
How Does It React With the Metals Magnesium, Zinc, and Iron?	3.	4.
How Does It React with Carbonates?	5.	6.
What Color Does It Turn Litmus?	7.	8.

Building Vocabulary

Answer the following questions in the spaces provided.

9. What does *corrosive* mean?

_____

_____

10. If a substance reacts with a metal to produce hydrogen gas, what may you infer about the substance?

_____

_____

11. What is an indicator?

_____

_____

12. Why do you think bases are often described as the "opposites" of acids?

_____

_____

_____

© Pearson Education, Inc., publishing as Pearson Prentice Hall. All rights reserved.

Acids, Bases, and Solutions

Acids, Bases, and Solutions · *Enrich*

Acidic Paper

From the fifteenth through the eighteenth centuries, the paper in many books was made from linen. Linen is made from the fibers of flax plants. By the nineteenth century, the printing of books had increased dramatically and, as a result, so did the demand for inexpensive paper. In response, a method was developed to produce cheap paper from wood. This process involved the use of a chemical called *alum*, which greatly increased the acidity of paper. Eventually, this acidity causes such paper to become brittle and fall apart. Thus, many books made during the ninteenth and twentieth centuries are slowly becoming too fragile to read, while older books made with linen paper are often in better condition.

Scientists have developed several chemical methods to preserve books made with acidic paper. These methods involve reacting the acid in the paper with a base. The products of these reactions are not acidic, and so the paper is protected from further damage due to acidity. The diagram below illustrates one of these processes. Today, some publishers use acid-free paper in their books. In fact, important documents are sometimes printed on paper that is basic rather than acidic.

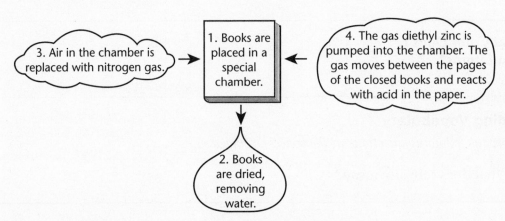

Answer the following questions on a separate sheet of paper.

1. The bases used to treat books containing acidic paper are usually gases rather liquid solutions. Why do you think this is so?

2. Is paper made from linen more or less acidic than paper made from wood? Which type of paper lasts longer?

3. Why do you think that printing a document on basic paper will help to ensure that it lasts for a very long time?

4. How might the process of making paper from wood be changed to produce paper that is not acidic?

© Pearson Education, Inc., publishing as Pearson Prentice Hall. All rights reserved.

Acids and Bases in Solution

⏱ *3–4 periods, 1 1/2–2 blocks*

Ability Levels Key
L1 Basic to Average
L2 For All Students
L3 Average to Advanced

Objectives

L.3.4.1 State what kinds of ions acids and bases form in water.

L.3.4.2 Explain what pH tells you about a solution.

L.3.4.3 Describe what happens in a neutralization reaction.

Key Terms

• hydrogen ion (H^+) • hydroxide ion (OH^-)
• pH scale • neutralization • salt

Local Standards

PRETEACH

Build Background Knowledge
Students answer questions about a common acid solution as an introduction to acids and bases in solution.

 **Discover Activity** *What Can Cabbage Juice Tell You?* **L1**

Targeted Resources

❏ **All in One Teaching Resources**
  L2 Reading Strategy Transparency L34: Previewing Visuals
❏ ◎ **Presentation-Pro CD-ROM**

INSTRUCT

Acids and Bases in Solution Guide students in understanding how acids and bases produce ions in water.
Strength of Acids and Bases Use a questioning strategy to help students recognize what determines the strength of acids and bases.
Acid-Base Reactions Define and discuss neutralization.

 **Consumer Lab** *The Antacid Test* **L2**

Targeted Resources

❏ **All in One Teaching Resources**
  L2 Guided Reading, pp. 209–211
  L2 Transparencies L35, L36, L37, L38
  L2 Lab: *The Antacid Test*, pp. 214–217
❏ 📼 **Lab Activity Video/DVD**
  Consumer Lab: *The Antacid Test*
❏ **PHSchool.com** Web Code: cgd-2034
❏ ◎ **Student Edition on Audio CD**

ASSESS

Section Assessment Questions
🔄 Have students use their completed graphic organizers to answer the questions.

Reteach
Students use the key terms in sentences.

Targeted Resources

❏ **All in One Teaching Resources**
  Section Summary, p. 208
  L1 Review and Reinforce, p. 212
  L3 Enrich, p. 213

Acids, Bases, and Solutions

© Pearson Education, Inc., publishing as Pearson Prentice Hall. All rights reserved.

Name _____ Date _____ Class _____

Acids, Bases, and Solutions · *Section Summary*

Acids and Bases in Solution

Guide for Reading

- What kinds of ions do acids and bases form in water?

- What does pH tell you about a solution?

- What happens in a neutralization reaction?

Many acids have formulas that begin with hydrogen. The acids you will learn about are made of hydrogen ions and various kinds of negative ions in solution with water. A **hydrogen ion (H^+)** is an atom of hydrogen that has lost its electron. **An acid is any substance that produces hydrogen ions (H^+) in water.** Hydrogen ions cause the properties of acids.

Many bases are made of positive ions combined with hydroxide ions. The **hydroxide ion (OH^-)** is made of oxygen and hydrogen. It has a negative charge. When bases dissolve in water, the positive ions and hydroxide ions separate. **A base is any substance that produces hydroxide ions (OH^-) in water.** Hydroxide ions are responsible for the bitter taste and slippery feel of bases. Hydroxide ions also turn red litmus paper blue.

Acids and bases may be strong or weak. Strength refers to how well an acid or base produces ions in water. In a strong acid, most of the molecules react to form ions in solution. In a weak acid, fewer molecules react. Similarly, strong bases produce more OH^- ions in solution than equal concentrations of weak bases.

Chemists use a numeric scale called pH to describe the concentration of hydrogen ions in a solution. The **pH scale** is a range of values from 0 to 14. **A low pH tells you that the concentration of hydrogen ions is high. In contrast, a high pH tells you that the concentration of hydrogen ions is low.** When the pH is low, the concentration of hydrogen ions is high. A solution with a pH lower than 7 is acidic. A solution with a pH higher than 7 is basic. If the pH is exactly 7, the solution is neutral.

A reaction between an acid and a base is called a **neutralization**. After neutralization, an acid-base mixture is not as acidic or basic as the individual starting solutions were.

A **salt** is any ionic compound made from the neutralization of an acid with a base. A salt is made of the positive ion of a base and the negative ion of an acid. **In a neutralization reaction an acid reacts with a base to produce a salt and water.**

© Pearson Education, Inc., publishing as Pearson Prentice Hall. All rights reserved.

Acids and Bases in Solution

This section explains what kinds of ions acids and bases form in water. It also describes how the concentrations of ions are measured in a solution.

Use Target Reading Skills

Before you read, preview the diagram in your textbook that shows a neutralization reaction. Then, complete the graphic organizer by writing two questions about the diagram. As you read, answer your questions.

Neutralization

Q. What is a neutral solution?
A.
Q.
A.

Acids and Bases in Solution

1. What is a hydrogen ion (H^+)?

   _____

   _____

   _____

2. What do acids in water separate into?

   _____

3. Any substance that produces hydrogen ions (H^+) in water can be called a(n)

   _____.

4. What is a hydroxide ion (OH^-)?

   _____

   _____

© Pearson Education, Inc., publishing as Pearson Prentice Hall. All rights reserved.

Acids and Bases in Solution *(continued)*

5. Any substance that produces hydroxide ions (OH^-) in water can be called a(n) _____.

Strength of Acids and Bases

6. Circle the letter of each sentence that is true about the strength of acids and bases.

   a. A strong base produces more OH^- ions than a weak base.
   b. A weak acid produces more OH^- ions than a strong acid.
   c. A strong acid produces more H^+ ions than a weak acid.
   d. A weak base produces more H^+ ions than a strong base.

7. What is the pH scale?

   _____

   _____

   _____

8. On the scale below, add labels to show the pH of these substances: milk, soap, water, vinegar, lemon, and ammonia.

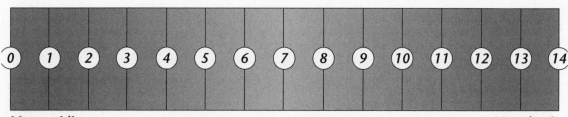

Most acidic   *Most basic*

9. Is the following sentence true or false? A strong acid is safe as long as it's in a dilute solution. _____

10. When the pH of a solution is low, is the concentration of hydrogen ions high or low? _____

11. Circle the letter of each sentence that is true about pH.

    a. A pH lower than 7 is acidic.
    b. A pH of 7 is neutral.
    c. A pH lower than 7 is basic.
    d. A pH higher than 7 is acidic.

© Pearson Education, Inc., publishing as Pearson Prentice Hall. All rights reserved.

Acids, Bases, and Solutions · *Guided Reading and Study*

Acid-Base Reactions

12. A reaction between an acid and a base is called a(n)

_____.

13. Is the following sentence true or false? An acid-base mixture is always more acidic than the starting solutions were. _____

14. What is a salt?

_____

_____

_____

15. What two substances does a neutralization reaction produce?

a. _____

b. _____

© Pearson Education, Inc., publishing as Pearson Prentice Hall. All rights reserved.

Acids, Bases, and Solutions • *Review and Reinforce*

Acids and Bases in Solution

Understanding Main Ideas

Complete the concept map shown below and answer the following questions on a separate sheet of paper.

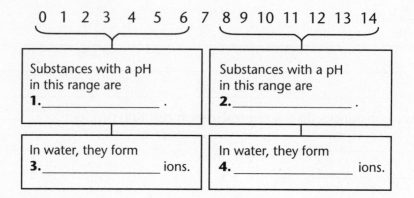

0 1 2 3 4 5 6 7 8 9 10 11 12 13 14

Substances with a pH in this range are
1. _____ .

In water, they form
3. _____ ions.

Substances with a pH in this range are
2. _____ .

In water, they form
4. _____ ions.

5. What is the difference between a strong acid and a weak acid?

6. What is the difference between a strong base and a weak base?

7. Which solution has a greater concentration of hydrogen ions (H^+), a solution with a pH of 3 or one with a pH of 7? Explain.

8. What are the products formed when a base reacts with an acid?

9. What is the pH of a neutral solution?

Building Vocabulary

Match each term with its definition by writing the letter of the correct symbol or definition on the line beside the term in the left column.

_____ **10.** hydroxide ion

_____ **11.** pH scale

_____ **12.** hydrogen ion

_____ **13.** neutralization

_____ **14.** salt

a. ionic compound that can form from the reaction of an acid with a base

b. reaction between an acid and a base

c. series of numbers that indicates the concentration of hydrogen ions in solution

d. H^+

e. OH^-

© Pearson Education, Inc., publishing as Pearson Prentice Hall. All rights reserved.

Acids, Bases, and Solutions • *Enrich*

Swimming Pool Basics

If chemicals are not added to swimming pools, tiny organisms such as bacteria and algae can multiply in the water. Algae growth can turn the water in a swimming pool cloudy and make the sides and bottom of the pool slimy. Disease-causing bacteria can make swimmers sick. One chemical added to pools contains hypochlorite ions (OCl^-). A hypochlorite ion reacts with water in the pool to produce hypochlorous acid ($HOCl$) and a hydroxide ion. Hypochlorous acid kills algae and bacteria. The equation for this reaction is:

OCl^-	+	H_2O	$\rightarrow$	$HOCl$	+	OH^-
Hypochlorite ion		Water		Hypochlorous acid		Hydroxide ion

The amount of hypochlorous acid that is produced by this reaction depends on the pH of the pool water. The ideal pH for the above reaction is 7.4. Therefore, the pH of the pool water must be carefully controlled. If the pH is too high (above 7.6), the reverse of the reaction shown above occurs:

$HOCl$	+	OH^-	$\rightarrow$	OCl^-	+	H_2O
Hypochlorous acid		Hydroxide ion		Hypochlorite ion		Water

As a result, there will not be enough hypochlorous acid in the pool water to control the bacteria and algae. Problems also occur when the pH of the pool water is too low (less than 7.2). Pool water having a low pH can damage the sides and bottom of the pool. Pool water having pH levels that are either too high or too low can cause eye irritation in swimmers. The graph below shows how the relative amounts of hypochlorous acid and hypochlorite ions vary with the pH of the pool water.

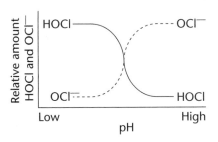

Answer the following questions on a separate sheet of paper.

1. What happens to the amount of hypochlorous acid ($HOCl$) in a swimming pool as the pH increases? What happens to the amount of hypochlorite ion (OCl^-)?

2. What type of chemical could you add to a swimming pool to decrease the pH of the water? Explain.

3. What type of chemical could you add to a swimming pool to increase the pH of the water? Explain.

© Pearson Education, Inc., publishing as Pearson Prentice Hall. All rights reserved.

Acids, Bases, and Solutions · *Consumer Lab*

The Antacid Test

Problem

Which antacid neutralizes stomach acid with the smallest number of drops?

Skills Focus

designing experiments, interpreting data, measuring

Materials

3 plastic droppers

dilute hydrochloric acid (HCl), 50 mL

liquid antacid, 30 mL of each brand tested

small plastic cups

methyl orange solution, 1 mL

Procedure  *Review the safety guidelines in Appendix A of your textbook.*

Part 1

1. Using a plastic dropper, put 10 drops of hydrochloric acid (HCl) into one cup. **CAUTION:** *HCl is corrosive. Rinse spills and splashes immediately with water.*

2. Use another plastic dropper to put 10 drops of liquid antacid into another cup.

3. Record the colors of HCl and the antacid in the data table on the next page.

4. Add 2 drops of methyl orange solution to each cup. Record the colors you see.

5. Test each of the other antacids. Discard all the solutions and cups as directed by your teacher.

© Pearson Education, Inc., publishing as Pearson Prentice Hall. All rights reserved.

Acids, Bases, and Solutions ▪ *Consumer Lab*

Part 2

6. Methyl orange changes color at a pH of about 4. Predict the color of the solution you expect to see when an antacid is added to a mixture of methyl orange and HCl. Write your prediction on the lines below.

_____

_____

_____

_____

7. Design a procedure for testing the reaction of each antacid with HCl. Decide how many drops of acid and methyl orange you need to use each time.

8. Devise a plan for adding the antacid so that you can detect when a change occurs. Decide how much antacid to add each time and how to mix the solutions in order to be sure the indicator is giving accurate results.

9. Make a second data table to record your observations.

10. Carry out your procedure and record your results.

11. Discard the solutions and cups as directed by your teacher. Rinse the plastic droppers thoroughly.

12. Wash your hands thoroughly when done.

Data Table

Substance	Original Color	Color With Indicator
HCl		
Antacid Brand A		
Antacid Brand B		

© Pearson Education, Inc., publishing as Pearson Prentice Hall. All rights reserved.

Acids, Bases, and Solutions

Name _____ Date _____ Class _____

Acids, Bases, and Solutions ▪ *Consumer Lab*

The Antacid Test *(continued)*

Analyze and Conclude
Write your answers in the spaces below.

1. **Designing Experiments** What is the function of the methyl orange solution?

   _____

   _____

   _____

2. **Interpreting Data** Do your observations support your predictions from Step 6? Explain why or why not.

   _____

   _____

   _____

   _____

3. **Inferring** Why do you think antacids reduce stomach acid? Explain your answer, using the observations you made.

   _____

   _____

   _____

   _____

4. **Controlling Variables** Explain why it is important to use the same number of drops of HCl in each trial.

   _____

   _____

   _____

   _____

5. **Measuring** Which antacid neutralized the HCl with the smallest number of drops? Give a possible explanation for the difference.

   _____

   _____

   _____

6. **Calculating** If you have the same volume (number of drops) of each antacid, which one can neutralize the most acid?

   _____

© Pearson Education, Inc., publishing as Pearson Prentice Hall. All rights reserved.

Acids, Bases, and Solutions • *Consumer Lab*

7. **Drawing Conclusions** Did your procedure give results from which you could draw conclusions about which brand of antacid was most effective? Explain why or why not.

_____

_____

_____

_____

_____

8. **Communicating** Write a brochure that explains to consumers what information they need to know in order to decide which brand of antacid is the best buy.

_____

_____

_____

_____

_____

_____

_____

_____

_____

_____

_____

_____

_____

_____

_____

_____

_____

_____

Design an Experiment

A company that sells a liquid antacid claims that its product works faster than tablets to neutralize stomach acid. Design an experiment to compare how quickly liquid antacids and chewable antacid tablets neutralize hydrochloric acid. *Obtain your teacher's permission before carrying out your investigation.*

© Pearson Education, Inc., publishing as Pearson Prentice Hall. All rights reserved.

Digestion and pH

Ability Levels Key
L1 Basic to Average
L2 For All Students
L3 Average to Advanced

1–2 periods, 1/2–1 block

Objectives
L.3.5.1 Explain why the body must digest food.
L.3.5.2 Describe how pH affects digestion.

Key Terms
• digestion • mechanical digestion
• chemical digestion

Local Standards

PRETEACH

Build Background Knowledge
Students use their knowledge of hydrochloric
acid to predict its role in digestion.

 **Discover Activity** *Where Does Digestion
Begin?* **L1**

Targeted Resources

❑ **All in One Teaching Resources**
  L2 Reading Strategy Transparency L39:
  Sequencing
❑ ⊙ **Presentation-Pro CD-ROM**

INSTRUCT

What Is Digestion? Work with students to
compare and contrast mechanical and chemical
digestion.
pH in the Digestive System Use the diagram of
the digestive system to tell what the pH is at
particular locations. Help students infer why pH
changes.

Targeted Resources

❑ **All in One Teaching Resources**
  L2 Guided Reading, pp. 220–221
  L2 Transparency L40
❑ **www.SciLinks.org** Web Code: scn-1235
❑ ⊙ **Student Edition on Audio CD**

ASSESS

Section Assessment Questions
↻ Have students use their completed flow-
charts to answer the questions.

Reteach
Students fill in the missing information in an
overhead transparency of the digestive system
without the labels.

Targeted Resources

❑ **All in One Teaching Resources**
  Section Summary, p. 219
  L1 Review and Reinforce, p. 222
  L3 Enrich, p. 223

© Pearson Education, Inc., publishing as Pearson Prentice Hall. All rights reserved.

Acids, Bases, and Solutions · *Section Summary*

Digestion and pH

Guide for Reading

- Why must your body digest food?

- How does pH affect digestion?

Foods must be broken down into simpler substances that your body can use for raw materials and energy. The process of **digestion** breaks down the complex molecules of food into smaller molecules.

Digestion involves two parts—mechanical and chemical digestion. **Mechanical digestion** is a physical process in which large pieces of food are torn and ground into smaller pieces. The size of the food is reduced, but the foods aren't changed into other compounds. **Chemical digestion** breaks large molecules into smaller molecules. Some molecules provide your body with energy. Others serve as building blocks for the molecules in muscle, bone, blood, skin, and other organs. Chemical digestion takes place with the help of enzymes, catalysts that speed up reactions in living things. **Some digestive enzymes work at a low pH. For others, the pH must be high or neutral.**

Digestion begins in your mouth. Your teeth chew and mash the food. The food gets wet with a fluid called saliva. Saliva has a pH near 7, the neutral point. Saliva contains amylase, an enzyme that helps break down the carbohydrate starch into smaller sugar molecules. Amylase works best when the pH is near 7.

Next, the food is swallowed and arrives in your stomach. This muscular organ starts the chemical digestion of foods that contain protein. Cells in the lining of your stomach release enzymes and hydrochloric acid. The pH in your stomach is very acidic—about 2. The main enzyme that works in your stomach is pepsin. It helps break down proteins into small molecules called amino acids. Pepsin works best in acids.

Your stomach empties its contents into the small intestine. Here, other digestive fluids containing bicarbonate ions surround the food. These ions create a slightly basic solution—the pH in the small intestine is about 8. Enzymes in the small intestine complete the breakdown of carbohydrates, fats, and proteins. These enzymes work best in a slightly basic solution.

Acids, Bases, and Solutions

© Pearson Education, Inc., publishing as Pearson Prentice Hall. All rights reserved.

Acids, Bases, and Solutions • *Guided Reading and Study*

Digestion and pH

This section explains why it is necessary for your body to digest food. It also explains how pH affects digestion.

Use Target Reading Skills

As you read about how pH changes as food moves through the digestive system, fill in the flowchart to show the steps in the process.

pH During Digestion

At a pH near 7, enzymes in the **a.** _____ start to break down carbohydrates.

↓

At a pH near **b.** _____ stomach enzymes break down **c.** _____ .

↓

d. _____

_____

_____

What Is Digestion?

1. The process that breaks down the complex molecules of foods into smaller molecules is called _____ .

2. Why must foods be broken down in your body?

_____

_____

_____

3. Complete the table about the two processes of digestion.

Digestion	
Digestive Process	**Description**
a. Mechanical digestion	
b. Chemical digestion	

© Pearson Education, Inc., publishing as Pearson Prentice Hall. All rights reserved.

4. Circle the letter of each sentence that is true about digestive enzymes.

   a. Enzymes require just the right temperature and pH to work.
   b. The pH must be neutral for all enzymes to work.
   c. Some enzymes require the pH to be high.
   d. Some enzymes require the pH to be low.

pH in the Digestive System

5. Is the following sentence true or false? The pH is not the same in all parts of the digestive system. _____

6. What is amylase?

   _____

   _____

7. Amylase works best when the pH is near _____.

8. The stomach begins the chemical digestion of foods containing

   _____.

9. What occurs in your stomach that drops the pH to a very acidic level of about 2 ?

   _____

   _____

   _____

10. What does pepsin do?

    _____

    _____

11. Why is the pH in the small intestine about 8?

    _____

    _____

    _____

12. Is the following sentence true or false? Enzymes in the small intestine work best in a slightly basic solution. _____

13. Most chemical digestion is completed in the _____.

© Pearson Education, Inc., publishing as Pearson Prentice Hall. All rights reserved.

Name _____ Date _____ Class _____

Digestion and pH

Understanding Main Ideas

Label the diagram as directed below and answer the questions in the spaces provided.

a._____

b._____

c._____

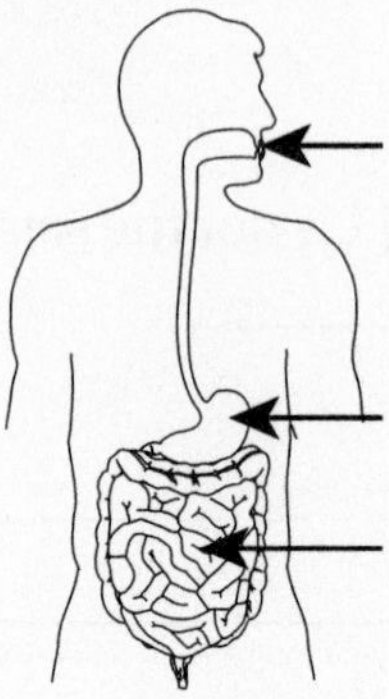

1. Label parts a, b, and c in the diagram above.
2. Beneath each label, write the pH of the fluids in that part of the digestive system.
3. What is the purpose of digestion?

   _____

   _____

4. Why are the differences in the pH of the mouth, stomach, and small intestine important for digestion?

   _____

   _____

Building Vocabulary

Define each of the following terms in the spaces provided.

5. digestion

   _____

   _____

6. mechanical digestion

   _____

   _____

7. chemical digestion

   _____

   _____

© Pearson Education, Inc., publishing as Pearson Prentice Hall. All rights reserved.

Acids, Bases, and Solutions · *Enrich*

Blood and pH

You learned that pH varies within the digestive system. In other organ systems, however, it is important that pH remain constant. For example, blood pH is about 7.4 throughout the circulatory system. Serious medical conditions and even death can result if the blood's pH rises or falls outside a narrow range.

In blood, pH is maintained by the interaction of carbonic acid (H_2CO_3), bicarbonate ion ($HCO3^-$), hydrogen ion (H^+), and carbon dioxide (CO_2). The table below describes what happens when blood pH becomes too low or too high.

What Happens When Blood pH is Low	What Happens When Blood pH is High
1. Hydrogen ions react with bicarbonate ions to produce carbonic acid. $H^+ + HCO_3^- \rightarrow H_2CO_3$	**1.** The breathing rate decreases, so less carbon dioxide is exhaled from the body.
2. Carbonic acid decomposes to produce carbon dioxide and water. $H_2CO_3 \rightarrow CO_2 + H_2O$	**2.** The concentration of carbon dioxide in the blood increases.
3. The concentration of carbon dioxide in the blood increases.	**3.** Carbon dioxide and water in the blood react to produce carbonic acid. $CO_2 + H_2O \rightarrow H_2CO_3$
4. Increased carbon dioxide in the blood causes the breathing rate to increase. More carbon dioxide is exhaled from the body.	**4.** Carbonic acid dissolves to produce hydrogen ions and bicarbonate ions. $H_2CO_3 \rightarrow H^+ + HCO_3-$

Answer the following questions on a separate sheet of paper.

1. How do the reactions on the left side of the table compare with the reactions on the right side of the table?
2. Which reaction removes hydrogen ions from the blood? Which reaction adds hydrogen ions?
3. When molecules in food react in cells to produce energy, carbon dioxide forms as a waste product. The carbon dioxide then enters the blood. How could this addition of carbon dioxide lead to a decrease in blood pH?
4. The reaction of carbon dioxide and water to produce carbonic acid occurs very slowly unless a specific enzyme is present. How would a person who lacked this enzyme be affected?

© Pearson Education, Inc., publishing as Pearson Prentice Hall. All rights reserved.

Key Terms

Match each definition in the left column with the correct term in the right column. Then write the number of each term in the appropriate box below. When you have filled in all the boxes, add up the numbers in each column, row, and two diagonals. All the sums should be the same.

A. A very well-mixed mixture

B. The part of a solution that is present in the smaller amount

C. A compound that changes color when in contact with an acid or a base

D. A substance that turns blue litmus paper red

E. A mixture that has a lot of solute dissolved in it

F. A negative ion made of oxygen and hydrogen

G. A process that breaks down the complex molecules of food into smaller molecules

H. The part of a solution that is present in the larger amount

I. Any ionic compound made from the neutralization of an acid with a base

1. solute

2. digestion

3. hydroxide ion (OH^-)

4. salt

5. concentrated solution

6. solution

7. acid

8. indicator

9. solvent

A. _____	**B.** _____	**C.** _____
D. _____	**E.** _____	**F.** _____
G. _____	**H.** _____	**I.** _____

= _____

= _____

= _____

= _____

= _____   = _____   = _____

_____   _____   _____   = _____

© Pearson Education, Inc., publishing as Pearson Prentice Hall. All rights reserved.

Acids, Bases, and Solutions • *Connecting Concepts*

Connecting Concepts

Develop a concept map that uses Key Concepts and Key Terms from this chapter. The concept map shown is one way to organize how the information in this chapter is related. You may use an extra sheet of paper.

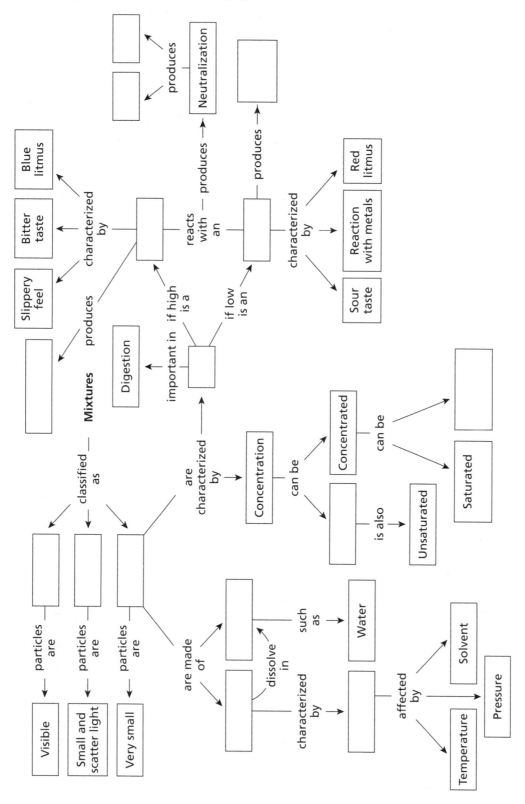

© Pearson Education, Inc., publishing as Pearson Prentice Hall. All rights reserved.

Acids, Bases, and Solutions

Determining Solubility

Key Concept

Solubility is a measure of how much of a given material will dissolve in a particular solvent under a determined set of conditions.

Skills Focus

inferring, measuring, calculating, graphing

Time

40 minutes

Materials

small piece of paper, about 15 cm × 15 cm

balance

25 g potassium nitrate

10-mL graduated cylinder

tongs

2 test tubes

thermometer

hot plate

two 250-mL beakers

ice

spatula

Safety

Remind students to use tongs or wear oven mitts when handling hot glassware.

Alternate Materials

You could substitute other nitrates for potassium nitrate, but they don't have as large a range of solubility over a wide temperature range.

Teaching Tips

Assign each student one temperature above room temperature and one below. The class as a whole should test a variety of different temperatures between 0°C and 100°C.

© Pearson Education, Inc., publishing as Pearson Prentice Hall. All rights reserved.

Acids, Bases, and Solutions ▪ *Laboratory Investigation*

Determining Solubility

Pre-Lab Discussion

Solubility is how much of a solid can dissolve in a liquid. Suppose, for example, you stir salt (the solute) into a glass of water (the solvent) a little at a time. The salt dissolves until the saltwater solution is saturated. After that, added salt crystals will no longer disappear.

Now suppose you took an identical glass of water and made a saturated solution of sugar. You could stir in a lot more sugar than salt before the solution becomes saturated. In fact, you could tell the two samples apart by observing how much of each dissolves in the same amount of water. The water has to be the same temperature, however, or your results would not be comparable. The amount of sugar that could dissolve in cold water is different than the amount that can dissolve in the same amount of warm water.

In this investigation, you will determine the amount of a solute that can dissolve in water at different temperatures.

1. What is a solution?

   _____

   _____

2. What is a saturated solution?

   _____

   _____

3. How do you know when a solution is saturated?

   _____

   _____

Problem

How can you determine the solubility of a substance in water?

Materials

small piece of paper, about 15 cm × 15 cm

balance

25 g potassium nitrate

10-mL graduated cylinder

tongs

2 test tubes

thermometer

hot plate

two 250-mL beakers

ice

spatula

© Pearson Education, Inc., publishing as Pearson Prentice Hall. All rights reserved.

Acids, Bases, and Solutions

Acids, Bases, and Solutions • *Laboratory Investigation*

Determining Solubility (continued)

Safety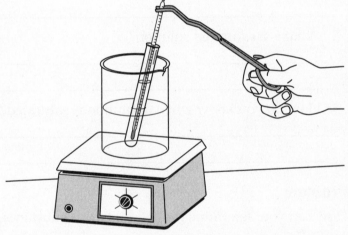

Review the safety guidelines in Appendix A of your textbook.

Handle the thermometer carefully. If it breaks, tell the teacher. Use tongs or an oven mitt when handling hot objects.

Procedure

1. Your teacher will assign you a high and a low temperature to use in the lab.

2. Use a balance to find the mass of the small sheet of plain paper. In the Data Table on the next page, record the mass of the paper.

3. Adjust the balance so that it registers 25 g more than the mass of the paper alone. Slowly and carefully add potassium nitrate to the paper until the balance is again level. In this way, you have poured out 25 g of potassium nitrate. Record this amount in the Data Table. Add and record the total mass of the paper and potassium nitrate.

4. Pour 10 mL of water into a test tube. Put the test tube in a half-filled beaker of water. Place the beaker on the hot plate. See Figure 1. Insert a thermometer in the test tube. You will need to hold the thermometer so that the end is in the water but not touching the bottom.

5. Heat the test tube in the water bath over the hot plate until the water reaches the high temperature assigned to you. **CAUTION:** *Use tongs to hold the thermometer in the test tube. Try to maintain this temperature during the next step by adjusting the dial on the hot plate.*

Figure 1

6. Use as spatula to put a small amount of the 25 g of potassium nitrate into the test tube. Stir carefully with the thermometer. If the potassium nitrate dissolves completely, add a little more. Continue adding small amounts of potassium nitrate until no more dissolves and a few small grains settle to the bottom of the test tube. Now you have a saturated solution.

7. In the Data Table, record the exact temperature of the solution when it has become saturated.

8. Find the mass of the paper and the remaining potassium nitrate. Subtract this amount from the mass before dissolving to find the amount of potassium nitrate you used. Record the amount used in the Data Table.

© Pearson Education, Inc., publishing as Pearson Prentice Hall. All rights reserved.

Acids, Bases, and Solutions ▪ *Laboratory Investigation*

9. Half-fill a beaker with ice. Pour 10 mL of water into another test tube. Set the test tube on the ice. Insert a thermometer so that the end is in the water but not touching the bottom. Cool the water until it reaches the second temperature assigned to you. Try to maintain this temperature during the next step by periodically removing the test tube from the ice.

10. Repeat steps 6–8.

11. Report your data to your teacher, who will compile all the information obtained by the class. In this way, you will find out how much potassium nitrate dissolves in 10 mL of water over a wide temperature range.

12. Graph the class's results on the grid provided in Observations.

Observations

Data Table

Mass of paper	
Mass of potassium nitrate	
Mass of paper and potassium nitrate before dissolving	
Temperature of heated solution when saturated	
Mass of paper and potassium nitrate after saturation	
Mass of potassium nitrate used to saturate	
Temperature of cooled solution	
Mass of paper and potassium nitrate before dissolving	
Mass of paper and potassium nitrate after saturation	
Mass of potassium nitrate used to saturate	

© Pearson Education, Inc., publishing as Pearson Prentice Hall. All rights reserved.

Name _____ Date _____ Class _____

Determining Solubility (continued)

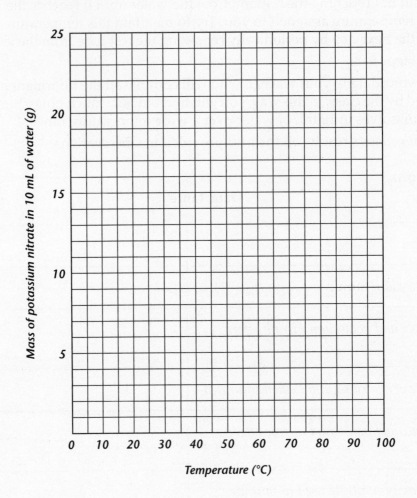

Analyze and Conclude

1. What effect does temperature have on the amount of potassium nitrate that can dissolve in a given amount of water?

_____

_____

2. From your graph, predict how much potassium nitrate would dissolve in 10 mL of water at 60°C.

3. How much potassium nitrate do you think could dissolve in 100 mL of water at 60°C? Show your calculations.

4. What temperature would 10 mL of water have to be for 14 g of potassium nitrate to just dissolve completely?

_____

© Pearson Education, Inc., publishing as Pearson Prentice Hall. All rights reserved.

Acids, Bases, and Solutions ▪ *Laboratory Investigation*

Critical Thinking and Applications

1. If the temperature of a saturated solution of potassium nitrate dropped, what would you see?

   _____

   _____

   _____

2. Based on the graph, how much potassium nitrate do you think would dissolve in 190 mL of water at 100°C? Show your calculations.

3. Suppose you measured the solubility of potassium nitrate only at 10°C and at 90°C. Would this affect the accuracy of your solubility graph? Give a reason for your answer.

   _____

   _____

   _____

   _____

   _____

4. If 10 mL of a saturated solution of potassium nitrate cooled from 60°C to 10°C, how much potassium nitrate would be on the bottom of the test tube? Show your calculations.

© Pearson Education, Inc., publishing as Pearson Prentice Hall. All rights reserved.

Acids, Bases, and Solutions

Determining Solubility *(continued)*

More to Explore

New Problem What is the solubility of sodium chloride under the same conditions as in this lab? Does its graph differ from the graph for potassium nitrate?

Materials Use the same equipment as in this lab.

Safety Handle the thermometer carefully. If it breaks, tell your teacher. Use tongs or an oven mitt when handling hot objects. Wear your safety goggles and apron.

Procedure Decide how, if at all, you should adjust the previous procedure to solve this new problem. Have the teacher approve your procedure before you carry out the investigation.

Observations Plot the data on the same graph in Observations.

Analyze and Conclude

1. How does the solubility graph for soidum chloride compare to the graph for potassium nitrate?

   _____

   _____

   _____

   _____

2. Use your graph to find the temperature at which sodium chloride and potassium nitrate have the same solubility.

   _____

   _____

   _____

   _____

© Pearson Education, Inc., publishing as Pearson Prentice Hall. All rights reserved.

Clean Money

Students are presented with the problem of determining which of four solutions is the best at cleaning pennies and whether the pH of a solution is related to its cleaning ability. To solve this problem, students will apply the concepts they have learned about pH and solutions of acids and bases.

Expected Outcome

Students will test solutions of lemon juice, vinegar, liquid soap, and baking soda. They should place four dirty pennies in each solution. Students should begin to notice color changes after 5 to 10 minutes. After students remove their pennies from the solutions, they will assign a numerical value to each penny by comparing it to a color scale. These values will indicate the cleaning ability of each solution. Students will average the results of the four pennies for each solution. They will also measure and record the pH of the solutions. In general, students should find that the best penny cleaner is lemon juice, followed by vinegar, liquid soap, and finally baking soda. Individual results may vary. The approximate pHs of the solutions are as follows: lemon juice, about 2; vinegar, between 2 and 3; baking soda, between 8 and 9; and liquid soap, about 10, depending on the brand used. Students should use their results to draw a conclusion about how the pH of a solution is related to its cleaning ability.

Content Assessed

This activity tests students' understanding of pH and acidic and basic solutions.

Skills Assessed

developing a hypothesis, designing an experiment, controlling variables, drawing conclusions, applying concepts

Materials

Each student will need 16 discolored pennies. The pennies should rank darkest on the color scale described in Advance Preparation.

Each student will also need four paper cups, one or two stirring rods, paper towels, a spoon, water, and pH testing paper with a pH color scale.

One bottle of vinegar, one box of baking soda, and one container of liquid hand soap should be sufficient for the entire class. You may wish to supply students with fresh lemons or bottled lemon juice, depending on cost and availability. Several students will be able to share a single penny color scale.

Advance Preparation

To make a penny color scale, glue 8 to 10 pennies to a strip of cardboard. The first penny on the scale should be the brightest and shiniest. The last penny on the scale should be the darkest. The rest of the pennies should be arranged between these two according to how bright or dark they are. Write a number under each penny with 1 being the brightest and 8 or 10 being the darkest.

Time

40 minutes

Monitoring the Task

Before students begin their experiments, discuss with them how they will control variables such as the length of time the pennies are left in solution, whether the pennies are put in solution face up or face down, and what side of the penny they will compare to the color scale.

© Pearson Education, Inc., publishing as Pearson Prentice Hall. All rights reserved.

Acids, Bases, and Solutions

Clean Money

In assessing students' performance, use the following rubric.

	4	3	2	1
Designing and Conducting Experiment	Student clearly states a hypothesis. Student accurately measures the pH of each solution. Student records four values for each solution and accurately averages the results. Data table is neat and complete. Student ranks the cleaners based on collected data. Student attempts to control all important variables. Student revises hypothesis if necessary.	Student states a hypothesis. Student makes a minor error in measuring the pH of the solutions. Student records four values for each solution and makes a minor error in averaging the results. Data table is complete. Student ranks the cleaners based on collected data. Student attempts to control several variables. Student revises hypothesis if necessary.	Student's hypothesis is unclear. Student makes two minor errors in measuring the pH of the solutions. Student makes more than one error in averaging the results. Data table is missing one or two pieces of data. Student ranks the cleaners, but ranking is not based on collected data. Students attempts to control one or two variables. Student does not revise hypothesis if necessary.	Student's hypothesis is incorrectly stated. Student makes one or more major errors in measuring the pH of the solutions. Student does not record all data and does not average the results. Data table is missing several pieces of data. Student incorrectly ranks the cleaners based on collected data. Student fails to control variables. Student does not revise hypothesis if necessary.
Concept Understanding	Student demonstrates a mastery of concepts related to pH and acidic and basic solutions.	Student demonstrates a good understanding of concepts related to pH and acidic and basic solutions.	Student demonstrates a partial understanding of concepts related to pH and acidic and basic solutions.	Student demonstrates a minimal understanding of concepts related to pH and acidic and basic solutions.

© Pearson Education, Inc., publishing as Pearson Prentice Hall. All rights reserved.

Name _____ Date _____ Class _____

Clean Money

Problem
How can you test solutions of vinegar, baking soda, liquid soap, and lemon juice to determine which is best at cleaning pennies?

Suggested Materials

16 discolored pennies	4 paper cups	pH testing paper with color scale
vinegar	lemon juice	
liquid soap	baking soda	paper towels
water	spoon	penny color scale

Devise a Plan

1. Form a hypothesis about whether acids or bases will clean pennies better. Record your hypothesis on a separate sheet of paper.

2. Decide how you will use the materials to test your hypothesis. You will need to make solutions of liquid soap and baking soda by mixing them with water.

3. Make a data table similar to the one shown below. Include a row for each solution. For each solution, you will test four pennies. After the pennies have been cleaned, rate the color of each penny by comparing it to the penny color scale provided by your teacher. Record these values in the columns headed Penny 1 through Penny 4. Then average the data for each set.

Solution	pH	Penny 1	Penny 2	Penny 3	Penny 4	Average
Lemon juice						
Vinegar						

4. Conduct your tests and collect your data.

Analyze and Conclude

Answer the following questions on a separate sheet of paper.

1. Which solution was the best at cleaning pennies? Which was the worst?

2. Is there a relationship between how well a solution cleaned the pennies and its pH? If so, what is this relationship? What does pH tell you about a solution?

3. Which solutions were acids and which were bases? What other properties could you use to determine if each solution was an acid or base?

© Pearson Education, Inc., publishing as Pearson Prentice Hall. All rights reserved.

Acids, Bases, and Solutions

Acids, Bases, and Solutions

Multiple Choice

Write the letter of the correct answer on the line at the left.

_____ 1. A mixture in which particles can be seen and easily separated by settling or filtration is a

    a. suspension.   **b.** solution.

    c. solute.   **d.** solvent.

_____ 2. A neutral solution has a pH of

    a. 3.   **b.** 7.

    c. 5.   **d.** 9.

_____ 3. A base

    a. tastes sour.

    b. corrodes metals.

    c. does not react with carbonates.

    d. turns litmus red.

_____ 4. Solutes lower the freezing point of water by

    a. stopping water molecules from moving.

    b. forming crystals.

    c. making it harder for water to form crystals.

    d. making the water molecules move faster.

_____ 5. A polar solvent will most likely dissolve

    a. any solute.   **b.** polar solutes.

    c. nonpolar solutes.   **d.** no solute.

_____ 6. Sodium hydroxide, potassium hydroxide, and magnesium hydroxide all produce hydroxide ions in water and are therefore

    a. salts.   **b.** acids.

    c. bases.   **d.** low in pH.

_____ 7. If you add a small amount of hydrochloric acid to 4 liters of water, what type of solution would you expect to have?

    a. concentrated solution   **b.** basic solution

    c. dilute solution   **d.** saturated solution

_____ 8. The pH scale

    a. is numbered from 1 to 12.

    b. measures the concentration of bases.

    c. measures the concentration of acids.

    d. measures the concentration of hydrogen ions.

© Pearson Education, Inc., publishing as Pearson Prentice Hall. All rights reserved.

_____ **9.** Neutralization
   a. is a reaction between an acid and a base.
   b. occurs when acid is dissolved in water.
   c. forms an acid and a base.
   d. does not change the pH of a solution.

_____ **10.** The pH in the digestive system is highest in the
   a. mouth.   **b.** stomach.
   c. small intestine.   **d.** large intestine.

Completion

Fill in the line to complete each statement.

11. If you add solute to a dilute solution, the solution becomes a more
_____ solution.

12. Acids are described as being _____, because they
dissolve some metals.

13. A(n) _____ is a substance that turns different colors
in an acid or a base.

14. A(n) _____ is a mixture containing small,
undissolved particles that do not settle out.

15. The process of chemical _____ breaks down the
complex molecules of food into smaller molecules.

True or False

If the statement is true, write true. *If it is false, change the underlined word or words
to make the statement true.*

_____ **16.** When a base reacts with an acid, water and a(n)
<u>salt</u> forms.

_____ **17.** When acids react with carbonate compounds,
<u>carbon dioxide</u> forms.

_____ **18.** A(n) <u>base</u> forms hydrogen ions when it dissolves
in water.

_____ **19.** The <u>solute</u> is the part of a solution present in the
largest amount.

_____ **20.** Solutes <u>decrease</u> the boiling point of a solvent.

© Pearson Education, Inc., publishing as Pearson Prentice Hall. All rights reserved.

Acids, Bases, and Solutions • *Chapter Test*   **Scoring Rubric**

Using Science Skills: Interpreting Diagrams

Use the diagram below to answer the following questions.

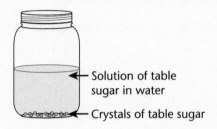

21. The jar in the diagram has been shaken and allowed to sit for a day. What can you infer about the concentration of the solution? Explain.

    _____

    _____

    _____

    _____

22. Describe the changes that would take place to the materials in the jar if the jar were to be cooled. What would happen if the jar were heated instead?

    _____

    _____

    _____

    _____

    _____

    _____

    _____

    _____

Essay

Write an answer for each of the following on a separate sheet of paper.

23. What happens to the particles of a solid solute when the solute is dissolved in a solvent?

24. Why must the pH values of the mouth, stomach, and small intestine be different?

25. In what two ways is adding antifreeze to the water in a car radiator useful?

© Pearson Education, Inc., publishing as Pearson Prentice Hall. All rights reserved.

Acids, Bases, and Solutions • *Chapter Test*   **Scoring Rubric**

Using Science Skills

Use the equation below to answer the following questions in the spaces provided.

$$NH_3 + H_2O \longrightarrow NH_4^+ + OH^-$$

26. Interpreting Diagrams Is ammonia (NH_3) an acid or a base? How do you know?

_____

_____

27. Applying Concepts If you did not know the products of the resulting solution, how could you determine whether it contains ions or a dissolved molecular solid?

_____

_____

_____

Essay

Write an answer for each of the following in the spaces provided.

28. The water in some lakes is basic because the rock underneath the lake is limestone rock made up of calcium carbonate. What chemical reaction happens when acid rain falls on a lake such as this? What happens to the lake's pH?

_____

_____

_____

_____

29. How is a weak acid different from a dilute acid?

_____

_____

_____

_____

30. How are the dissolved particles of a molecular solid, such as sugar, different from the dissolved particles of an ionic solid, such as table salt?

_____

_____

_____

_____

_____

_____

Acids, Bases, and Solutions

© Pearson Education, Inc., publishing as Pearson Prentice Hall. All rights reserved.

Chapter Project
Worksheet 1

1. Answers will vary. Sample: cherries, blueberries, and grass

2. Answers will vary. Sample: Cut 5 g of cherries into small pieces and place in blender. Blend for two minutes, adding water 2 mL at a time if the cherry mixture is too dry. Pour mixture through cheesecloth, squeezing out as much liquid as possible. Store the liquid in a labeled container in the refrigerator.

3. Answers will vary. Sample: Brand X cleaning solution, Brand Y bleach, apple juice, Brand Z baby shampoo.

Worksheet 2

1. A good indicator should show distinct colors for different pH values (e.g., bright red for a pH of 1, pink for a pH of 2, etc.). Students may notice that some of their indicators worked better for acids than bases and vice versa. Good acid and base indicators could be used together when making a test kit.

2. A bad indicator is one that either does not change for various pH values or shows only slight variations in color, for example making it difficult to distinguish a pH of 1 from a pH of 4.

3. Check that answers reflect actual experiences doing the research, including both successes and problems.

4. Answers will vary, depending on the particular indicators chosen. Check that answers reflect actual observations from the data table. Some substances may work fairly well as indicators, others may work poorly. Some indicators will only test acids, while others will test only bases. It is probable that some will only work well for strong acids or for strong bases, or a limited range of pH.

5. Answers will vary. Samples: Class presentation, poster display, demonstration of testing and results of the best indicator. The list of materials will include the substances to test, the indicators to do the testing, and test tubes and bottles to hold the substances.

Understanding Solutions
Guided Reading and Study

Use Target Reading Skills
Sample answers:

a. Detail A solvent is the part of a solution that is present in the largest amount and that dissolves other substances.

b. Detail A solute is present in a smaller amount and is dissolved by th solvent.

c. Detail Water is often called the "universal solvent" because so many substances can form solutions in water.

d. Detail Solutions can also be made with solvents other than water using any combination of gasses, liquids, or solids.

Understanding Solutions
Guided Reading and Study

1. solution
2. a. Solvent
   b. Solute
   c. Water
   d. Sugar
3. solute; solvent
4. Water dissolves so many substances.
5. false
6. A colloid is a mixture containing small, undissolved particles that do not settle out.
7. larger
8. a, c
9. A suspension is a mixture in which particles can be seen and easily separated by settling or filtration.
10. Unlike a solution, a suspension does not have the same properties throughout. It contains visible particles that are larger than the particles in solutions or colloids.
11. The particles of the solute leave each other and become surrounded by particles of the solvent.
12. c, d
13. salt solution
14. a, b

© Pearson Education, Inc., publishing as Pearson Prentice Hall. All rights reserved.

Understanding Solutions
Review and Reinforce

1. Suspension; The particles are visible and they have separated.
2. Solution; The particles are too small to see.
3. Colloid; The particles are too small to be seen, but scatter light.
4. In an ionic solid, the positive and negative ions are surrounded by water molecules. In a molecular solid, the particles break into individual neutral molecules, which are surrounded by water molecules.
5. Solutes lower the freezing point and raise the boiling point of a solvent.
6. solute
7. solvent
8. colloid
9. suspension
10. solution

Understanding Solutions
Enrich

1. The water would freeze at a higher temperature than the other ingredients do. All of the water in ice cream would exist as ice. Large crystals of ice would form, which would prevent the ice cream from having a smooth texture.
2. As the particles of the colloid clump together, the air would escape from the mixture.
3. There would be no point in adding air to the mixture until the particles became sufficiently mixed and their temperature is cool enough to trap the air.
4. Milk is more stable because it remains a colloid at a much wider range of temperatures than does ice cream.

Design Your Own Lab
Speedy Solutions

For answers, see the Teacher's Edition.

Concentration and Solubility
Guided Reading and Study

Use Target Reading Skills
Sample answers:
dilute solution: I put just a dash of salt in the boiling water while I made dinner, making a dilute solution.
concentrated solution: I left the tea bag in my cup a long time, making a concentrated solution.
solubility: My aunt's iced tea was so sweet, I wondered if sugar's solubility in water is actually higher than what I'd learned in my textbook.
saturated solution: My aunt's super sweet tea must have been a saturated solution.
unsaturated solution: On the other hand, my uncle makes a weak sweetened tea that surely must be an unsaturaed solution.
supersaturated solution: If you heated my aunt's sweet tea, I supose you might get a bit more sugar to dissolve in it, making it a supersaturated solution.

1. b
2. a
3. You can add more solute or you can add or remove solvent.
4. To measure concentration, you compare the amount of solute to the amount of solvent or to the total amount of solution.
5. Solubility is a measure of how well a solute can dissolve in a solvent at a given temperature.
6. saturated solution
7. unsaturated solution
8. sugar
9. true
10. pressure; type of solvent; temperature
11. more
12. false
13. a, b, d

Acids, Bases, and Solutions

© Pearson Education, Inc., publishing as Pearson Prentice Hall. All rights reserved.

Concentration and Solubility
Review and Reinforce

1. To measure concentration, you compare the amount of solute to the amount of solvent or to the total amount of solvent.

2. You could measure the solubility of the white powder in water at 0°C and compare it to a table of solubilities.

3. A solution under high pressure will have more gas dissolved in it.

4. Ionic and polar compounds usually dissolve in polar solvents. Nonpolar compounds do not usually dissolve in polar solvents.

5. For most solids, solubility increases as the temperature increases.

6. d

7. f

8. a

9. c

10. e

11. b

Concentration and Solubility
Enrich

1. For both graphs, solubility is the responding variable and temperature is the manipulated variable.

2. In general, the solubilities of solids increase with increasing temperature. The solubilities of gases decrease with increasing temperature.

3. No. $Yb_2(SO_4)_3$ is less soluble at higher temperatures. The solubility of NaCl is relatively constant.

4. The solubility of KNO_3 increases significantly between 30°C and 80°C.

5. The particles of a gas have much more energy at higher temperatures and escape from the liquid solvent more easily.

Describing Acids and Bases
Guided Reading and Study

Use Target Reading Skills
Sample answers:
Q. What is an acid?
A. An acid is a substance that tastes sour, reacts with metals and carbonates, and turns blue litmus paper red.
Q. What is a base?
A. A base is a substance that tastes bitter, feels slippery, and turns red litmus paper blue.
Q. What are uses of acids and bases?
A. Uses of acids include cleaning products, fertilizers, and car batteries; uses of bases include cleaning products, baking ingredients, and cement manufacturing.

1. It tastes sour. It reacts with metals and carbonates. It turns blue litmus paper red.

2. Scientists never taste chemicals in order to identify them. Many acids are not safe to eat.

3. Acids eat away at other materials.

4. Carbon dioxide gas forms.

5. indicator

6. It turns blue litmus paper red because lemon juice is acidic.

7. It tastes bitter. It feels slippery. It turns red litmus paper blue.

8. false

9. true

10. home; industry

11. acids

© Pearson Education, Inc., publishing as Pearson Prentice Hall. All rights reserved.

Describing Acids and Bases
Review and Reinforce

1. Sour
2. Bitter
3. Corrosive to magnesium, zinc, and iron; eats them away and produces bubbles of hydrogen gas
4. Doesn't react with metals
5. Produces carbon dioxide
6. Doesn't react with carbonates
7. Red
8. Blue
9. Corrosive describes a substance that can eat away certain materials.
10. The substance is an acid.
11. An indicator is a substance that turns different colors in an acid or a base.
12. Bases are bitter rather than sour, turn litmus paper blue rather than red, and don't react with metals or carbonates as acids do.

Describing Acids and Bases
Enrich

1. Answers may vary. Sample: Placing a book in a liquid solution would be much like soaking the book in water. The pages would become rippled, the ink might run, and the binding could be ruined.
2. Linen paper is less acidic than wood-based papers. Linen paper lasts much longer.
3. Basic paper would not become brittle and fall apart as acidic paper does. In addition, the base in the paper would react with any acid the paper might come into contact with.
4. Answers may vary. Samples: A base might be added after the stage in which alum is added, or a process for making paper without the chemical alum could be developed.

Acids and Bases in Solution
Guided Reading and Study

Use Target Reading Skills
Sample questions and answers:
Q. What is a neutral solution?
A. A neutral solution is one that has a pH close to 7.
Q. What is neutralization?
A. Neutralization is a reaction between an acid and a base.

1. A hydrogen ion is an atom of hydrogen that has lost its electron.
2. hydrogen ions and negative ions
3. acid
4. A hydroxide ion is a negative ion made of oxygen and hydrogen.
5. base
6. a, c
7. The pH scale is a range of values from 0 to 14. It express the concentration of hydrogen ions in a solution.
8. Milk: about 6.5; soap: 10; water: 7; vinegar: about 2.8; lemon: about 2.2; ammonia: about 11.5
9. false
10. high
11. a, b
12. neutralization
13. false
14. A salt is any ionic compound made from the neutralization of an acid with a base.
15. water; a salt

Acids, Bases, and Solutions

© Pearson Education, Inc., publishing as Pearson Prentice Hall. All rights reserved.

Acids and Bases in Solution
Review and Reinforce

1. acids
2. bases
3. hydrogen
4. hydroxide
5. In a strong acid, most of the molecules break up into ions in solution. In a weak acid, fewer molecules break up into ions.
6. In a strong base, most of the molecules break up into ions in solution. In a weak base, fewer molecules break up into ions.
7. The solution with a pH of 3 has a greater concentration of hydrogen ions. As pH values decrease, the concentration of hydrogen ions increases.
8. Water and a salt
9. 7
10. e
11. c
12. d
13. b
14. a

Acids and Bases in Solution
Enrich

1. As pH increases, the amount of hypochlorous acid decreases and the amount of hypochlorite ion increases.
2. An acid added to the water will decrease the pH. The acid will separate into hydrogen ions and negative ions. As the concentration of hydrogen ions increases, pH decreases.
3. A base added to the water will increase pH. The base will neutralize some of the acid in the water to produce water and a salt. This reaction will remove hydrogen ions from the water. As the concentration of hydrogen ions decreases, pH increases.

Consumer Lab
The Antacid Test

For answers, see the Teacher's Edition.

Digestion and pH
Guided Reading and Study

Use Target Reading Skills
Sample answers:
a. mouth
b. 2
c. proteins
d. At a pH near 8, enzymes in the small intestine complete the breakdown of carbohydrates, fats, and proteins.

1. digestion
2. Foods must be broken down into simpler substances that the body can use for raw materials and energy.
3. a. A physical process in which large pieces of food are torn and ground into smaller pieces
   b. Chemical reactions break large molecules into smaller ones.
4. a, c, d
5. true
6. Amylase is an enzyme in saliva that breaks down starch into smaller sugar molecules.
7. 7
8. proteins
9. Cells in the lining of the stomach release hydrochloric acid.
10. Pepsin breaks down proteins into amino acids.
11. Digestive fluid in the small intestine contains bicarbonate ions, which create a slightly basic solution.
12. true
13. small intestine

© Pearson Education, Inc., publishing as Pearson Prentice Hall. All rights reserved.

Digestion and pH
Review and Reinforce

1-2. a. mouth, 7

     b. stomach, 2

     c. small intestine, 8

3. Digestion supplies raw materials and energy from foods to the body.

4. The various digestive enzymes work best at different pH levels.

5. The process of breaking down complex molecules of foods into smaller molecules the body can use

6. Physical process in which large food particles are torn and ground into smaller pieces

7. Chemical process where large molecules are broken down into smaller molecules with the help of enzymes

Digestion and pH
Enrich

1. The reactions on the left side of the table are the reverse of those on the right side.

2. The reaction $H^+ + HCO_3^- \rightarrow H_2CO_3$ removes hydrogen ions. The reaction $H_2CO_3 \rightarrow H^+ + HCO_3^-$ adds hydrogen ions.

3. The carbon dioxide could react with water to produce carbonic acid. The carbonic acid could decompose to produce bicarbonate ions and hydrogen ions. The increase of hydrogen ions causes a decrease in pH.

4. Without the enzyme, less carbonic acid would be produced and fewer hydrogen ions would be produced. That means that blood pH would be high.

Key Terms

A. 6

B. 1

C. 8

D. 7

E. 5

F. 3

G. 2

H. 9

 I. 4

Sums: 15

© Pearson Education, Inc., publishing as Pearson Prentice Hall. All rights reserved.

Acids, Bases, and Solutions

Connecting Concepts

This concept map is only one way to represent the main ideas and relationships in this chapter. Accept other logical answers from students.

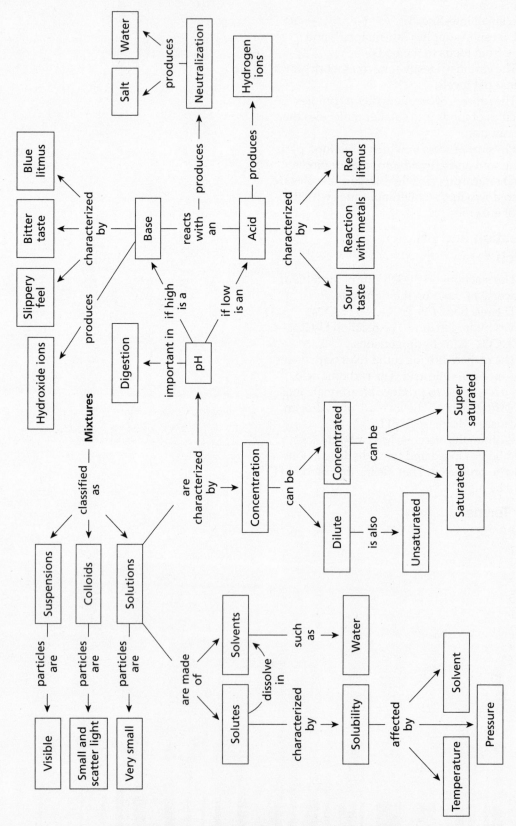

© Pearson Education, Inc., publishing as Pearson Prentice Hall. All rights reserved.

Laboratory Investigation
Determining Solubility

Pre-Lab Discussion

1. A solution is a well-mixed mixture that contains a solvent and at least one solute.

2. In a saturated solution, no more solute can be dissolved in the solvent.

3. More solute added to the solvent will not dissolve and will remain visible in the solvent.

Observations

The data in each student's table will vary depending on the temperatures you assigned. Each student should begin with 25 g of potassium nitrate. Make sure they add the mass of the paper.

The data plotted in the graph should be the same for each student as each student graphs the class data. The mass of potassium nitrate dissolved in water will increase with increasing temperature. Sample data: At 0°C, about 1.3 g of potassium nitrate will dissolve. At 60°C, about 15.3 g of potassium nitrate will dissolve. At 100°C, about 24.7 g of potassium nitrate will dissolve.

Analyze and Conclude

1. More potassium nitrate can dissolve in warmer water.

2. Answers will vary. Sample answer: About 15.3 g of potassium nitrate would dissolve.

3. The volume of water increases by a factor of 10, so the amount of solute will increase by about the same factor. For the sample data, this will be 153 g of potassium nitrate, or ten times the amount in 10 mL of water at 60°C.

4. Answers will vary. Sample answer: 54°C

Critical Thinking and Applications

1. The solubility of potassium nitrate would decrease, and some would precipitate on the bottom of the test tube.

2. Answers will vary. For the sample data, 24.7 g of potassium nitrate will dissolve in 10 mL of water at 100°C. Therefore, $19 \times 24.7 \text{ g} \cong 469$ g of potassium nitrate will dissolve in 190 mL of water at 100°C.

3. A graph of two points is a straight line. If the mathematical relationship is not linear and some curvature is actually present, the two data points won't show this relationship, and the graph would be inaccurate. In addition, the fewer data points you have, the more likely it is that measurement errors will result in an incorrect graph.

4. 15.3 g at 60°C minus 3.6 g at 10°C = 11.7 g

More to Explore

1. Compared to potassium nitrate, more sodium chloride dissolves in water at 0°C, and less dissolves in water at 100°C. So the line has a much flatter slope.

2. Sample answer: At about 10°C. Sodium chloride is much more soluble in water at lower temperatures than potassium nitrate is. But it is much less soluble than potassium nitrate at higher temperatures. Sodium chloride's solubility in water differs very little between 0°C and 100°C.

Acids, Bases, and Solutions

© Pearson Education, Inc., publishing as Pearson Prentice Hall. All rights reserved.

Performance Assessment

1. Answers may vary. Most students will find that lemon juice is the best cleaner and baking soda the worst.

2. Answers may vary. Most students will find that solutions with lower pH clean the pennies better. pH is a measure of the concentration of hydrogen ions (H^+) in a solution.

3. Lemon juice and vinegar are acids because their pH levels are less than 7. The soapy water and baking soda solutions are bases because their pH levels are greater than 7. In addition to having pH levels below 7, acids react with metals and carbonates, and turn blue litmus paper red. In addition to having pH levels above 7, bases feel slippery, and turn red litmus blue.

Chapter Test

1. a
2. b
3. c
4. c
5. b
6. c
7. c
8. d
9. a
10. c
11. concentrated
12. corrosive
13. indicator
14. colloid
15. digestion
16. true
17. true
18. acid
19. solvent
20. increase
21. You can infer that the solution is a saturated solution of sugar in water because sugar crystals remain on the bottom. This means that as much sugar as possible has dissolved in the water.
22. Cooling the jar lowers the solubility of sugar in water. Since the solution is already saturated, more of the sugar will come out of the solution as it is cooled. The amount of solid sugar on the bottom of the jar would increase. If the jar was heated (lid off, of course) instead of cooled, the solubility of sugar would increase. More sugar would dissolve, and there would be fewer or no sugar crystals on the bottom.

23. The solute particles break away from each other and become surrounded by particles of the solvent. The solute and solvent become evenly mixed.
24. The mouth, stomach, and small intestine produce enzymes that function best at specific and different pH levels. If the pH is not at the correct level for each organ, the enzymes won't be able to work and food will not be digested properly.
25. Adding antifreeze to the water lowers the freezing point and raises the boiling point. The antifreeze and water solution does not freeze in very cold weather as water alone would. It also protects the engine from overheating because it boils at a higher temperature than pure water would.
26. Ammonia is a base because it forms hydroxide ions in water.
27. If the solution is composed of ions in water, it will conduct electricity. Solutions of dissolved molecular solids do not conduct electricity.
28. A neutralization reaction takes place as the acidic rain and basic lake water react. A salt is formed, and the pH of the lake decreases.
29. A weak acid is one that doesn't easily form H^+ ions in water. A dilute acid is one in which a small amount of acid has been dissolved in water.
30. The dissolved particles of a molecular solid are completely surrounded by the solvent particles, but they remain as neutral molecules. An ionic solid in a solvent separates into positive and negative ions.

© Pearson Education, Inc., publishing as Pearson Prentice Hall. All rights reserved.

Carbon Chemistry

© Pearson Education, Inc., publishing as Pearson Prentice Hall. All rights reserved.

Lab zone Chapter Project ▶ Check Out the Fine Print

The following steps will walk you through the Chapter Project. Use the hints as you guide your students through the collection and interpretation of food labels.

Chapter Project Overview

In this project, students will collect food labels and read the ingredient lists to find carbon compounds. Then, they will classify the carbon compounds found into the categories of polymers found in living things.

Before introducing the project, read the ingredients from a familiar packaged food to the class. See if anyone can identify this food. Explain to students that even though many ingredients have long, strange-sounding names, it is possible to figure out the category of compounds the ingredient belongs to.

Have students read the Chapter Project Overview. Review the project's rules and hand out the Scoring Rubric you will use for scoring students' work. Discuss with students what is expected of them.

Set a deadline for the project presentation and interim dates for the Keep Students on Track at the ends of Section 1 and Section 3. Encourage students to copy the dates in the Project Time Line.

Before students begin collecting labels, organize them into groups. Have them brainstorm a list of packaged foods from which they can easily obtain labels. You might distribute some sample labels for the students to discuss. They should begin to identify familiar ingredients.

Distribute copies of Worksheet 1. Have students do this activity with the labels they have collected. This activity will help students evaluate the nutritional information supplied on the food labels.

Distribute Worksheet 2. This worksheet will help students organize the data on the food labels in preparation for their presentations.

Materials and Preparation

Students will need labels from packaged foods, biology textbooks, health textbooks, chemistry textbooks, and encyclopedias (*A Consumer's Dictionary of Food Additives* by Ruth Winter may be helpful).

Consider organizing the class into groups to do this project. If time is limited, you may want to have the whole class examine the same labels, possibly ones that you collected in advance.

Students should select their labels from a wide variety of packaged foods. Some suggestions include breakfast cereals, instant soups, candy bars, potato chips, fruit drinks, canned soups, tuna fish, processed meats like bologna or salami, ice cream, and "natural" foods.

Explain to students that ingredients are listed in order of decreasing amount, and that the first ingredients are the most plentiful in the food.

Alert students to the fact that some ingredients they find at the ends of label lists may be dyes, preservatives, or emulsifiers. These ingredients may have names that are unrecognizable as organic or inorganic compounds, although they may be either.

Keep Students on Track— Section 1

Make sure students have obtained at least a dozen different labels to use in this project. You might suggest they collect a few labels from different brands of the same type of food so that they can compare nutritional data.

Assist students in reading their labels. Students should understand that the ingredients are listed in order of decreasing amount.

Show students a typical table of nutritional facts contained on all labels. Explain that the percentages of daily values are based on a diet of 2,000 calories per day.

© Pearson Education, Inc., publishing as Pearson Prentice Hall. All rights reserved.

Keep Students on Track— Section 3

Have students begin this part of the project by classifying as organic or inorganic as many ingredients on their labels as possible. Prefixes that indicate organic compounds include *meth-, eth-, prop-, but-, phen-, -amino-, carboxy-, acet-,* and *benz-*. Some organic suffixes include *-ane, -ene, -yne, -ate, -one,* and *-ol*.

Students might need help identifying other organic compounds, such as ascorbic or citric acid (vitamin C), niacin (vitamin B3), thiamin (vitamin B1), riboflavin (vitamin B2), caffeine, cellulose, cholesterol, citrates, and peptides.

If necessary, assist students in identifying the organic compounds as carbohydrates, proteins, lipids, or vitamins and in identifying the minerals among the inorganic compounds.

Even after using reference materials, students may not be able to identify or classify all label ingredients. Suggest that students keep a list of these ingredients.

Decide how you want students to classify specific foods such as apples, onions, beef, etc. Remind students that some ingredients can be classified as more than one type of organic compound.

Chapter Project Performance

Students should be able to answer questions from classmates about the foods they chose and the ingredients in them.

They should also point out the chemicals that appeared in the majority of the foods chosen.

After everyone has presented their displays, have students discuss the nutritional content of the foods examined. They can compare the ingredients of each food and tell which ones should be included in a healthy diet.

Extension

Consider grouping students and having different groups examine several brands of the same type of food. They should be able to compare the brands and select one that they believe to be superior. Have each group present their findings to the class and justify their selections.

Have students contact people at local bakeries and food processors to discuss why certain ingredients are put into food. For example, is the ingredient a flavoring, a preservative, or something else? Students could ask about the function of label ingredients they were unable to identify.

To simplify this project, students could examine only the first two or three ingredients listed on each label instead of all the ingredients.

© Pearson Education, Inc., publishing as Pearson Prentice Hall. All rights reserved.

Carbon Chemistry • *Chapter Project*   **Overview**

Chapter Project Check Out the Fine Print

There are many different substances used to make packaged foods. Fresh-squeezed orange juice contains only the juice from oranges, but packaged juice drinks often contain a long list of ingredients. Is one ingredient better for you than the other? Do additional chemicals increase a food's nutritional value?

For this project, you will collect a dozen labels from different packaged foods. You will examine the ingredients in these foods and classify as many ingredients as you can as organic (containing carbon) or inorganic (not containing carbon). You will further identify the organic compounds as carbohydrates, proteins, lipids, or vitamins. You will identify any minerals among the inorganic compounds. Finally, you will compare the different foods based on their nutritional information.

Project Rules

- You must collect labels from at least twelve different packaged foods.

- All food labels must list at least five ingredients.

- You must classify as many ingredients as possible as organic or inorganic.

- You must classify the organic compounds as proteins, lipids, carbohydrates, or vitamins.

- You must identify the minerals among the inorganic compounds.

- You must compare the nutritional information for the ingredients found in the different foods that you studied.

- You must present all information in an organized display.

Suggested Materials

You should select your labels from a wide variety of packaged foods. Some suggestions include breakfast cereals, instant soups, candy bars, potato chips, fruit drinks, canned soups, tuna fish, processed meats like bologna or salami, ice cream, and "natural" foods.

© Pearson Education, Inc., publishing as Pearson Prentice Hall. All rights reserved.

Carbon Chemistry ▪ *Chapter Project*   **Overview**

Project Hints

- Many chemical compounds have long names. However, most names will have a prefix, a suffix, or some other signal that can tell you what type of compound it is. Here are some prefixes used for naming organic compounds: *meth-, eth-, prop-, but-, phen-, amino-, carboxy-, acet-,* and *benz-*.

- Some suffixes used for naming organic compounds are *-ol, -ate,* and *-one.* Skim through the chapter to discover other suffixes that indicate organic compounds. Realize that even though you may not see the word "sugar" listed in the ingredients, the food may still contain sugar. The suffix *-ose* indicates a sugar.

- Some organic compounds have unfamiliar names such as ascorbic or citric acid (vitamin C), niacin (vitamin B3), thiamin (vitamin B1), riboflavin (vitamin B2), caffeine, cellulose, cholesterol, citrates, and peptides.

- Watch for minerals such as iron, calcium, phosphorus, sodium, potassium, sulfur, iodine, zinc, and chlorine.

- The ingredients on food labels are listed in order of decreasing amount.

- Serving sizes are standardized based on different food categories. Make sure you take these serving sizes into account when comparing different products.

- When considering which foods are healthy, you might want to examine the tables that contain percentages of recommended daily values for different nutrients.

Project Time Line

Task	Due Date
1. Labels collected.	_____
2. List of organic and inorganic ingredients completed.	_____
3. Polymers, lipids, vitamins, and minerals identified.	_____
4. Table completed and display materials ready.	_____
5. Class presentation completed.	_____

© Pearson Education, Inc., publishing as Pearson Prentice Hall. All rights reserved.

Reading Food Labels

Food manufacturers use attractive packaging, catchy jingles, and flashy advertisements to convince you to purchase their products. As an informed consumer, you should not base your decision to buy certain foods on these advertising devices. Instead, you should make an educated decision using information provided to you on the food labels. The U.S. Food and Drug Administration (FDA) requires all packaged foods to contain a list of ingredients and nutritional information. The following tasks will help you use this information to make healthy food choices. Using the labels that you collected, answer the following questions on a separate sheet of paper.

1. Name five ingredients that are present in large amounts in the foods you have chosen.

2. How many calories are contained in one serving of each food?

3. What percent of the daily value for saturated fat does one serving of each food contain?

4. Which of these foods contains more than 30% of the daily value for sodium? Do you think those foods would be a good choice for someone trying to include only small amounts of sodium in their diet? Why or why not?

5. What vitamins and minerals are found in quantities higher than 25% in the foods you have chosen?

6. Women often try to incorporate calcium into their diet. Which of the foods you're investigating would you recommend for that purpose?

7. Iron is a mineral that helps transport oxygen in the blood. Do any of your foods provide more than 10% of the daily value of iron?

8. Which of your foods would you consider to be the healthiest choice? Consider such things as sugar content, vitamin and mineral content, sodium content, and fat content.

© Pearson Education, Inc., publishing as Pearson Prentice Hall. All rights reserved.

Carbon Chemistry • *Chapter Project*   **Worksheet 2**

Recording and Analyzing Data

Complete the following tasks on a separate sheet of paper. When they are completed, you are ready to put together your presentation for the class.

1. Make a list of all the organic compounds listed on the package labels. Make a list of all the inorganic compounds. If there are any compounds you cannot classify as organic or inorganic, write them down in a separate list.

2. Use your data to create a table similar to the one below. Use the table to record the information about the ingredients present in each of your chosen foods.

Food Item	Carbohydrates	Proteins	Lipids	Vitamins	Minerals	Other Ingredients

3. Which ingredients are the most common in the foods you examined? Which ingredients are the least common?

4. Group your foods according to the organic compound(s) they contain. Remember that some foods will contain more than one class of organic compound.

5. Write several sentences summarizing your research and your observations based on your data table.

6. Decide how you want to communicate what you have learned to your classmates. Make a list of the things you want to tell your classmates during your presentation.

© Pearson Education, Inc., publishing as Pearson Prentice Hall. All rights reserved.

Carbon Chemistry ▪ *Chapter Project*   **Scoring Rubric**

Lab zone™ Chapter Project

Check Out the Fine Print

In evaluating how well you complete the Chapter Project, your teacher will judge your work in four categories. In each, a score of 4 is the best rating.

	4	3	2	1
Recording Data	Student collects at least twelve labels from different packaged foods. Data table is complete and organized.	Student collects at least ten labels from different packaged foods. Data table is complete and organized.	Student collects at least eight labels from different packaged foods. Data table is fairly complete but not very organized.	Student collects fewer than six labels from different packaged foods. Data table is incomplete and unorganized.
Applying Chapter Concepts	Student is able to distinguish between organic and inorganic compounds. Student is able to categorize all organic compounds as carbohydrates, proteins, lipids, or vitamins. Student is able to identify minerals.	Student is able to distinguish between organic and inorganic compounds. Student is able to categorize most organic compounds as carbohydrates, proteins, lipids, or vitamins. Student is able to identify some minerals.	Student is able to distinguish most organic and inorganic compounds. Student is able to categorize only a few organic compounds as carbohydrates, proteins, lipids, or vitamins. Student is able to identify a few minerals.	Student is able to distinguish only a few organic and inorganic compounds. Student is unable to categorize organic compounds as carbohydrates, proteins, lipids, or vitamins. Student is unable to identify any minerals.
Presenting Results	Student makes a thorough, well-organized presentation, displaying data table, classifying all ingredients, and comparing the nutritional composition of chosen foods.	Student's presentation adequately organizes and classifies the ingredients and compares the nutritional composition of chosen foods.	Student's presentation is somewhat organized, and attempts to classify the ingredients and compare the nutritional composition of some of the chosen foods.	Student's presentation is unorganized and hard to follow. Chart does not classify the ingredients and does not address the nutritional composition of different foods.

© Pearson Education, Inc., publishing as Pearson Prentice Hall. All rights reserved.

Properties of Carbon

1–2 periods, 1/2–1 block

Ability Levels Key
L1 Basic to Average
L2 For All Students
L3 Average to Advanced

Objectives

L.4.1.1 Describe how carbon is able to form a huge variety of compounds.

L.4.1.2 Identify four forms of pure carbon

Key Terms

• diamond • graphite • fullerene • nanotube

Local Standards

PRETEACH

Build Background Knowledge

Students explain why they think people value diamonds.

 **Discover Activity** *Why Do Pencils Write?* **L1**

Targeted Resources

❏ **All in One Teaching Resources**
L2 Reading Strategy Transparency L42:
Using Prior Knowledge
❏ **Presentation-Pro CD-ROM**

INSTRUCT

Carbon Atoms and Bonding Use dot diagrams and structural diagrams to lead a discussion describing how carbon bonds to itself and to other elements.

Forms of Pure Carbon Ask questions to lead the class in completing a compare/contrast table of the forms of pure carbon.

Targeted Resources

❏ **All in One Teaching Resources**
L2 Guided Reading, pp. 259–260
L2 Transparencies L43, L44
❏ **PHSchool.com** Web Code: cgp-2041
❏ **Student Edition on Audio CD**

ASSESS

Section Assessment Questions

Have students use their completed graphic organizers to answer the questions.

Reteach

Students diagram how carbon atoms form bonds with other elements.

Targeted Resources

❏ **All in One Teaching Resources**
Section Summary, p. 258
L1 Review and Reinforce, p. 261
L3 Enrich, p. 262

© Pearson Education, Inc., publishing as Pearson Prentice Hall. All rights reserved.

Carbon Chemistry ▪ *Section Summary*

Properties of Carbon

Guide for Reading
- How is carbon able to form a huge variety of compounds?

- What are the four forms of pure carbon?

Carbon has four valence electrons—the electrons available for forming chemical bonds. A chemical bond is the force that holds two atoms together. A chemical bond between two atoms is made up of the atoms' valence electrons. **Few elements have the ability of carbon to bond with both itself and other elements in so many different ways. With four valence electrons, each carbon atom is able to form four bonds.** It is possible to form substances with many carbon atoms. It is possible to arrange carbon atoms in different ways. When they combine to make compounds, carbon atoms can form straight chains, branched chains, and rings.

Because of the ways in which carbon forms bonds, carbon can exist in different forms as a pure element. **Diamond, graphite, fullerenes, and nanotubes are four forms of the element carbon.**

The hardest mineral—**diamond**—forms deep within Earth under very high pressure and temperature. Solid diamond crystals are extremely hard and unreactive because each carbon atom in diamond is strongly bonded to four other carbon atoms. Diamonds are used in industry as cutting tools and also in jewelry as gems.

The "lead" in a lead pencil is actually **graphite**, another form of the element carbon. In graphite, carbon atoms are bonded tightly together in flat layers. However, the bonds between atoms in different layers are very weak, so the layers slide easily past one another. Because it is so slippery, graphite makes an excellent lubricant in machines.

In 1985, a new form of the element carbon was made. The new form consists of carbon atoms arranged in the shape of a hollow sphere. This form is called **fullerene.** In 1991, another form of carbon was made—the nanotube. In a **nanotube**, carbon atoms are arranged in the shape of a long, hollow tube. Nanotubes are tiny, light, flexible, and very strong. They are also good conductors of heat and electricity.

Chemists are looking for ways to use fullerenes and nanotubes. Because fullerenes enclose a ball-shaped open area, they may be able to carry substances, such as medicines, inside them. Nanotubes may also be used as conductors in electical devices.

© Pearson Education, Inc., publishing as Pearson Prentice Hall. All rights reserved.

Carbon Chemistry · *Guided Reading and Study*

Properties of Carbon

This section explains why carbon can form a huge variety of different compounds. It also describes the different forms of pure carbon.

Use Target Reading Skills

Before your read, write what you know about carbon in the top box. As you read, write what you learn in the bottom box.

What You Know
1. Carbon atoms have 6 electrons.
2.
3.
4.
5.

What You Learned
1.
2.
3.
4.
5.

Carbon Atoms and Bonding

1. Circle the letter of the number of valence electrons a carbon atom has available for bonding.

   a. 2   **b.** 4   **c.** 6   **d.** 8

2. The transfer or sharing of valence electrons creates chemical _____.

3. Is the following sentence true or false? Carbon atoms form more bonds than most other atoms. _____

© Pearson Education, Inc., publishing as Pearson Prentice Hall. All rights reserved.

Carbon Chemistry • *Guided Reading and Study*

Properties of Carbon *(continued)*

4. Circle the letter of the number of bonds each carbon atom is able to form.

   a. 2   **b.** 4   **c.** 6   **d.** 8

5. What are three ways carbon atoms bond to form the backbones for molecules?

   a. _____ **b.** _____

   c. _____

Forms of Pure Carbon

6. Why can the pure element of carbon exist in different forms?

   _____

   _____

7. Complete the table about forms of pure carbon.

Forms of Carbon			
Form	**Arrangement of Carbon Atoms**	**Properties**	**Use**
a. Diamond			
b.		Soft, slippery	Pencils, lubricants
c.	Hollow sphere	Enclose an open area	Possibly carry medicines through the body
d.	Long, hollow tube		Conductors in electronic devices

8. Under what conditions do diamonds form?

   _____

   _____

© Pearson Education, Inc., publishing as Pearson Prentice Hall. All rights reserved.

Name _____ Date _____ Class _____

Carbon Chemistry · *Review and Reinforce*

Properties of Carbon

Understanding Main Ideas

For items 1–4, correctly label each structure as one of the forms of elemental carbon.

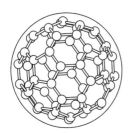 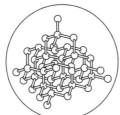 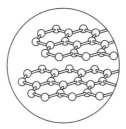 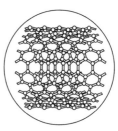

1. _____ 2. _____ 3. _____ 4. _____

Fill in the blank with the word or words that best completes each sentence.

5. Each carbon atom has _____ valence electrons for forming bonds.

6. Carbon atoms can bond with other _____ and with other elements in many different ways.

Building Vocabulary

Answer the following questions in the spaces provided.

7. Which form of carbon in the figure above is the hardest?

_____

8. Which form of carbon in the figure above feels slippery?

_____

9. Which form of carbon in the figure above may possibly be used to carry other substances inside the molecule?

_____

10. Which form of carbon in the figure above is also good a conductor of electricity and heat?

_____

© Pearson Education, Inc., publishing as Pearson Prentice Hall. All rights reserved.

Carbon Chemistry • *Enrich*

Charcoal

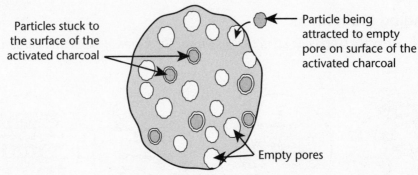

Particles stuck to the surface of the activated charcoal

Particle being attracted to empty pore on surface of the activated charcoal

Empty pores

Grain of Activated Charcoal

If you've ever built a campfire or a fire in a fireplace, you know what is left after the fire goes out—charcoal. Charcoal is the black material formed when wood is burned. It is actually an impure form of graphite. Charcoal has lots of very small openings, or pores, throughout its structure. Another form of charcoal, called activated charcoal, is made by burning wood at very high temperatures with very little air. This process produces an even greater number of these extremely small pores throughout the charcoal.

Because of the tiny pores throughout the material, charcoal and activated charcoal are very useful. These openings can attract molecules and make them stick to their surfaces as shown in the figure above.

Activated charcoal can be used to remove harmful chemicals and bacteria from drinking water. It is also used in aquarium filters to keep the water in the tank clean. As the water flows through the pores in the activated charcoal, some of the substances in the water, such as pesticides, bacteria, and particles, are attracted to the surfaces of the pores. These materials then stick to the charcoal and are removed from the water.

Answer the following on a separate sheet of paper.

1. Another use for activated charcoal is in treating people and animals who have swallowed poisonous substances. How do you think activated charcoal removes a poison from a person's or an animal's body?

2. As well as removing particles from water and other liquids, activated charcoal can also remove particles from the air. Give examples of how activated charcoal might be used in this way.

3. Some backpackers carry a special kind of straw with them that contains a small filter made of activated charcoal. The straw is for use when clean drinking water is not available. How can the special straw be used to obtain clean drinking water?

4. Bacteria that is removed from drinking water by activated charcoal remains stuck to the surface of the charcoal. If the same activated charcoal is used for a long period of time to remove bacteria, a quantity of bacteria can build up on it. Manufacturers of drinking water filters made of activated charcoal recommend that the filter material be changed at least once a year. Why do you think this is a good idea?

© Pearson Education, Inc., publishing as Pearson Prentice Hall. All rights reserved.

SECTION LESSON PLAN

Carbon Compounds

3–4 periods, 1 1/2–2 blocks

Ability Levels Key
L1 Basic to Average
L2 For All Students
L3 Average to Advanced

Objectives

L.4.2.1 List properties of organic compounds.
L.4.2.2 Identify properties of hydrocarbons.
L.4.2.3 Describe the kind of structures and bonding that hydrocarbons have.
L.4.2.4 Identify characteristics of substituted hydrocarbons, esters, and polymers.

Local Standards

Key Terms

• organic compound • hydrocarbon • structural formula • isomer
• saturated hydrocarbon • hydroxyl group • unsaturated hydrocarbon • alcohol
• substituted hydrocarbon • organic acid • carboxyl group • ester • polymer • monomer

---

PRETEACH

Build Background Knowledge
Students describe properties of gasoline that they have observed.

 **Discover Activity** *What Do You Smell?* **L1**

Targeted Resources

❏ **All in One Teaching Resources**
  L2 Reading Strategy Transparency L45: Outlining
❏ ⊙ **Presentation-Pro CD-ROM**

INSTRUCT

Organic Compounds Use the definition of *organic compound* in a discussion of their properties.
Hydrocarbons Lead a discussion about the properties of hydrocarbons.
Structure and Bonding in Hydrocarbons Use structural formulas of different hydrocarbons to discuss different ways that carbon can form bonds
Substituted Hydrocarbons Use structural formulas of methanol and formic acid in a discussion about substituted hydrocarbons.
Esters Lead a discussion about the characteristics of esters.
Polymers Model monomers and polymers to illustrate what polymers are and how they form.

Skills Lab *How Many Molecules?* **L2**

Targeted Resources

❏ **All in One Teaching Resources**
  L2 Guided Reading, pp. 265–268
  L2 Transparencies L46, L47, L48, L49, L50
  L2 Lab: *How Many Molecules?*, pp. 271–272
❏ **Lab Activity Video/DVD**
  Skills Lab: *How Many Molecules?*
❏ **www.SciLinks.org** Web Code: scn-1242
❏ ⊙ **Student Edition on Audio CD**

ASSESS

Section Assessment Questions
↻ Have students use their completed outlines to answer the questions.

Reteach
Students relate hydrocarbons, substituted hydrocarbons, esters, and polymers in a concept map.

Targeted Resources

❏ **All in One Teaching Resources**
  Section Summary, p. 264
  L1 Review and Reinforce, p. 269
  L3 Enrich, p. 270

Carbon Chemistry

© Pearson Education, Inc., publishing as Pearson Prentice Hall. All rights reserved.

Carbon Chemistry ▪ *Section Summary*

Carbon Compounds

Guide for Reading

- What are some properties of organic compounds?

- What are some properties of hydrocarbons?

- What kind of structures and bonding do hydrocarbons have?

- What are some characteristics of substituted hydrocarbons, esters, and polymers?

With some exceptions, a compound that contains carbon is called an **organic compound. Many organic compounds have similar properties in terms of melting points, boiling points, odor, electrical conductivity, and solubility.**

A **hydrocarbon** is a compound that contains only the elements carbon and hydrogen. **Like many other organic compounds, hydrocarbons mix poorly with water. Also, all hydrocarbons are flammable.** Hydrocarbons differ in the number of carbon and hydrogen atoms in each molecule. This is shown in a chemical formula. The chemical formula for methane is CH_4. Methane has one carbon atom and four hydrogen atoms. **The carbon chains in a hydrocarbon may be straight, branched, or ring-shaped.**

A **structural formula** shows the kind, number, and arrangement of atoms in a molecule. Compounds that have the same chemical formula but different structures are called **isomers**. Each isomer is a different substance with its own characteristic properties.

In addition to forming a single bond, two carbon atoms can form a double bond or a triple bond. Hydrocarbons made up of only single bonds are classified as **saturated hydrocarbons**. Hydrocarbons with double or triple bonds are classified as **unsaturated hydrocarbons**.

If just one atom of another element is substituted for a hydrogen atom in a hydrocarbon, a different compound is created. In a **substituted hydrocarbon**, atoms of other elements replace one or more hydrogen atoms in a hydrocarbon. Substituted hydrocarbons include halogen-containing compounds, alcohols, and organic acids.

The group –OH is made of an oxygen atom and a hydrogen atom, and is called a **hydroxyl group**. An **alcohol** is a substituted hydrocarbon that contains one or more hydroxyl groups.

An **organic acid** is a substituted hydrocarbon with one or more carboxyl group. A **carboxyl group** is written as –COOH. Citric acid is an organic acid found in oranges and lemons.

If an alcohol and an organic acid are chemically combined, the resulting compound is called an **ester. Many esters have pleasant, fruity smells.**

A very large molecule made of a chain of many smaller molecules bonded together is called a **polymer**. The smaller molecules are called **monomers. Organic compounds, such as alcohols, esters, and others, can be linked together to build polymers with thousands or even millions of atoms.** Some polymers are made naturally by living things. Others are manufactured in factories.

© Pearson Education, Inc., publishing as Pearson Prentice Hall. All rights reserved.

Name _____ Date _____ Class _____

Carbon Chemistry · *Guided Reading and Study*

Carbon Compounds

This section describes the properties that many carbon compounds have in common. It also describes carbon compounds that contain only the elements carbon and hydrogen.

Use Target Reading Skills

As you read, complete the outline about carbon compounds. Use the red headings for the main ideas and the blue headings for supporting ideas.

Carbon Compounds

I. Organic compounds

II. Hydrocarbons
    A.
    B.

III.
    A.
    B.
    C.

IV.
    A.
    B.
    C.
V.

VI.

Organic Compounds

1. Most compounds that contain carbon are called
_____.

2. Why are many organic compounds liquid or gas at room temperature?
_____
_____

© Pearson Education, Inc., publishing as Pearson Prentice Hall. All rights reserved.

Carbon Chemistry

Name _____ Date _____ Class _____

Carbon Chemistry • *Guided Reading and Study*

Carbon Compounds (continued)

3. Circle the letter of each sentence that is true about organic compounds.
    a. They generally have strong odors.
    b. They have high boiling points.
    c. Many don't dissolve well in water.
    d. They are good conductors of electric currents.

Hydrocarbons

4. What is a hydrocarbon?

   _____

   _____

5. Why are hydrocarbons used for fuel in stoves, cars, and airplanes?

   _____

   _____

6. This is the chemical formula for a hydrocarbon called propane: C_3H_8. What does this formula tell you about a molecule of propane?

   _____

   _____

   _____

Structure and Bonding in Hydrocarbons

7. What are three carbon chains that form in hydrocarbons?

   a. _____ b. _____

   c. _____

8. What does a structural formula show about a molecule of a compound?

   _____

   _____

9. Each dash in a structural formula represents a chemical

   _____.

© Pearson Education, Inc., publishing as Pearson Prentice Hall. All rights reserved.

10. The partially complete structural formula below shows the "backbone" for a propane molecule. Complete the structural formula of this hydrocarbon by showing all the hydrogen atoms that are bonded to the carbon chain.

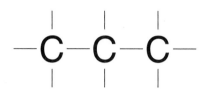

Propane (C_3H_8)

11. Compounds that have the same molecular formula but different structures are called _____.

12. Is the following sentence true or false? Carbon atoms can only form a single bond between other carbon atoms. _____

13. Complete the table about saturated and unsaturated hydrocarbons.

Saturated and Unsaturated Hydrocarbons			
Type of Hydrocarbon	Bonds	Ending on Names	Example
a.	Single bonds		Ethane
b.	Double or triple bonds	*-ene* or *-yne*	

Substituted Hydrocarbons

14. A hydrocarbon in which one or more hydrogen atoms have been replaced by atoms of other elements is called a(n) _____.

© Pearson Education, Inc., publishing as Pearson Prentice Hall. All rights reserved.

Carbon Chemistry · *Guided Reading and Study*

Carbon Compounds *(continued)*

15. In compounds that contain halogens, what replaces hydrogen atoms?

    _____

    _____

16. Circle the letter of the hydroxyl group.

    a. –HO   **b.** –COOH
    c. –OH   **d.** –COH

17. A substituted hydrocarbon that contains one or more hydroxyl groups
    is called a(n) _____.

18. Circle the letter of each alcohol.

    a. freon   **b.** ethanol
    c. acetic acid   **d.** methanol

19. Circle the letter of the carboxyl group.

    a. –HO   **b.** –COOH
    c. –OH   **d.** –COH

20. A substituted hydrocarbon that contains one or more carboxyl groups is
    called a(n) _____.

Esters

21. An organic compound made by chemically combining an alcohol and an
    organic acid is called a(n) _____.

22. Is the following sentence true or false? Many esters have pleasant, fruity
    smells. _____

Polymers

23. What is a polymer?

    _____

    _____

    _____

24. The smaller molecules that make up polymers are called

    _____.

25. Circle the letter of each synthetic polymer.

    a. wool   **b.** polyester
    c. silk   **d.** nylon

© Pearson Education, Inc., publishing as Pearson Prentice Hall. All rights reserved.

Name _____ Date _____ Class _____

Carbon Compounds

Understanding Main Ideas

Answer the following questions on a separate sheet of paper.

1. What kinds of carbon chains are shown in Figures 1 through 3?

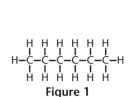
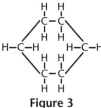

Figure 1   Figure 2   Figure 3

2. Write the chemical formulas for the three compounds shown above.

3. The compounds in Figure 1 and Figure 2 have the same number of carbon and hydrogen atoms. This fact makes them what type of compounds? ?

Building Vocabulary

Match each term with its definition by writing the letter of the correct definition in the right column on the line beside the term in the left column.

_____ 4. substituted hydrocarbon

_____ 5. organic compound

_____ 6. ester

_____ 7. polymer

_____ 8. hydroxyl group

_____ 9. structural formula

_____ 10. hydrocarbon

_____ 11. alcohol

_____ 12. carboxyl group

_____ 13. monomer

_____ 14. organic acid

a. a compound that contains carbon

b. –OH

c. very large molecule made of a chain of many smaller molecules bonded together

d. a substituted hydrocarbon with one or more hydroxyl groups

e. a compund containing only the elements carbon and hydrogen

f. –COOH

g. a hydrocarbon with an atom of another element in place of hydrogen

h. the compound that results when an alcohol and an organic acid are chemically combined

i. shows the kind, number, and arrangement of atoms of a molecule

j. the smaller molecules that make up a polymer

k. a substituted hydrocarbon with one or more carboxyl groups

© Pearson Education, Inc., publishing as Pearson Prentice Hall. All rights reserved.

Carbon Chemistry • *Enrich*

Simplest Hydrocarbons

The simplest hydrocarbons belong to a family called alkanes. The alkane family is made up of compounds that contain only carbon and hydrogen atoms. The carbon atoms in an alkane are connected to one another by single bonds only. The table below shows the first ten alkanes, their formulas, their states at room temperature, and their melting and boiling points. The carbon atoms in each compound form a straight chain.

Name	Formula	State at Room Temperature	Melting Point (°C)	Boiling Point (°C)
Methane	CH_4	gas	−184	−161.4
Ethane	C_2H_6	gas	−172	−88.3
Propane	C_3H_8	gas	−189.9	−44.5
Butane	C_4H_{10}	gas	−135	−0.55
Pentane	C_5H_{12}	liquid	−131.5	36.2
Hexane	C_6H_{14}	liquid	−94.3	69
Heptane	C_7H_{16}	liquid	−90	98.4
Octane	C_8H_{18}	liquid	−56.5	124.6
Nonane	C_9H_{20}	liquid	−51	150.6
Decane	$C_{10}H_{22}$	liquid	−32	174

Answer the following questions on a separate sheet of paper.

1. As the number of carbon atoms in the compound increases, what pattern do you see in the boiling points? What general pattern do you see in the melting points?
2. The alkane with a formula of $C_{14}H_{30}$ is a liquid at room temperature. Predict the state of the compound $C_{12}H_{26}$ at room temperature. Explain your reasoning.
3. There is a relationship between the number of hydrogen atoms and the number of carbon atoms in an alkane. This relationship does not change, no matter how many carbon atoms an alkane contains. Describe that relationship in a statement or as a mathematical formula.
4. Based on the table and your answer to item 3, what is the chemical formula of the alkane that contains 40 carbon atoms?

© Pearson Education, Inc., publishing as Pearson Prentice Hall. All rights reserved.

Carbon Chemistry ▪ *Skills Lab*

How Many Molecules?

Problem

In this lab you will use gumdrops to represent atoms and toothpicks to represent bonds. How many different ways can you put the same number of carbon atoms together?

Skills Focus

making models

Materials

toothpicks

multicolored gumdrops

other materials supplied by your teacher

Procedure

1. You will need gumdrops of one color to represent carbon atoms and gumdrops of another color to represent hydrogen atoms. When building your models, always follow these rules:

   ▪ Eash carbon atom forms four bonds.

   ▪ Each hydrogen atom forms one bond.

   CAUTION: *Do not eat any of the food substances in this experiment.*

2. Make a model of CH_4 (methane).
3. Now make a model of C_2H_6 (ethane).
4. Make a model of C_3H_8 (propane). Is there more than one way to arrange the atoms in propane? (*Hint:* Are there any branches in the carbon chain or are all the carbon atoms in one line?)
5. Now make a model of C_4H_{10} (butane) in which all the carbon atoms are in one line.
6. Make a second model of butane with a branched chain.
7. Compare the branched-chain model with the straight-chain model of butane. Are there other ways to arrange the atoms?
8. Predict how many different structures can be formed from C_5H_{12} (pentane).

   _____

   _____

9. Test your prediction by building as many different models of pentane as you can.

© Pearson Education, Inc., publishing as Pearson Prentice Hall. All rights reserved.

Carbon Chemistry

Name _____ Date_____ Class _____

Carbon Chemistry • *Skills Lab*

How Many Molecules? *(continued)*

Analyze and Conclude

1. **Making Models** Did any of your models have a hydrogen atom between two carbon atoms? Why or why not?

_____

_____

_____

2. **Observing** How does a branched chain differ from a straight chain?

_____

_____

_____

3. **Drawing Conclusions** How many different structures have the formula C_3H_8? C_4H_{10}? C_5H_{12}? Use diagrams to explain your answers.

_____

_____

_____

4. **Predicting** If you bend a straight chain of carbons, do you make a different structure? Why or why not?

_____

_____

_____

5. **Communicating** Compare the information you can get from models to the information you can get from formulas like C_6H_{14}. How does using models help you understand the structure of a molecule?

_____

_____

_____

More to Explore

Use a third color of gumdrops to model an oxygen atom. An oxygen atom forms two bonds. Use the rules in this lab to model as many different structures for the formula $C_4H_{10}O$ as possible.

© Pearson Education, Inc., publishing as Pearson Prentice Hall. All rights reserved.

Life With Carbon

⏱ *3–4 periods, 1 1/2–2 blocks*

Ability Levels Key
L1 Basic to Average
L2 For All Students
L3 Average to Advanced

Objectives

L.4.3.1 List the four main classes of organic compounds in living things.

L.4.3.2 Explain how the organic compounds in living things differ from one another.

Local Standards

Key Terms

- carbohydrate • glucose
- complex carbohydrate • starch • cellulose
- protein • amino acid • lipid • fatty acid
- cholesterol • nucleic acid • DNA • RNA
- nucleotide

PRETEACH

Build Background Knowledge

Invite students to compare and contrast different foods.

 **Discover Activity** *What Is in Milk?* **L1**

Targeted Resources

☐ **All in One** **Teaching Resources**
  L2 Reading Strategy Transparency L51: Asking Questions
☐ 💿 **Presentation-Pro CD-ROM**

INSTRUCT

Carbohydrates Lead a discussion in which students compare and contrast simple and complex carbohydrates.

Proteins Use the structural formulas of alanine and serine to discuss protein structure.

Lipids Ask questions in a discussion about lipids contrasted with carbohydrates.

Nucleic Acids Lead a discussion about the structure of nucleic acids and their importance to living things.

Other Compounds in Foods Ask questions in a discussion about vitamins and minerals.

 **Consumer Lab** *Are You Getting Your Vitamins?* **L2**

Targeted Resources

☐ **All in One** **Teaching Resources**
  L2 Guided Reading, pp. 275–278
  L2 Transparencies L52, L53
  L2 Lab: *Are You Getting Your Vitamins?*, pp. 281–283
☐ 📼 **Lab Activity Video/DVD**
  Consumer Lab: *Are You Getting Your Vitamins?*
☐ **www.SciLinks.org** Web Code: scn-1243
☐ **PHSchool.com** Web Code: cgh-2040
☐ 💿 **Student Edition on Audio CD**

ASSESS

Section Assessment Questions

🔄 Have students use their questions and answers to answer the questions.

Reteach

Students relate the key terms in a concept map.

Targeted Resources

☐ **All in One** **Teaching Resources**
  Section Summary, p. 274
  L1 Review and Reinforce, p. 279
  L3 Enrich, p. 280

Carbon Chemistry

© Pearson Education, Inc., publishing as Pearson Prentice Hall. All rights reserved.

Carbon Chemistry · *Section Summary*

Life With Carbon

Guide for Reading

- What are the four main classes of organic compounds in living things?

- How are the organic compounds in living things different from one another?

Nutrients are the building blocks of all living things. Nutrients are organinc compounds. Foods provide organic compounds. **The four classes of organic compounds required by living things are carbohydrates, proteins, lipids, and nucleic acids.**

A **carbohydrate** is an energy-rich organic compound made of the elements carbon, hydrogen, and oxygen. The simplest carbohydrates are sugars. **Glucose** is a sugar found in your body. A **complex carbohydrate** is made of a long chain of simple carbohydrates bonded to each other. Two complex carbohydrates are starch and cellulose, both of which are made of glucose. **Starch and cellulose are both polymers built from glucose, but the glucose molecules are arranged differently in each case.** Plants store energy in the form of the complex carbohydrate **starch**. Starches are found in many foods. The body breaks starch down into glucose, which it uses for energy. Plants build strong stems and roots with the complex carbohydrate **cellulose**. The body cannot break down cellulose into glucose molecules. However, undigested cellulose keeps the digestive tract healthy.

Proteins are polymers formed from monomers called **amino acids**. There are 20 kinds of amino acids found in living things. **Different proteins are made when different sequences of amino acids are linked into long chains.** Each amino acid molecule has a carboxyl group (–COOH). Good sources of protein include meat, fish, eggs, and milk.

Like carbohydrates, **lipids** are energy-rich compounds made of carbon, oxygen and hydrogen. **Gram for gram, lipids release twice as much energy in your body as do carbohydrates.** Lipids include fats, oils, waxes, and cholesterol. Each fat or oil molecule is made of three **fatty acids** and one alcohol. Another important lipid is **cholesterol**, a waxy substance found in all animal cells.

Nucleic acids are very large organic molecules made up of carbon, oxygen, hydrogen, nitrogen, and phosporous. **DNA** are the initials that stand for one type of nucleic acid, called deoxyribonucleic acid. The other type of nucleic acid, ribonucleic acid, has the initials **RNA**. The building blocks of nucleic acids are called **nucleotides**. **The differences among living things depend on the order of nucleotides in their DNA.**

Your body also needs vitamins, minerals, water, and salts. **Unlike the nutrients discussed so far, vitamins and minerals are needed only in small amounts.** Vitamins are organic compounds that serve as helper molecules in a variety of chemical reactions in your body. Minerals are elements in the form of ions needed by your body. Minerals are not organic compounds.

© Pearson Education, Inc., publishing as Pearson Prentice Hall. All rights reserved.

Carbon Chemistry ▪ *Guided Reading and Study*

Life With Carbon

This section describes the four main classes of polymers in living things.

Use Target Reading Skills

Before your read, preview the red headings. In the graphic organizer below, ask a what *question for each heading. As you read, write the answers to your questions.*

Question	Answer
What is a carbohydrate?	A carbohydrate is . . .

Introduction

1. What are the four classes of polymers found in all living things?

   _____

   _____

Carbohydrates

2. What is a carbohydrate?

   _____

   _____

3. The sugar with the molecular formula of $C_6H_{12}O_6$ is called

   _____ .

© Pearson Education, Inc., publishing as Pearson Prentice Hall. All rights reserved.

Carbon Chemistry • *Guided Reading and Study*

Life With Carbon *(continued)*

4. Why is glucose sometimes called "blood sugar"?

_____

_____

_____

5. A large chainlike molecule made of simple carbohydrates is called a(n)
_____.

6. Complete the table about complex carbohydrates.

Complex Carbohydrates		
Type	**Description**	**Contained in These Foods**
a. Starch		
b. Cellulose		

Proteins

7. Polymers formed from smaller molecules called amino acids are
_____.

8. Is the following sentence true or false? There are four different kinds of amino acids. _____

9. How are different proteins made?

_____

_____

_____

10. Circle the letter of each food that is a good source of protein.

   a. fish   **b.** beans   **c.** potatoes   **d.** meat

11. What does the body use proteins for?

_____

_____

© Pearson Education, Inc., publishing as Pearson Prentice Hall. All rights reserved.

Carbon Chemistry ▪ *Guided Reading and Study*

Lipids

12. What are lipids?

_____

_____

_____

13. What are four types of lipids?

_____

_____

14. Gram for gram, which stores more energy, lipids or carbohydrates?

_____

15. What is each fat or oil made of?

_____

_____

_____

16. A waxy lipid found in all animal cells is called

_____.

Nucleic Acids

17. What are nucleic acids?

_____

_____

_____

18. Complete the table about types of nucleic acids.

Nucleic Acids		
Common Name	**Full Name**	**Composed of**
a.	Deoxyribonucleic acid	Four kinds of
b.	Ribonucleic acid	Four kinds of

© Pearson Education, Inc., publishing as Pearson Prentice Hall. All rights reserved.

Carbon Chemistry · *Guided Reading and Study*

Life With Carbon *(continued)*

19. The building blocks of nucleic acids are called

_____.

20. What do the differences among living things depend on?

_____

_____

_____

21. Complete the flowchart about nucleic acids.

The order of nucleotides in _____ determines

↓

The order of nucleotides in _____ , which determines

↓

The sequence of _____ in proteins.

Other Compounds in Foods

22. Complete the table about other compounds in foods.

Vitamins and Minerals		
Nutrient	**Definition**	**Examples**
a. Vitamins		
b. Minerals		

23. Is the following sentence true or false? Vitamins and minerals are only needed by your body in small amounts. _____

© Pearson Education, Inc., publishing as Pearson Prentice Hall. All rights reserved.

Carbon Chemistry · *Review and Reinforce*

Life With Carbon

Understanding Main Ideas

Answer the following questions on a separate sheet of paper.

1. What are the four main classes of organic compounds in living things?
2. Why are starch and cellulose considered different compounds even though they are both built from glucose?
3. How does DNA determine the differences among living things?
4. Describe your body's requirements for vitamins and minerals.

Building Vocabulary

Fill in the blank with the word or words that best completes each sentence.

glucose	carbohydrate	starch	RNA
cellulose	proteins	amino acids	DNA
nucleic acid	fatty acids	cholesterol	lipids
complex	carbohydrate	nucleotide	

5. Twenty different _____ make up proteins.

6. Each lipid molecule is composed of three _____ and one alcohol.

7. Different _____ are made when different sequences of amino acids are linked into long chains.

8. Gram for gram, _____ release twice as much energy in your body as do _____.

9. A very large organic compound made up of carbon, oxygen, hydrogen, nitrogen, and phosphorus is called a(n) _____.

10. _____ and _____ are the two types of nucleic acids.

11. The monomer that makes up a nucleic acid is a(n) _____.

12. A long chain of energy-rich organic compounds made of carbon, hydrogen, and oxygen is called a(n) _____

13. _____ is a waxy substance found in all animal cells.

14. _____ is a simple carbohydrate. Both _____ and _____ are complex carbohydrates.

© Pearson Education, Inc., publishing as Pearson Prentice Hall. All rights reserved.

Carbon Chemistry · *Enrich*

Protein Structures

The bodies of all mammals, such as humans, cows, sheep, whales, and horses, contain similar but not identical proteins. One of these proteins is called *insulin*. Insulin helps to regulate the concentration of sugar in a mammal's blood. What makes one mammal's insulin different from another is the sequence of amino acids within the molecule. Each mammal listed in the table below has 51 amino acids in its insulin molecule. Most of the molecule is the same for all of these mammals. However, one portion of the molecule is different. The table shows that portion, and the sequence in which the different amino acids combine. The full names of the amino acids are abbreviated in the table. The amino acids used in the table are cyst, ala, ser, val, cys, thr, ileu, and gly.

Mammal	Amino Acid Sequence
cows	-cyst-ala-ser-val-cys-
whale	-cyst-thr-ser-ileu-cys-
sheep	-cyst-ala-gly-val-cys-
horse	-cyst-thr-gly-ileu-cys-
human	-cyst-thr-ser-ileu-cys-

Answer the following questions on a separate sheet of paper.

1. Which two insulin molecules are most alike?

2. Based on the table, how does the sequence of amino acids in horse insulin differ from the sequence in whale insulin?

3. Scientists think that the structure of proteins may reveal how closely related different animals are. Based on this assumption, which are more closely related: horses and cows or sheep and cows? Explain your answer.

4. The first medical treatment for diabetes, a disease in which the body lacks insulin, was to provide insulin from another animal. Based on the information above, suggest a hypothesis to explain why such treatment could work.

© Pearson Education, Inc., publishing as Pearson Prentice Hall. All rights reserved.

Name _____ Date _____ Class _____

Carbon Chemistry · *Consumer Lab*

Are You Getting Your Vitamins?

Problem

Fruit juices contain vitamin C, an important nutrient. Which juice should you drink to obtain the most vitamin C?

Skills Focus

controlling variables, interpreting data, inferring

Materials

6 small cups

6 plastic droppers

starch solution

iodine solution

vitamin C solution

samples of beverages to be tested (orange juice, apple juice, sports drink, fruit-flavored drink)

Procedure

Part 1 Vitamin C Test

1. Using a plastic dropper, place 25 drops of tap water into one of the small cups. Add 2 drops of starch solution.

2. Add 1 drop of iodine solution to the cup. **CAUTION:***Iodine solution can stain skin or clothing.* Observe the color of the mixture. Save this cup to use for comparison in Step 4.

3. Using a fresh dropper, place 25 drops of vitamin C solution into another cup. Add 2 drops of starch solution.

4. Add 1 drop of iodine solution to the cup and swirl. Continue adding iodine a drop at a time, swirling after each drop, until you get a dark blue color similar to the color obtained in Step 2. Record the number of iodine drops in the data table on the next page.

5. Save the cup from Step 4 and use it for comparison during Part 2.

© Pearson Education, Inc., publishing as Pearson Prentice Hall. All rights reserved.

Name _____ Date _____ Class _____

Carbon Chemistry • *Consumer Lab*

Are You Getting Your Vitamins? *(continued)*

Part 2 Comparison Test

6. Record your information in the data table below.

7. Which beverage sample do you think has the most vitamin C? Which do you think has the least? Rank your beverage samples according to your predictions in the data table below.

8. Adapt the procedure from Part 1 so you can compare the amount of vitamin C in your beverage samples to the vitamin C solution.

9. Carry out your procedure after your teacher approves.

Data Table

Test Sample	Drops of Iodine	Predicted Rank	Actual Rank
vitamin C			
orange juice			
apple juice			
sports drink			
fruit-flavored drink			

Analyze and Conclude

Write your answers in the space provided.

1. **Controlling Variables** What was the purpose for the test of the mixture of starch and water in Step 2?

    _____

    _____

    _____

2. **Controlling Variables** What was the purpose for the test of the starch, water, and vitamin C in Step 4?

    _____

    _____

    _____

© Pearson Education, Inc., publishing as Pearson Prentice Hall. All rights reserved.

Carbon Chemistry ▪ *Consumer Lab*

3. **Drawing Conclusions** What do you think caused differences between your data from Step 2 and Step 4?

   _____

   _____

4. **Controlling Variables** Why did you have to add the same amount of starch to each of the beverages?

   _____

   _____

5. **Predicting** What would happen if someone forgot to add the starch to the beverage before they began adding iodine?

   _____

   _____

6. **Measuring** Of the four drinks you tested, which took the most drops of iodine before changing color? Which took the fewest?

   _____

   _____

7. **Interpreting Data** Which beverage had the most vitamin C? Which had the least? How do you know?

   _____

   _____

8. **Inferring** When you tested orange juice, the color of the first few drops of the iodine faded away. What do you think happened to the iodine?

   _____

   _____

9. **Communicating** If a beverage scored low in your test for vitamin C, does that mean it isn't good for you? Write a paragraph in which you explain what other factors might make a beverage nutritious or take away from its nutrient value?

   _____

   _____

   _____

   _____

Design an Experiment

Foods are often labeled with expiration dates. Labels often also say to "refrigerate after opening." Design an experiment to find out if the vitamin C content of orange juice changes over time at different temperatures. *Obtain your teacher's permission before carrying out your investigation.*

© Pearson Education, Inc., publishing as Pearson Prentice Hall. All rights reserved.

Carbon Chemistry

Key Terms

Use the clues below to identify Key Terms from the chapter. Write the terms on the lines, putting one letter in each blank. When you finish, the word enclosed in the diagonal will reveal an important term related to the chemistry of living things. Define the term.

Clues

1. A form of pure carbon with atoms arranged in the shape of a long, hollow tube.

2. A form of pure carbon with atoms arranged in the shape of a hollow sphere.

3. A substituted hydrocarbon that contains one or more hydroxyl groups

4. A simple sugar found in the body

5. A complex carbohydrate that strengthens plant stems and roots

6. A –COOH group found in organic acids

7. A formula that shows the kind, number, and arrangement of atoms in a molecule

8. The monomers in a protein molecule

9. A compound that contains only the elements carbon and hydrogen

10. An organic compound made by chemically combining an alcohol and an organic acid

1. ___ ___ ___ ___ ___ ___ ___

2. ___ ___ ___ ___ ___ ___ ___ ___

3. ___ ___ ___ ___ ___ ___

4. ___ ___ ___ ___ ___ ___

5. ___ ___ ___ ___ ___ ___ ___ ___

6. ___ ___ ___ ___ ___ ___ ___ ___ ___

7. ___ ___ ___ ___ ___ ___ ___ ___ ___ ___ ___

8. ___ ___ ___ ___ ___ ___ ___ ___

9. ___ ___ ___ ___ ___ ___ ___ ___

10. ___ ___ ___ ___

Hidden Term: _____

Definition: _____

_____

© Pearson Education, Inc., publishing as Pearson Prentice Hall. All rights reserved.

Connecting Concepts

Develop a concept map that uses Key Concepts and Key Terms from this chapter. The concept map shown is one way to organize how the information in this chapter is related. You may use an extra sheet of paper.

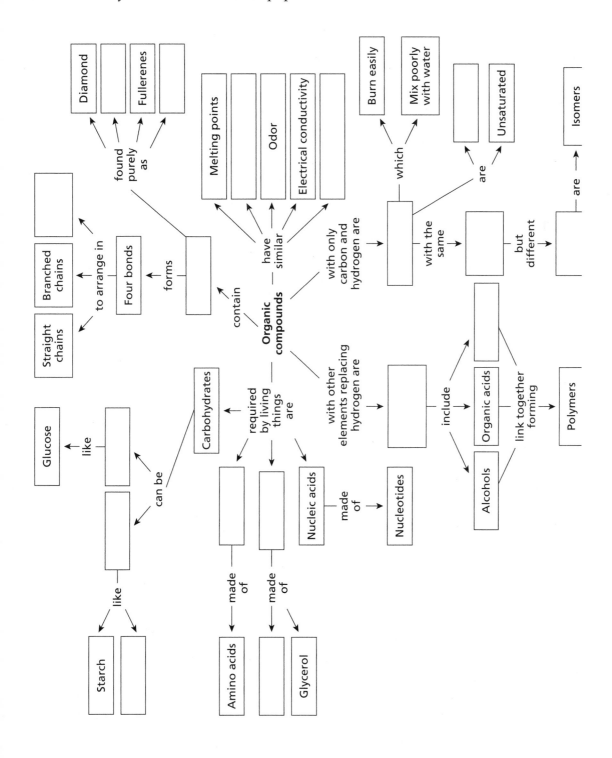

© Pearson Education, Inc., publishing as Pearson Prentice Hall. All rights reserved.

Testing Unsaturated Cooking Oils

Key Concept

An unsaturated bond will absorb iodine to make a saturated bond.

Skills Focus

observing, inferring, classifying, measuring

Time

30 minutes the first day

15 minutes the second day

Materials

10 test tubes

10 stoppers for test tubes

test-tube rack

balance

several vegetable oils such as corn, olive, sunflower, safflower, and soybean oil

tincture of iodine

3 plastic droppers

glass-marking pencil

paper towels

Safety

- Remind students to wear safety goggles and lab aprons at all times.

- Iodine can stain skin and clothing. Clean up any spills immediately.

Advance Preparation

- Gather a few vegetable oils with a range of unsaturated fats and with nutrient labels. Safflower and corn oils are polyunsaturated, olive and canola oils are monounsaturated, and coconut and palm oils are saturated.

- Tincture of iodine is used as an antiseptic and can be purchased at any drug store. You can also prepare it yourself by mixing 4 g potassium iodide and 2 g iodine in 100 mL of ethanol. Store the mixture in a dark bottle.

Teaching Tips

- Use liquid vegetable oils for this experiment rather than solid fats. Solid fats would have to be melted or dissolved in an organic solvent, such as methylene chloride.

- The oil's reaction with iodine is slow; it will take a few hours or overnight to occur. You may want to practice this test before the lab, so you are prepared to help students recognize and interpret the color change.

- Assign different oils for each group to test. Students will need to enter data from one other oil into their Data Tables. Compile students' data on a class data table and rank the oils for amount of saturation. The following oils are in order from most unsaturated to least unsaturated: canola and safflower (about 93%); olive and sunflower (about 89%); corn, soybean, and peanut (about 80%); palm (about 50%); and coconut (about 10%).

- Tincture of iodine is not readily soluble in oil and must be shaken well to mix and react with the oil. The orange color of the tincture of iodine gradually disappears as the oil absorbs the iodine. The oil absorbs the iodine as long as any carbon-carbon double bond remains. If any unreacted iodine remains, an orange color will be visible.

© Pearson Education, Inc., publishing as Pearson Prentice Hall. All rights reserved.

Carbon Chemistry • *Laboratory Investigation*

Testing Unsaturated Cooking Oils

Pre-Lab Discussion

The nutrition labels on packages of food tell you how much saturated fat is in a serving. Why should you care? Fats are made mostly of saturated fatty acids. Research shows that unsaturated fatty acids are better for your health than saturated fatty acids are. Oils, which are usually liquid at room temperature, are made mostly of unsaturated fatty acids. If you are health conscious, you might choose to cook with oils rather than with solid fats.

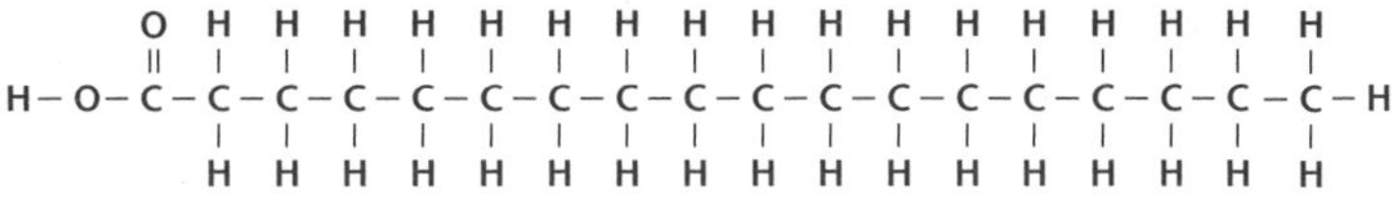

Stearic acid, a saturated fatty acid

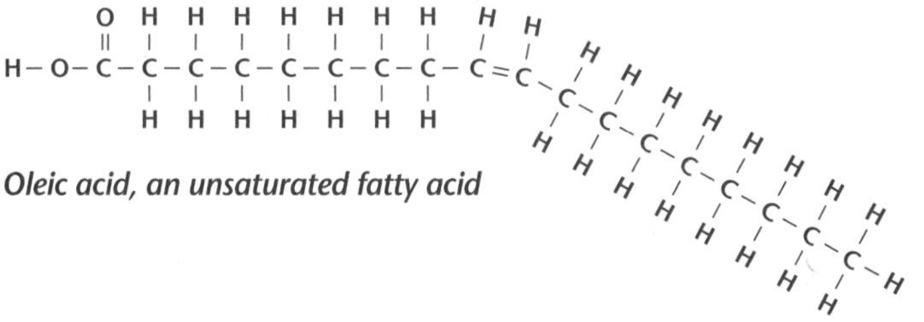

Oleic acid, an unsaturated fatty acid

Figure 1

Figure 1 shows the difference between molecules of saturated and unsaturated fatty acids. Unsaturated fatty acids have at least one double bond between two carbon atoms. Saturated fatty acids have only single bonds between carbon atoms.

How can you find out how unsaturated the fatty acids in a fat or an oil are? You can mix the chemical iodine with the fat or oil. As iodine reacts with the molecules of unsaturated fatty acids, it loses its color. The more iodine that disappears, the more unsaturated fatty acid is in the fat or oil. When the iodine no longer changes color, the reaction is complete. In this investigation, you will determine the relative amount of unsaturated fatty acid in some cooking oils.

1. How does a saturated fatty acid differ from an unsaturated fatty acid?

   _____

   _____

2. What happens as iodine reacts with fat or oil?

   _____

   _____

© Pearson Education, Inc., publishing as Pearson Prentice Hall. All rights reserved.

Carbon Chemistry • *Laboratory Investigation*

Testing Unsaturated Cooking Oils (continued)

Problem

How can you tell how unsaturated an oil is?

Materials

10 test tubes

10 stoppers for test tubes

test-tube rack

balance

several vegetable oils such as corn, olive, sunflower, safflower, and soybean oil

tincture of iodine

3 plastic droppers

glass-marking pencil

paper towels

Safety 🧍 👃 🥽 ✋ 🧤 *Review the safety guidelines in Appendix A of your textbook.*

Handle tincture of iodine carefully; it will stain your skin and clothes. Clean up any spills immediately and notify the teacher.

Procedure

1. You will be given one oil to test. Label 10 test tubes with the name of the oil. Number them 1 through 10. The number tells you how many drops of iodine to add to each test tube.

2. Add 20 drops (1 mL) of oil to each test tube. Record the color in the Data Table.

3. **CAUTION:***Wipe up any spilled iodine immediately, especially on the outside of the test tube and stopper.* Add one drop of iodine to the first test tube and put the stopper on. Shake the test tube while holding the stopper and carefully observe the reaction of the oil and iodine. Record your observations in the Data Table.

4. Now add 2 drops of iodine to the test tube marked 2. Stopper it, shake it, and observe.

5. Add the corresponding number of drops to the remaining test tubes in order. Shake each test tube thoroughly to mix the contents.

6. Allow the test tubes to sit with stoppers on in the test tube rack overnight. The next day observe any color changes. On a separate piece of paper, record the color change for each test tube in a chart.

7. Record in your Data Table the lowest number of drops of iodine used where the color remained.

8. Provide your results to your teacher so they may be shared with your classmates. Enter the data from one additional oil into your Data Table.

9. Clean up the equipment with soapy water. Wash your hands as well.

© Pearson Education, Inc., publishing as Pearson Prentice Hall. All rights reserved.

Name _____ Date _____ Class _____

Carbon Chemistry · *Laboratory Investigation*

Observations

Data Table

	Oil _____ Oil	*Oil* _____ Oil
Color before adding iodine		
Color and other observations after adding iodine (first day)		
Color after iodine color stops changing (second day)		
Drops of iodine needed for permanent color change		

Analyze and Conclude

1. Why did the oil react with the iodine?

_____

_____

_____

_____

2. Which of the oils is the most unsaturated? Give evidence to support your conclusion.

_____

_____

_____

_____

© Pearson Education, Inc., publishing as Pearson Prentice Hall. All rights reserved.

Carbon Chemistry ▪ *Laboratory Investigation*

Testing Unsaturated Cooking Oils (continued)

Critical Thinking and Applications

1. The iodine was orange when added to the oil. Why did the color disappear?

   _____

   _____

   _____

   _____

2. Is the iodine-oil reaction a physical change or a chemical change? Give a reason for your answer.

   _____

   _____

   _____

3. Why did the iodine color remain when the reaction was complete?

   _____

   _____

   _____

4. How can you use the data from this lab to improve your health?

   _____

   _____

   _____

   _____

More to Explore

Do the relative amounts of unsaturated fatty acids from your tests agree with the relative amounts on the nutrition labels for the oils? On a separate sheet of paper, make a data table that compares the two sets of figures. Discuss why the relative amounts are or are not comparable.

© Pearson Education, Inc., publishing as Pearson Prentice Hall. All rights reserved.

More Molecular Models

Students are presented with the problem of creating models of six molecules, each containing six carbon atoms. To solve this problem, students will apply the concepts they have learned about hydrocarbons and structural formulas.

Expected Outcome

Students will use toothpicks to represent bonds between atoms, and combinations of raisins, gumdrops (or other soft candies), and dried fruits to represent carbon, hydrogen, and oxygen atoms. Students should model at least one molecule that fits each of the following descriptions: a straight carbon chain, a branched carbon chain, a carbon ring, a saturated hydrocarbon, an unsaturated hydrocarbon, and an alcohol. Double or triple bonds can be modeled by using two or three toothpicks to connect the materials used as elements. An alcohol can be modeled by connecting an oxygen atom to both a hydrogen atom and a carbon atom.

Students will use data tables to indicate which of the required characteristics each of their models possesses. Some models will necessarily have more than one characteristic. Then students will exchange their models with a partner and identify each characteristic of their partner's models in a separate column of their data tables.

Content Assessed

This activity assesses students' understanding of carbon-containing molecules and structural formulas.

Skills Assessed

making models, creating a data table, applying concepts

Materials

Each student will need approximately 120 toothpicks (60 if broken in half). They also need raisins, gumdrops (or other soft candies), and dried fruits. They will need at least 36 pieces of one item for carbon atoms, approximately 84 pieces of a second item for hydrogen atoms, and at least one piece of a third item for oxygen atoms. Caution students not to eat any of their modeling materials.

Time

40 minutes

Monitoring the Task

Review the difference between a branched carbon chain and a straight carbon chain that is merely "bent." Point out that in a straight chain, each carbon atom is bonded to only one or two other carbon atoms. In a branched carbon chain, at least one of the carbon atoms is bonded to more than two other carbon atoms. Draw on the board the structural formulas for several hydrocarbons, some branched and some unbranched but bent. Challenge volunteers to identify which of these molecules have branched chains.

Draw on the board the two representations of 2-methylpentane shown below. Lead students to realize that these two structures represent the same molecule.

2-methylpentane

© Pearson Education, Inc., publishing as Pearson Prentice Hall. All rights reserved.

More Molecular Models

In assessing students' performance, use the following rubric.

	4	3	2	1
Creating Models	Student models six different molecules that contain six carbons each. Student's models contain at least one example of each of the following: a straight carbon chain, a branched carbon chain, a carbon ring, a saturated hydrocarbon, an unsaturated hydrocarbon, and an alcohol. Student correctly identifies these examples in his or her own models and those of a partner.	Student models six different molecules that contain six carbons each. Student's models contain at least one example of all but one of the following: a straight carbon chain, a branched carbon chain, a carbon ring, a saturated hydrocarbon, an unsaturated hydrocarbon, and an alcohol. Student correctly identifies all but one example in his or her own models and those of a partner.	Student models six different molecules that contain six carbons each, but two of the models are identical. Student's models contain at least one example of all but two of the following: a straight carbon chain, a branched carbon chain, a carbon ring, a saturated hydrocarbon, an unsaturated hydrocarbon, and an alcohol. Student correctly identifies all but two examples in his or her own models and those of a partner.	Student models six molecules, but not all contain six carbons and at least two are identical. Student's models are missing an example of more than two of the following: a straight carbon chain, a branched carbon chain, a carbon ring, a saturated hydrocarbon, an unsaturated hydrocarbon, and an alcohol. Student fails to identify more than two examples in his or her own models and those of a partner.
Concept Understanding	Student demonstrates a clear understanding of how carbon atoms bond to other atoms and the kinds of compounds formed.	Student demonstrates an adequate understanding of how carbon atoms bond to other atoms and the kinds of compounds formed.	Student demonstrates a partial understanding of how carbon atoms bond to other atoms and the kinds of compounds formed.	Student demonstrates a minimal understanding of how carbon atoms bond to other atoms and the kinds of compounds formed.

© Pearson Education, Inc., publishing as Pearson Prentice Hall. All rights reserved.

Carbon Chemistry · *Performance Assessment*

More Molecular Models

Problem

How can you model six different molecules that each contain six carbon atoms?

Suggested Materials

dried fruits

gumdrops

raisins

toothpicks

Devise a Plan

1. Study the materials and think of a way you could use them to build models of molecules that contains six carbon atoms. Your models should include at least one molecule that fits each of the following descriptions: a straight carbon chain, a branched carbon chain, a carbon ring, a saturated hydrocarbon, an unsaturated hydrocarbon, and an alcohol. (*Hints:* Some of your models may have more than one of these characteristics. For example, you might build a saturated hydrocarbon with a branched carbon chain. Also, remember that oxygen atoms form two bonds and hydrogen atoms form one bond.)

2. Build your models and label them from 1 to 6. Next, make a data table with columns titled *Description* and *Model Number*. Then use your models to complete your table. For example, if your models numbered 1, 4, and 5 each had branched carbon chains, you would write *1, 4, 5* in the second column next to the words *branched carbon chain* in the first column.

3. Add a third column to your table, and title it *Partner's Model Number*. Trade models with a partner, and complete the third column of your table using your partner's models. Be sure to tell your partner which food item represents which type of atom.

Analyze and Conclude

After following the plan you devised, answer the following questions on a separate sheet of paper.

1. After you have finished, compare your data table to that of your partner. Do your data agree? If not, what differences were there?

2. What would be wrong with a model that had five bonds to a carbon atom? Two bonds to a hydrogen atom?

3. Do you think it would be possible for an oxygen atom to bond to two carbon atoms? Why or why not?

4. Write the chemical formulas of each of your models.

© Pearson Education, Inc., publishing as Pearson Prentice Hall. All rights reserved.

Carbon Chemistry ▪ *Chapter Test*

Carbon Chemistry

Multiple Choice

Write the letter of the correct answer on the line at the left.

_____ 1. The maximum number of bonds a carbon atom can form is

    a. one.   **b.** two.

    c. three.   **d.** four.

_____ 2. Many organic compounds

    a. have high melting points.

    b. have high boiling points.

    c. do not dissolve well in water.

    d. conduct electricity.

_____ 3. The monomers of complex carbohydrates are

    a. simple sugars.   **b.** amino acids.

    c. fatty acids.   **d.** glycerol.

_____ 4. Pure carbon exists as all the following forms EXCEPT

    a. graphite.   **b.** methane.

    c. fullerene.   **d.** diamond.

_____ 5. Carbohydrates are made up of carbon, hydrogen, and

    a. sulfur.   **b.** nitrogen.

    c. phosphorus.   **d.** oxygen.

_____ 6. The group –COOH is characteristic of

    a. hydrocarbons.   **b.** sugars.

    c. alcohols.   **d.** organic acids.

_____ 7. The names of saturated hydrocarbons end in

    a. -ane.   **b.** -ine.

    c. -ene.   **d.** -yne.

_____ 8. Substituted hydrocarbons include all of the following EXCEPT

    a. alcohols.

    b. halogen-containing compounds.

    c. minerals.

    d. organic acids.

_____ 9. All hydrocarbons

    a. burn easily.

    b. mix well with water.

    c. contain hydrogen, carbon, and oxygen.

    d. have ring-shaped molecules.

© Pearson Education, Inc., publishing as Pearson Prentice Hall. All rights reserved.

_____ **10.** The main classes of organic compounds in living things include all of the following EXCEPT

    a. carbohydrates.   **b.** proteins.

    c. alcohols.   **d.** lipids.

Completion

Fill in the blank to complete each statement.

11. Carbon atoms can form straight chains, _____, and rings.

12. Many _____ have pleasant, fruity smells.

13. Along with the four classes of organic compounds, _____ and minerals are other nutrients that contribute to a healthy diet.

14. With some exceptions, a compound that contains carbon is called a(n) _____.

15. A combination of an oxygen atom and a hydrogen atom, –OH, is called a(n) _____.

True or False

If the statement is true, write true. *If it is false, change the underlined word or words to make the statement true.*

_____ **16.** <u>Nucleotides</u> are polymers made of amino acids.

_____ **17.** A hydrocarbon with only single bonds in its carbon chain is called a(n) <u>unsaturated</u> hydrocarbon.

_____ **18.** Fats and oils are energy-rich organic compounds called <u>lipids</u>.

_____ **19.** Plants store energy in the form of the complex carbohydrate <u>starch</u>.

_____ **20.** DNA and RNA are examples of <u>cholesterol</u>.

© Pearson Education, Inc., publishing as Pearson Prentice Hall. All rights reserved.

Name _____ Date _____ Class _____

Carbon Chemistry • *Chapter Test*

Using Science Skills

Use the diagram below to answer the following questions in the spaces provided.

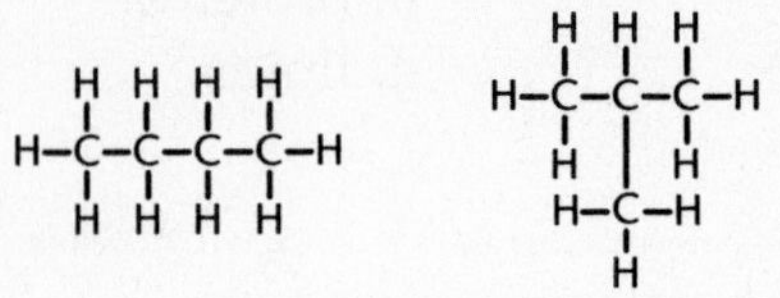

H H H H
H–C–C–C–C–H
H H H H

H H H
H–C–C–C–H
H | H
H–C–H
H

21. What type of formula is used to illustrate the two compounds shown above?

_____

22. Why are the organic compounds shown in the diagram called isomers?

_____

_____

_____

23. Are the compounds in the diagram saturated or unsaturated hydrocarbons? Are they substituted hydrocarbons? Explain your answers.

_____

_____

_____

Essay

Write an answer for each of the following in the spaces provided.

24. Describe graphite and diamond in terms of their hardness or softness. How does the arrangement of their atoms account for this characteristic?

_____

_____

_____

_____

_____

_____

25. What type of compounds are most nutrients, and why does your body need them?

_____

_____

_____

_____

© Pearson Education, Inc., publishing as Pearson Prentice Hall. All rights reserved.

Name _____ Date _____ Class _____

Carbon Chemistry ▪ *Chapter Test*

Using Science Skills

Use the diagram below to answer the following questions in the spaces provided.

$$
\begin{array}{cc}
\text{H} & \text{Cl} \\
| & | \\
\text{H}-\text{C}-\text{OH} & \text{Cl}-\text{C}-\text{Cl} \\
| & | \\
\text{H} & \text{Cl}
\end{array}
$$

Compound A   **Compound B**

26. Classifying What kind of substituted hydrocarbon is compound A in the diagram above? What kind is compound B? What is the chemical formula of each compound?

_____

_____

27. Inferring Do you think there are isomers of these compounds? Explain your answer.

_____

_____

_____

28. Applying Concepts Compounds A and B are both formed around a carbon atom. What characteristics of carbon enable it to form so many different compounds?

_____

_____

_____

_____

Essay

Write an answer for each of the following in the spaces provided.

29. Explain the structure of a polymer. Give an example of a natural and a synthetic polymer.

_____

_____

_____

_____

30. Why is it misleading to say that anything "organic" is a natural compound?

_____

_____

_____

_____

© Pearson Education, Inc., publishing as Pearson Prentice Hall. All rights reserved.

Chapter Project
Worksheet 1

1.–8. Students' answers will vary based on the packaged foods chosen. Make certain students have thoughtfully and correctly answered the questions based on the information provided on the food labels.

Worksheet 2

1.–6. Students' answers will vary based on the packaged foods chosen.

Properties of Carbon
Guided Reading and Study

Use Target Reading Skills
Sample questions and answers:
What You Know
1. Carbon atoms have 6 electrons
2. Carbon is not a metal.
3. Carbon has 4 valence electrons.
4. Diamond is one form of carbon.
5. Graphite is a form of carbon.
What You Learned
1. Carbon is able to form four bonds.
2. Carbon atoms can form straight chains, branched chains, and rings.
3. Few elements have the ability of carbon to form bonds.
4. Fullerenes, and nanotubes are two forms of pure carbon.
5. Nanotubes can conduct electricity and heat.
1. b
2. bonds
3. true
4. b
5. **a.** straight chain **b.** branched chain **c.** ring
6. Carbon can exist in different forms because of the ways it can form bonds
7. **a.** Crystal structure; Extremely hard and unreactive; Gems, cutting tools
    b. Graphite; Layers
    c. Fullerene
    d. Nanotube; Tiny, light, flexible, strong
8. Diamonds form at very high temperatures and pressures.

Properties of Carbon
Review and Reinforce

1. fullerene
2. diamond
3. graphite
4. nanotube
5. four
6. carbon atoms

7. diamond
8. graphite
9. fullerene
10. nanotube

Properties of Carbon
Enrich

1. The tiny pores in the activated charcoal will attract the molecules of poison and make them stick to the charcoal's surface. The poison molecules will then be passed out of the human or animal's body along with the activated charcoal.
2. Answers will vary. Sample: Activated charcoal can be used to filter out particles of pollution from air. It can also be used in gas masks to remove certain poisonous gas particles.
3. The backpacker can sip water from streams, lakes, and rivers through the special straw. The activated charcoal in the straw will attract and remove most bacteria from the water.
4. Answers may vary. Sample: A buildup of bacteria on the activated charcoal will eventually prevent the charcoal from attracting bacteria to its surface. This will cause the activated charcoal to stop working. Also, a layer of dead bacteria is a good place for live bacteria to grow and multiply. This would contaminate the water.

Carbon Compounds
Guided Reading and Study

Use Target Reading Skills
Sample outline:
I. Organic compounds
II. Hydrocarbons
    A. Properties of hydrocarbons
    B. Chemical formulas of hydrocarbons
III. Structure and bonding in hydrocarbons
    A. Structural formulas
    B. Isomers
    C. Double bonds and triple bonds
    D. Saturated and unsaturated hydrocarbons
IV. Substituted hydrocarbons
    A. Compounds containing halogens
    B. Alcohols
    C. Organic acids
V. Structure and bonding in hydrocarbons
VI. Structure and bonding in hydrocarbons
1. organic compounds
2. Organic compounds have low melting points and low boiling points.
3. a, c
4. A hydrocarbon is a compound that contains

© Pearson Education, Inc., publishing as Pearson Prentice Hall. All rights reserved.

only the elements carbon and hydrogen.

5. Hydrocarbons release a great deal of energy when they burn.

6. A molecule of propane has three carbon atoms and eight hydrogen atoms.

7. straight chains, branched chains, ring-shaped chains

8. It shows the kind, number, and arrangement of atoms in a molecule

9. bond

10. Students should draw an "H" at the end of each bond, for a total of eight hydrogen atoms.

11. isomers

12. false

13. a. Saturated hydrocarbon; –ane
b. Unsaturated hydrocarbon; Sample: Acetylene

14. substituted hydrocarbon

15. One or more halogen atoms replace the hydrogen atoms.

16. c

17. alcohol

18. b, d

19. b

20. organic acid

21. ester

22. true

23. A polymer is a very large molecule made of a chain of many smaller molecules bonded together.

24. monomers

25. b, d

Carbon Compounds
Review and Reinforce

1. Figure 1: a straight chain
Figure 2: a branched chain
Figure 3: a ring-shaped chain

2. C_6H_{14}, C_6H_{14}, C_6H_{12}

3. isomers

4. g

5. a

6. h

7. c

8. b

9. i

10. e

11. d

12. f

13. j

14. k

Carbon Compounds
Enrich

1. As the number of carbon atoms in the alkane increases, the boiling point of the compound increases. The pattern for the melting points is the same, with the exception of propane.

2. Liquid; melting points generally increase as the number of carbon atoms increases, and the melting points of $C_{10}H_{22}$ and $C_{14}H_{30}$ make them both liquids at room temperature. The melting point of any alkane between $C_{10}H_{22}$ and $C_{14}H_{30}$ should also make it a liquid.

3. The number of hydrogen atoms in an alkane equals twice the number of carbon atoms plus 2; CnH2n`2, or a similar expression is acceptable.

4. $C_{40}H_{82}$

How Many Molecules?
Skills Lab

For answers, see the Teacher's Edition.

Life With Carbon
Guided Reading and Study

Use Target Reading Skills
Sample questions and answers:
What is a carbohydrate? *(A carbohydrate is an energy-rich organic compound made of the elements carbon, hydrogen, and oxygen.)*
What are proteins? *(Proteins are polymers formed from amino acid monomers.)*
What are lipids? *(Lipids are energy-rich compounds made of carbon, oxygen, and hydrogen.)*
What are nucleic acids? *(Nucleic acids are very large organic molecules made up of carbon, oxygen, hydrogen, nitrogen, and phosphorus.)*
What are other compounds in foods? *(Other compounds in foods include vitamins, minerals, and water.)*

1. carbohydrates, lipids, proteins, nucleic acids

2. A carbohydrate is an energy-rich organic compound made of the elements carbon, hydrogen, and oxygen.

3. glucose

4. The body circulates glucose to all body parts through blood.

5. complex carbohydrate

6. a. The complex carbohydrate that is stored by plants for energy; Bread, cereal, pasta, rice, potatoes
b. The complex carbohydrate that gives plant stems and roots strength; Fruits and vegetables

© Pearson Education, Inc., publishing as Pearson Prentice Hall. All rights reserved.

7. proteins
8. false
9. Different proteins are made when different sequences of amino acids are linked into long chains.
10. a, b, d
11. The body uses proteins to build and repairs body parts.
12. Lipids are energy-rich compounds made of carbon, oxygen, and hydrogen.
13. fats, waxes, oils, cholesterol
14. lipids
15. Each fat or oil is made of three fatty acids and one alcohol named glycerol.
16. cholesterol
17. Nucleic acids are very large organic molecules made up of carbon, oxygen, hydrogen, nitrogen, and phosphorus.
18. a. DNA; nucleotides
    b. RNA; nucleotides
19. nucleotides
20. The differences depend on the order of nucleotides in their DNA.
21. DNA; RNA; amino acids
22. a. Organic compounds that serve as helper molecules in a variety of chemical reactions; Vitamin C, Vitamin D
    b. Elements needed by the body; Sodium, calcium, iron, iodine, potassium
23. true

Life With Carbon
Review and Reinforce

1. The four main classes of organic compounds in living things are carbohydrates, proteins, lipids, and nucleic acids.
2. Starch and cellulose are considered different compounds because their glucose molecules are arranged differently.
3. The differences among living things depend on the order of nucleotides in the DNA.
4. The body needs vitamins and minerals only in small amounts.
5. amino acids
6. fatty acids
7. proteins
8. lipids; carbohydrates
9. nucleic acid
10. DNA; RNA
11. nucleotide
12. complex carbohydrate
13. cholesterol
14. glucose; starch; cellulose

Life With Carbon
Enrich

1. Whale and human; they are identical.
2. The sequences differ in the third amino acid.
3. Sheep and cows; there is only one difference in the structure of their insulin molecules, there are three differences between horses and cows.
4. Insulin from another animal is enough like human insulin that it worked the same way.

Are You Getting Your Vitamins?
Consumer Lab

For answers, see the Teacher's Edition.

Key Terms

1. nanotube
2. fullerene
3. alcohol
4. glucose
5. cellulose
6. carboxyl group
7. structural formula
8. amino acids
9. hydrocarbon
10. ester

Hidden term: nucleotide
Definition: A nucleotide is the building block of nucleic acids.

© Pearson Education, Inc., publishing as Pearson Prentice Hall. All rights reserved.

Connecting Concepts

This concept map is only one way to represent the main ideas and relationships in this chapter. Accept other logical answers from students

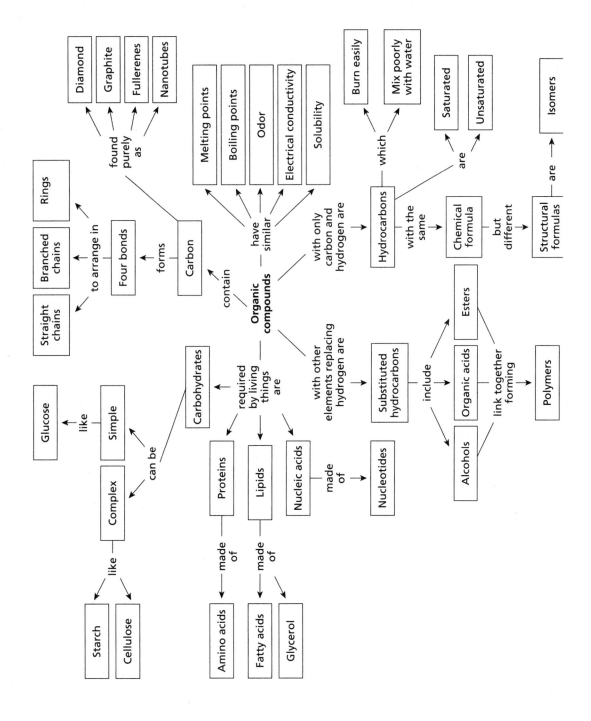

© Pearson Education, Inc., publishing as Pearson Prentice Hall. All rights reserved.

Laboratory Investigation

Testing Unsaturated Cooking Oils
Pre-lab Discussion

1. A saturated fatty acid has only single bonds between carbon atoms. An unsaturated fatty acid has one or more double bonds between carbon atoms.

2. As iodine reacts with the molecules of unsaturated fatty acids in the fat or oil, it loses its color.

Observations

Sample Data Table

	Oil Soybean Oil	Oil Canola Oil
Color before adding iodine	Pale yellow	Yellow, somewhat darker than soybean oil
Color and other observations after adding iodine (first day)	At first the orange iodine didn't mix with the oil. Shaking broke up the iodine and mixed the orange solution with the oil.	Same as for soybean oil
Color after iodine color stops changing (second day)	Orange	Orange
Drops of iodine needed for permanent color change	6	8

Analyze and Conclude

1. The oil has unsaturated fatty acids that combine with iodine. (One of the bonds in a double bond breaks, and each of the two carbon bonds to an iodine atom.)

2. Answers will vary depending on oils tested. For the sample data, the canola oil is the most saturated. The evidence is that more drops of iodine reacted with the canola oil than with the soybean oil.

Critical Thinking and Applications

1. Answers should indicate that chemical changes often result in color changes and other changes of properties. (The color of the iodine comes from the structure of iodine as I_2. When the iodine reacts with the oil, the I_2 separates into two iodine atoms that attach to double bonds and the resulting product does not have a color.)

2. It is a chemical change. The iodine combines chemically with the oil, as shown by the color change.

3. Iodine stopped reacting when no more double bonds were left. The excess iodine colors the oil orange.

4. From the data, students can conclude which oils are more unsaturated. They can choose these oils for cooking because unsaturated fats are more healthful than are saturated fats.

More to Explore

1. Because of measurement error, students' results may not correspond to the label if the two oils have small differences in percentages (less than 15%–20%).

Performance Assessment

Analyze and Conclude

1. Answers will vary. Sample: I said one of my partner's models had a straight chain, and he said that it had a branched chain. I showed him that his model wasn't really branched, it was just bent.

2. Carbon can form only four bonds, and hydrogen can form only one.

3. Yes, oxygen can form two bonds, so it could bond to two carbon atoms.

4. Answers will vary, but all models should contain six carbons.

Chapter Test

1. d
2. c
3. a
4. b
5. d
6. d
7. a
8. c
9. a
10. c
11. branched chains
12. esters
13. vitamins
14. organic compounds
15. hydroxyl group

© Pearson Education, Inc., publishing as Pearson Prentice Hall. All rights reserved.

16. Proteins
17. saturated
18. true
19. true
20. nucleic acids
21. A structural formula
22. They are called isomers because they have the same chemical formula (C_6H_{10}) but different structures.
23. Saturated hydrocarbons—they contain no double or triple bonds; they are not substituted hydrocarbons—they contain only carbon and hydrocarbon.
24. Graphite is softer than diamond and feels slippery. The carbon atoms in graphite are bonded together tightly in flat layers, but the bonds connecting the layers are very weak, allowing the layer to slide easily past one another. Diamond is one of the hardest substances on earth. The carbon atoms in a diamond are arranged in a crystal structure in which every atom is bonded to four other atoms. This arrangement results in an extremely hard solid.
25. Most nutrients are organic compounds. The body needs nutrients because they provide the energy and raw materials that they body needs to grow, repair worn parts, and function properly.
26. Compound A: alcohol; CH_3OH
   Compound B: halogen compound; CCL_4
27. No, these compounds do not have isomers because there is only one possible arrangement of the atoms in each compound.
28. Carbon has four valence electrons so that each carbon atom is able to form four bonds, making it possible to form many different molecules with one or more carbon atoms. Also, it is possible to arrange the same number of atoms in may different ways.
29. A polymer is a very large molecule made up of a chain of monomers bonded together. Samples: Plastics are synthetic polymers. Wool is a natural polymer.
30. Answers will vary. Sample: An organic compound is one that contains carbon. Many organic compounds come from living things, but others (such as plastics) must be produced in a laboratory or factory.

© Pearson Education, Inc., publishing as Pearson Prentice Hall. All rights reserved.

Transparencies

© Pearson Education, Inc., publishing as Pearson Prentice Hall. All rights reserved.

Atomic Models

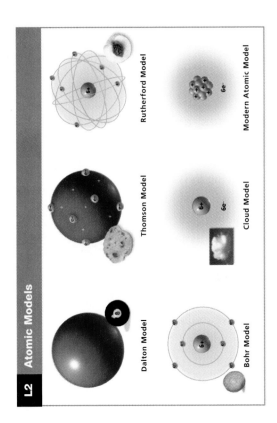

Dalton Model

Thomson Model

Rutherford Model

Bohr Model

Cloud Model

Modern Atomic Model

The Periodic Table

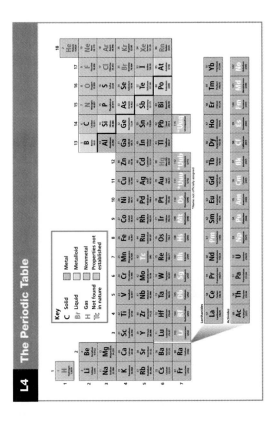

Target Reading Skill: Outlining

Elements and Atoms

I. The building blocks of matter

A. Elements, compounds, and mixtures

B.

II.

A.

B.

C.

D.

E.

F.

Rutherford's Gold Foil Experiment

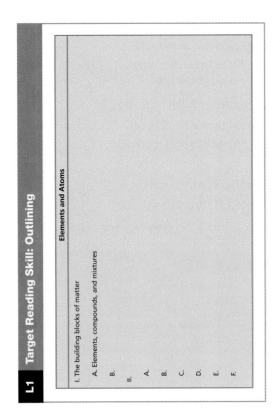

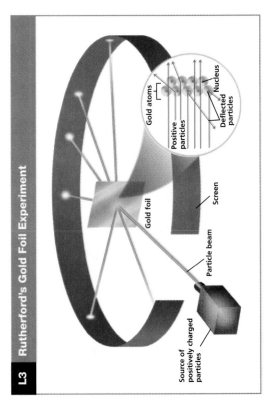

© Pearson Education, Inc., publishing as Pearson Prentice Hall. All rights reserved.

Transparencies

L6 Target Reading Skill: Previewing Visuals

Formation of an Ionic Bond

Q. What is an ionic bond?

A.

Q.

A.

Q.

A.

Q.

A.

L8 Formation of an Ionic Bond

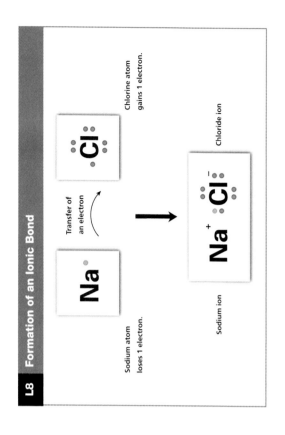

Sodium atom loses 1 electron.

Transfer of an electron

Chlorine atom gains 1 electron.

Sodium ion

Chloride ion

L5 Patterns of Valence Electrons

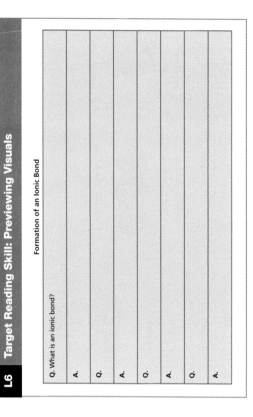

Li — Lithium
Be — Beryllium
B — Boron
C — Carbon
N — Nitrogen
O — Oxygen
F — Fluorine
Ne — Neon

Na — Sodium
Mg — Magnesium
Al — Aluminum
Si — Silicon
P — Phosphorus
S — Sulfur
Cl — Chlorine
Ar — Argon

L7 Ions and Their Charges

Ions and Their Charges

Name	Charge	Symbol or Formula
Lithium	1+	Li^+
Sodium	1+	Na^+
Potassium	1+	K^+
Ammonium	1+	NH_4^+
Calcium	2+	Ca^{2+}
Magnesium	2+	Mg^{2+}
Aluminum	3+	Al^{3+}
Fluoride	1–	F^-
Chloride	1–	Cl^-
Iodide	1–	I^-
Bicarbonate	1–	HCO_3^-
Nitrate	1–	NO_3^-
Oxide	2–	O^{2-}
Sulfide	2–	S^{2-}
Carbonate	2–	CO_3^{2-}
Sulfate	2–	SO_4^{2-}
Phosphate	3–	PO_4^{3-}

© Pearson Education, Inc., publishing as Pearson Prentice Hall. All rights reserved.

L9 Target Reading Skill: Asking Questions

Covalent Bonds

Question	Answer
How do covalent bonds form?	Covalent bonds form when . . .

L10 Formation of Covalent Bonds

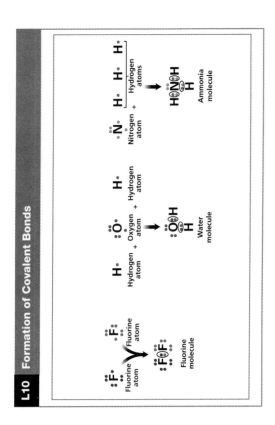

L11 Double and Triple Bonds

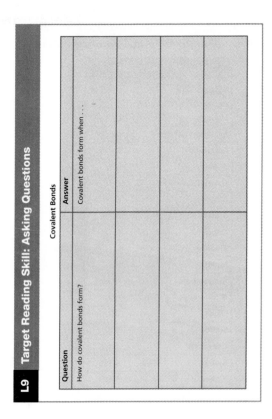

L12 Comparing Nonpolar and Polar Bonds

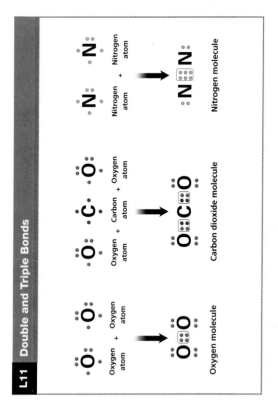

© Pearson Education, Inc., publishing as Pearson Prentice Hall. All rights reserved.

L14 Metallic Bonding

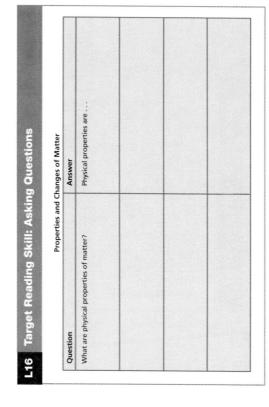

Metallic Bonding

Effect of a Force
on Metal

L16 Target Reading Skill: Asking Questions

Properties and Changes of Matter

Question	Answer
What are physical properties of matter?	Physical properties are . . .

L13 Target Reading Skill: Relating Cause and Effect

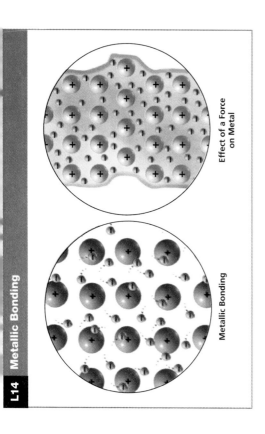

Cause

Metallic bonding

Effects

Electrical conductivity

L15 Organizing Information: Comparing and Contrasting

Types of Chemical Bonds

Feature	Ionic Bond	Polar Covalent Bond	Nonpolar Covalent Bond	Metallic Bond
How Bond Forms	a. ___	Unequal sharing of electrons	b. ___	c. ___
Charge on Bonded Atoms?	Yes; positive or negative	d. ___	e. ___	Yes; positive
Example	f. ___	g. ___	O_2 molecule	h. ___

© Pearson Education, Inc., publishing as Pearson Prentice Hall. All rights reserved.

L18 Energy of a Chemical Reaction

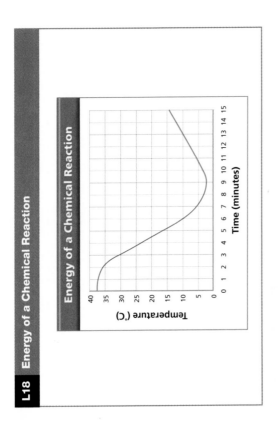

Energy of a Chemical Reaction

L20 Balancing an Equation

1 Write the equation.

$$H_2 + O_2 \longrightarrow H_2O$$

Reactants

2 Count the atoms.

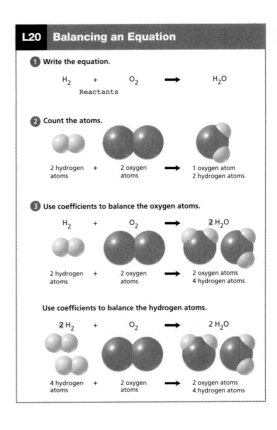

2 hydrogen atoms + 2 oxygen atoms → 1 oxygen atom 2 hydrogen atoms

3 Use coefficients to balance the oxygen atoms.

$$H_2 + O_2 \longrightarrow 2 H_2O$$

2 hydrogen atoms + 2 oxygen atoms → 2 oxygen atoms 4 hydrogen atoms

Use coefficients to balance the hydrogen atoms.

$$2 H_2 + O_2 \longrightarrow 2 H_2O$$

4 hydrogen atoms + 2 oxygen atoms → 2 oxygen atoms 4 hydrogen atoms

---

L17 Bonding and Chemical Change

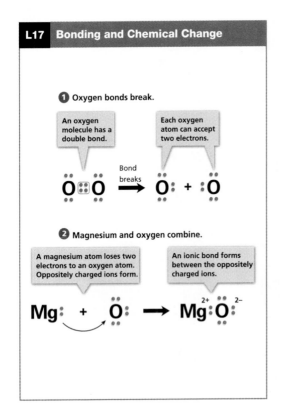

1 Oxygen bonds break.

An oxygen molecule has a double bond.

Each oxygen atom can accept two electrons.

Bond breaks

2 Magnesium and oxygen combine.

A magnesium atom loses two electrons to an oxygen atom. Oppositely charged ions form.

An ionic bond forms between the oppositely charged ions.

L19 Structure of a Chemical Equation

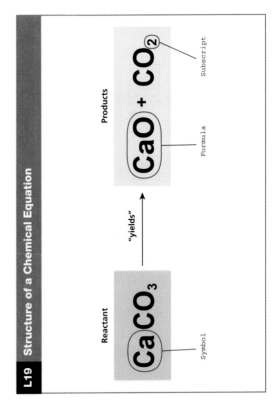

© Pearson Education, Inc., publishing as Pearson Prentice Hall. All rights reserved.

L22 Target Reading Skill: Relating Cause and Effect

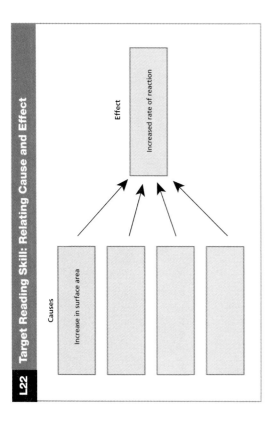

Causes

Increase in surface area

Effect

Increased rate of reaction

L24 Energy Changes in Chemical Reactions

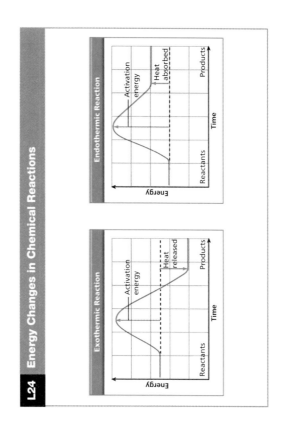

Exothermic Reaction

Energy

Reactants

Activation energy

Heat released

Products

Time

Endothermic Reaction

Energy

Reactants

Activation energy

Heat absorbed

Products

Time

L21 Types of Reactions

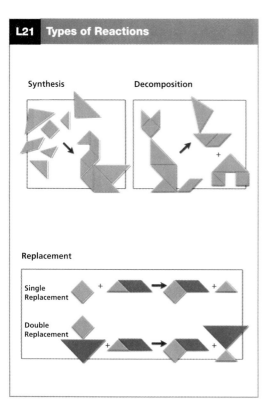

Synthesis

Decomposition

Replacement

Single Replacement

Double Replacement

L23 Modeling Activation Energy

© Pearson Education, Inc., publishing as Pearson Prentice Hall. All rights reserved.

What You Know

1. A fire needs fuel to burn.

2.

3.

4.

What You Learned

1.

2.

3.

4.

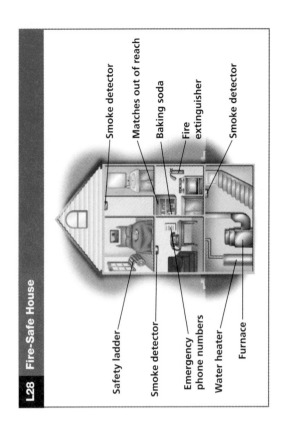

Smoke detector

Matches out of reach

Baking soda

Fire extinguisher

Smoke detector

Safety ladder

Smoke detector

Emergency phone numbers

Water heater

Furnace

L25 Enzyme Action

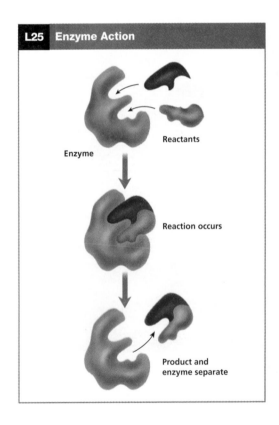

Enzyme

Reactants

Reaction occurs

Product and enzyme separate

L27 The Fire Triangle

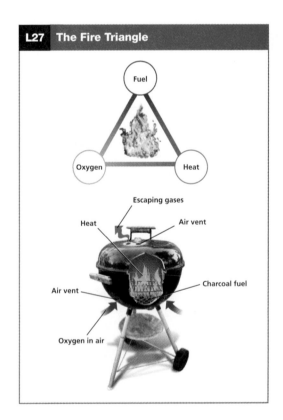

Fuel

Oxygen

Heat

Escaping gases

Heat

Air vent

Air vent

Charcoal fuel

Oxygen in air

© Pearson Education, Inc., publishing as Pearson Prentice Hall. All rights reserved.

Transparencies

L30 Target Reading Skill: Identifying Main Ideas

Main Idea

A solution consists of at least one solute in a well-mixed . . .

Detail

Detail

Detail

L32 Solubility of Potassium Nitrate

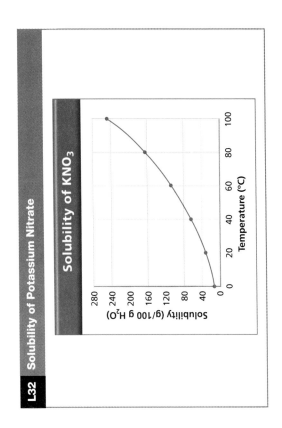

Solubility of KNO₃

L29 Organizing Information: Concept Mapping

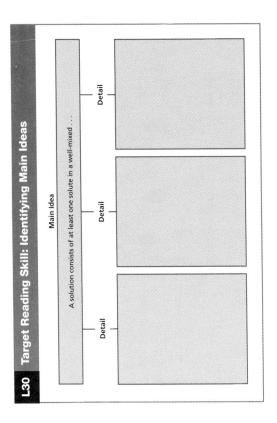

L31 Salt Dissolving in Water

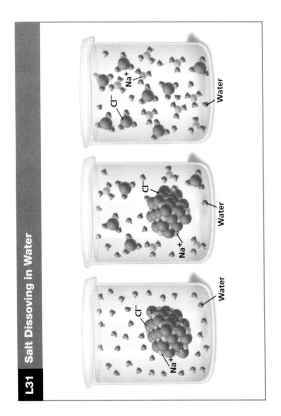

© Pearson Education, Inc., publishing as Pearson Prentice Hall. All rights reserved.

L33 Target Reading Skill: Asking Questions

Describing Acids and Bases

Question	Answer
What is an acid?	An acid is . . .

L34 Target Reading Skill: Previewing Visuals

Neutralization

Q. What is a neutral solution?

A.

Q.

A.

Q.

A.

Q.

A.

L35 Important Acids and Bases

Important Acids and Bases				
Acid	Formula	Base	Formula
Hydrochloric acid	HCl	Sodium hydroxide	NaOH
Nitric acid	HNO_3	Potassium hydroxide	KOH
Sulfuric acid	H_2SO_4	Calcium hydroxide	$Ca(OH)_2$
Carbonic acid	H_2CO_3	Aluminum hydroxide	$Al(OH)_3$
Acetic acid	$HC_2H_3O_2$	Ammonia	NH_3
Phosphoric acid	H_3PO_4	Calcium oxide	CaO

L36 Acids in Solution

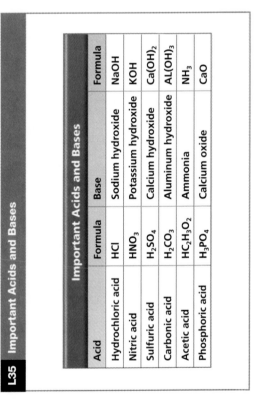

Strong Acid

Weak Acid

Key
- Chloride ion (Cl⁻)
- Hydrogen ion (H⁺)
- Acetic acid ($HC_2H_3O_2$)
- Acetate ion ($C_2H_3O_2{}^-$)

© Pearson Education, Inc., publishing as Pearson Prentice Hall. All rights reserved.

Transparencies

L38 Acid-Base Neutralization

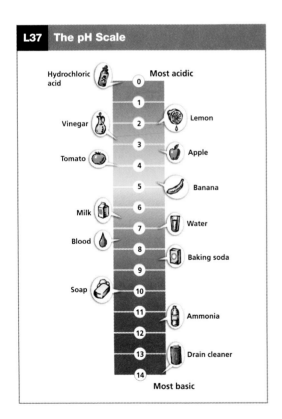

Base — pH = 13

Acid — pH = 2

pH = 8

L40 Digestive System

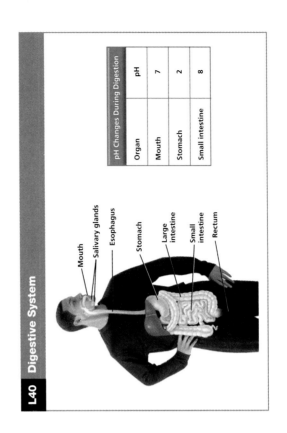

pH Changes During Digestion	
Organ	pH
Mouth	7
Stomach	2
Small intestine	8

Mouth
Salivary glands
Esophagus
Stomach
Large intestine
Small intestine
Rectum

L37 The pH Scale

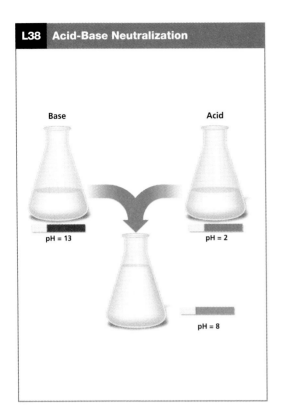

Most acidic

Hydrochloric acid — 0
1
Vinegar — 2 — Lemon
3
Tomato — 4 — Apple
5 — Banana
Milk — 6
7 — Water
Blood — 8 — Baking soda
9
Soap — 10
11 — Ammonia
12
13 — Drain cleaner
14

Most basic

L39 Target Reading Skill: Sequencing

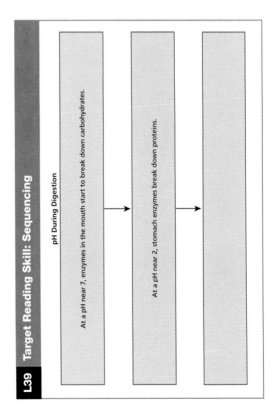

pH During Digestion

At a pH near 7, enzymes in the mouth start to break down carbohydrates.

At a pH near 2, stomach enzymes break down proteins.

© Pearson Education, Inc., publishing as Pearson Prentice Hall. All rights reserved.

What You Know

1. Carbon atoms have 6 electrons.
2.
3.
4.

What You Learned

1.
2.
3.
4.

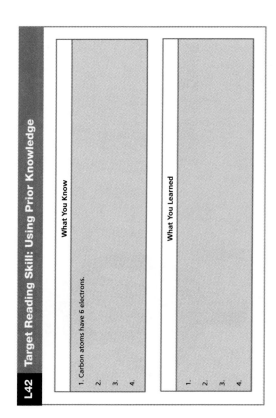

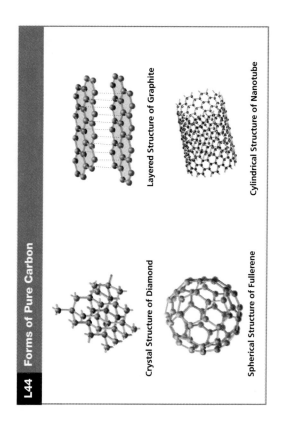

Layered Structure of Graphite

Cylindrical Structure of Nanotube

Crystal Structure of Diamond

Spherical Structure of Fullerene

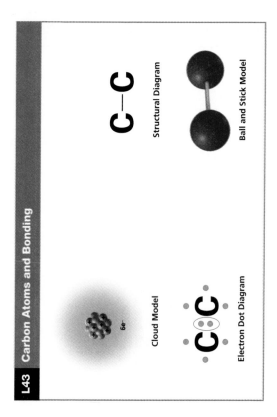

C—C

Structural Diagram

Ball and Stick Model

Cloud Model

Electron Dot Diagram

© Pearson Education, Inc., publishing as Pearson Prentice Hall. All rights reserved.

Transparencies

L46 Structural Formulas

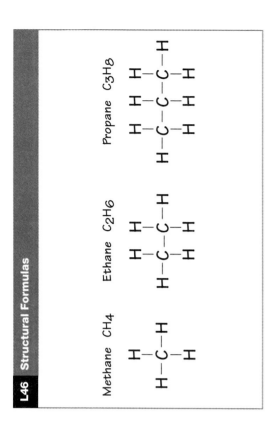

Methane CH₄   Ethane C₂H₆   Propane C₃H₈

L48 Isomers

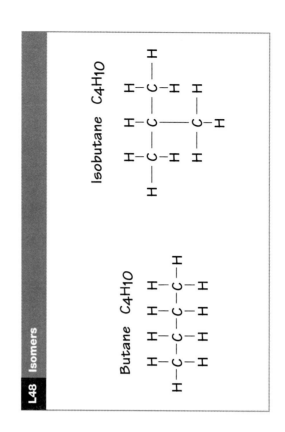

Butane C₄H₁₀   Isobutane C₄H₁₀

L45 Target Reading Skill: Outlining

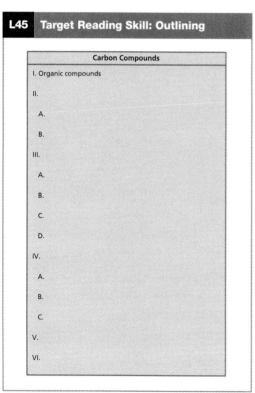

Carbon Compounds

I. Organic compounds

II.

  A.

  B.

III.

  A.

  B.

  C.

  D.

IV.

  A.

  B.

  C.

V.

VI.

L47 Boiling Points of Hydrocarbons

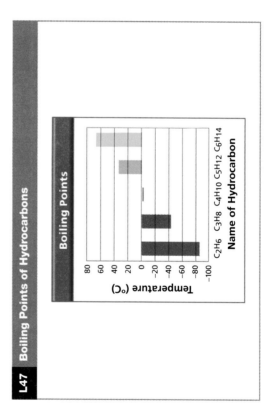

Boiling Points

© Pearson Education, Inc., publishing as Pearson Prentice Hall. All rights reserved.

L50 Substituted Hydrocarbons

Methanol CH_3OH

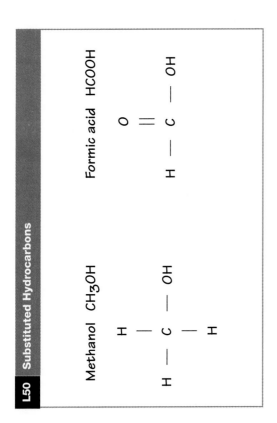

Formic acid $HCOOH$

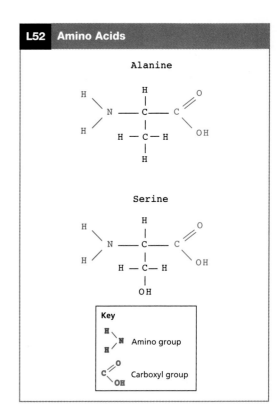

L52 Amino Acids

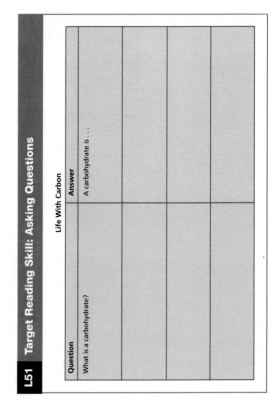

Alanine

Serine

Key

Amino group

Carboxyl group

L49 Unsaturated Hydrocarbons

Ethene C_2H_4

Acetylene (Ethyne) C_2H_2

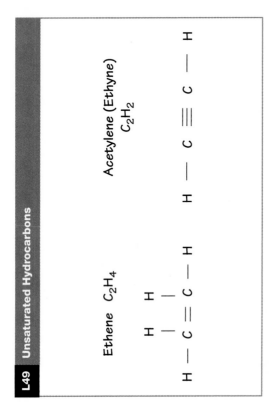

L51 Target Reading Skill: Asking Questions

Life With Carbon

Question	Answer
What is a carbohydrate?	A carbohydrate is . . .

© Pearson Education, Inc., publishing as Pearson Prentice Hall. All rights reserved.

L54 Organizing Information: Comparing and Contrasting

Proteins

Nucleic Acids

a.

b.

c.

Build and repair body parts

Made from nucleotides

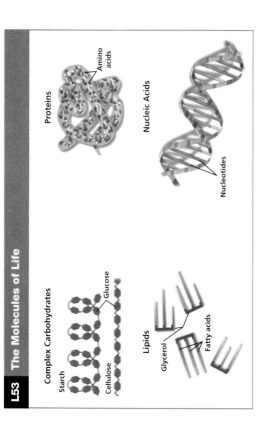

L53 The Molecules of Life

Complex Carbohydrates

Starch

Cellulose

Glucose

Proteins

Amino acids

Nucleic Acids

Nucleotides

Lipids

Glycerol

Fatty acids

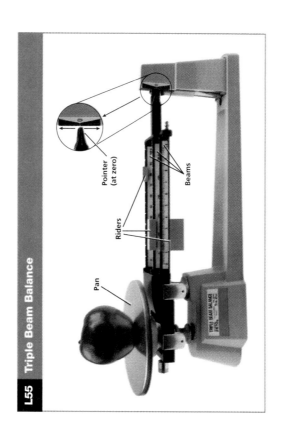

L55 Triple Beam Balance

Pointer (at zero)

Beams

Riders

Pan

© Pearson Education, Inc., publishing as Pearson Prentice Hall. All rights reserved.